CHARLOTTE
LAMB

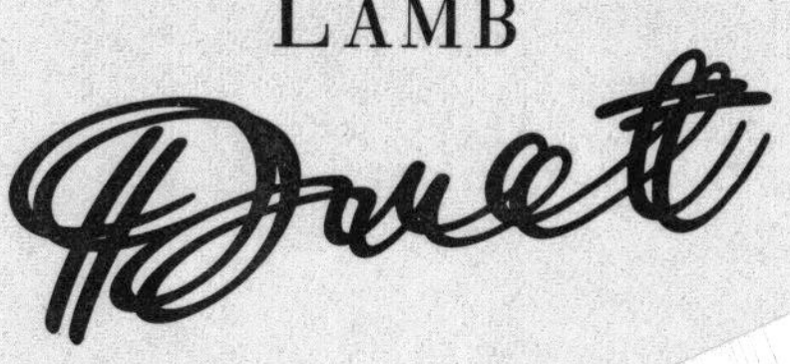

HEAT OF THE NIGHT

HEAT OF THE NIGHT

BY
CHARLOTTE LAMB

MILLS & BOON LIMITED
Eton House, 18-24 Paradise Road
Richmond, Surrey TW9 1SR

All the characters in this book have no existence outside the imagination of the Author, and have no relation whatsoever to anyone bearing the same name or names. They are not even distantly inspired by any individual known or unknown to the Author, and all the incidents are pure invention.

First published in Great Britain in 1986
by Mills & Boon Limited

Reprinted 1986
This edition 1993

ISBN 0 263 78208 5

Set in Times 11 on 11 1/4 pt.
19-9302-46143

Made and printed in Great Britain

CHAPTER ONE

SUSAN met her at Pisa airport, as they had arranged on the phone the day before, but Vicky could have walked right past her without being recognised. Susan's head didn't even turn, she was staring fixedly at the queues of people emerging through the barrier, and when Vicky touched her arm she jumped about three feet in the air.

'It's me,' Vicky hissed in a low voice, and watched her cousin's jaw drop with a sense of relieved satisfaction. If she could fool Susan she could fool anyone.

'Vicky?' Susan instinctively whispered too, her eyes as big as saucers. 'I don't believe it! What have you done to yourself?'

'Let's get out of here,' said Vicky. 'We can talk once we're sure we can't be overheard.' She headed for the exit with her case and Susan, after a stunned pause, followed.

'My car's just over there.' The airport building was surrounded by car parks which were almost full. Vicky felt the heat of the sun striking through her white wool jacket with faint surprise; she had forgotten that it was likely to be warmer in Italy than it had been in rain-drenched England. She had come away in such a rush that she hadn't done much thinking of any kind; she had merely fled to the only close relative she had in the world, knowing that she could trust Susan implicitly.

'Did you have a good flight? Not too bumpy over the Alps?' Susan asked as they walked across the tarmac towards the small red Fiat parked right at the back of the area. 'The last time we came back from London I almost last my lunch. It felt as if we were on the end of a bit of string being swung to and fro by an excited kid! It isn't usually that bumpy, but I bet you were glad to see the last of the mountains.'

'I was a little nervous, looking down on all those snowy peaks.' She had had too much on her mind, though, to indulge in flying nerves. Her only real fear during the flight had been that when she landed she might find a pushing, yelling mob of cameramen and reporters waiting for her. Compared to that nightmare, flying over the Alps had been a piece of cake. 'How's David?' she asked, and her cousin turned a smiling face towards her.

'Oh, fine. He loves working here. He gets on very well with his boss, and the countryside around Florence is so beautiful, every weekend we get out to discover new villages, marvellous scenery, have lunch under the trees in some open-air café. David's all for the culture bit, of course, you know how keen he is on Italian art, and heaven knows he can drown in the stuff round here. We still haven't even brushed the surface in Florence itself, but once the warm weather starts you can't move there for tourists, so we've concentrated on churches and the Tuscan hill towns.'

She had unlocked her car and lifted Vicky's case into the small boot as she talked—talked rather more than Susan usually did, and Vicky knew her well enough to guess why. Susan was curious and puzzled and worried, and tried to cover all three emotions by chattering away.

Susan was slim and pretty, with curly auburn hair and gentle brown eyes. Her colouring and nicely proportioned figure would have made her striking if she had been a little more assured, but even two years of marriage to the man she loved deeply had not lent her any more self-confidence—perhaps it never would. Susan's opinion of herself had been formed at too early an age by an overbearing, sarcastic and contemptuous father. However hard she tried, Susan had never been able to match up to Uncle George's standards; and it had left an indelible mark on her.

Vicky was leaning on the top of the car looking round her curiously. 'How far is it to Florence?'

'I forget exactly how many miles it is, but it takes me just under an hour. I set off at . . . oh, dear!' Susan, about to get into her seat, had stiffened, and Vicky felt her nerves prickle as she looked round to see who had put that look into her cousin's face. For a second she was afraid she would see the hounds of the press bearing down on her, baying for blood, but then she realised that Susan was giving a polite, uneasy smile, greeting a man who had just parked his car nearby.

'Hallo, Ricco.' Susan had flushed guiltily, almost as though it was she who was in hiding.

'*Ciao*, Susan.' The voice was deep and caressing, a voice with the sun in it. Vicky felt her cousin's agitation deepen and was curious—what was making Susan so uptight? She had assumed that Susan was nervous on her behalf, but it was far more than that—it was this man who was the root of her cousin's unease. Vicky studied him thoughtfully, secure behind her sunglasses. Their smoky lenses hid her eyes from him, which didn't stop him from staring back as if trying to probe through the dark glass.

'I'm here to meet someone off the London plane—is it in yet, do you know?' He sauntered over to the Fiat, his dark blue eyes making lazy forays over Vicky's figure in the white jacket and candy-pink pants, with which she wore a matching top under the jacket. The outfit was perfect for travelling in; practically uncreasable and machine washable, it was both light and cool once she shed the jacket, as she had done on the plane.

'Yes, most of the passengers have left, so you'd better hurry,' Susan told him.

He glanced at her and then at Vicky. 'Aren't you going to introduce us?'

Susan floundered, her eyes appealing to her cousin. 'Yes, I . . . this is . . .'

Vicky rescued her calmly. 'I'm Ann Lloyd, an old school friend of Susan's.'

She heard Susan give a muffled sigh of relief—they had forgotten to think of a false identity for her, but then this trip had been arranged in such a hurry there had been no time for lengthy explanations or discussions. She had just asked if she could come and Susan had said yes, of course, where else would you go?

'I'm Riccardo Salvatore, one of Susan and David's neighbours.' He offered his hand and she rather reluctantly took it. His skin was smooth and cool, the tanned hand firmly shaped and elegant with long, sensitive fingers, which clasped hers for a moment longer than she liked. His accent was only faintly Italian and his English extraordinarily good, a great deal better than her own Italian, but she hadn't needed to know his name to guess his nationality. He was distinctly Latin, a black-haired, long-limbed man of Mediterranean appearance, bronzed and lithe, with strikingly austere features and a mouth which contradicted them. Wide and strongly moulded, it held a mixture of sensuality, humour and cynicism which was at odds with his pared cheekbones, firm jaw and long, arrogant nose.

'Staying long?' he asked, and she shrugged, very conscious of his gaze on her short blonde hair, and hoping he wasn't noticing that it was not her natural colour. She wasn't used to being blonde herself, yet; when she looked into the mirror in the plane's loo she had done a double take for a second, confused and blinking, until she remembered that she had had her hair dyed. She had often wondered what it felt like to be a blonde, but so far she hadn't noticed much difference. Perhaps it was only casual interest that made Riccardo Salvatore stare like that? All the same, he looked as if not much escaped him. She must try not to see him again. How close a neighbour was he? It was clear that he knew Susan well, yet she had hardly been overjoyed to see him.

'Is this your first visit to Florence?'

'Yes.' It would be wisest to keep her replies short and succinct. That way she was less likely to make a slip-up.

'Then you have a unique opportunity ahead of you—I often wish I had new eyes to see my city with. I've lived here most of my life and know it too well. You must let me show you some of my favourite places.'

She smiled coolly, the delicately shaped mouth beneath the dark glasses curving very slightly without real warmth. 'How kind, but Susan has promised to give me a guided tour while I'm here.'

His eyes narrowed as he studied her, very cool, very English, with her smooth clear skin and fair hair that was shaped inwards to her long, slim neck. Vicky caught a glint of derisive impatience in his stare, but before he could say whatever was on the tip of his tongue someone called his name behind them.

'Ricco! Ricco, *caro, c'è qualcosa che . . .*'

They all turned to stare at the woman hurrying towards them on the most amazingly high heels, her slender body swaying in a way that held the eyes of her porter riveted as he followed behind her with what appeared to be enough luggage for a whole party of tourists on a trolley. As the woman came she talked in a melodic, fluid Italian of which Vicky understood about one word in a dozen. It was hard to tell whether she was furious, excited or rapturous to see Riccardo Salvatore, but whichever it was the lady felt it with every fibre. Her husky voice swooped and soared, she gesticulated with her hands, her black eyes flashed, and Riccardo Salvatore listened, smiling. She appeared to amuse him, and at last he interrupted her with a flow of Italian of his own.

The porter leaned on his trolley, enjoying the discussion. Once or twice he intervened to add a comment of his own. Both parties turned on him, and he threw up his hands, shrugging.

'*Va bene, va bene, mi scusi!*'

'Bianca, I want you to meet someone—now, calm down, I'm sorry I wasn't there to meet you, but I met a neighbour.' He murmured introductions as his lady friend turned her sultry eyes on Vicky and Susan. 'This is Bianca Fancelli.'

Susan shyly offered her hand and Bianca languidly brushed her fingers over it. '*Ciao.*' She was beautiful and she knew it, full-breasted, golden-skinned, with a cloud of curling black hair and hips that moved with molten grace. Her lower lip pouted as she gave Susan a reluctant glance and then turned to give Ricco an accusing stare.

'*Che ora è? Non mi sento bene . . .*'

'*Va bene*, Bianca. We'll be on our way in a moment.'

'*Partirò domani!*' she shrieked at him, tossing back her head, and that, at least, Vicky understood. The lady was threatening to leave tomorrow; she was very displeased. Riccardo Salvatore had offended her, he had hung around out in the car park chatting up other women when he should have been in the terminal, dancing attendance on Bianca.

Ricco seemed unperturbed. In fact, he smiled with deep amusement and said to Susan and Vicky, 'She's a singer, and if she keeps screaming like that she's going to ruin her voice; she has a very delicate throat and ought to have more sense.'

'Oh dear,' said Susan, bemused, quite unaware that he was actually talking to Bianca, who understood every word, but whose only response was to make a sound deep in her throat, something between a spitting noise and the snarl of a furious cat.

'Singers!' Ricco sighed. 'Crazy people.'

Vicky had had enough of this particular little soap opera. 'Shall we go?' she asked Susan, opening the passenger door of the Fiat and sliding into her seat. Susan, more politely, said, 'We really should be going . . . nice to see you, Ricco, Miss Fancelli.'

Ricco opened her door for her, put a hand under her elbow to assist her into her seat, threw a brief glance across her at Vicky and smiled mockingly. '*Ciao, a presto!*'

Her face remained cool and his mouth twisted. '*Parla italiano?*'

She shook her head. 'Sorry, I'm afraid not.'

'Then it's time you learnt,' he informed her. 'I'll be happy to give you a few lessons while I'm showing you round Florence.' Before she could snap back that he wasn't teaching her anything or showing her around anywhere, he had closed the door firmly and stood back.

'What does he want, a harem?' growled Vicky as they drove out of the car park. 'I'd have thought his hands were full with the demanding Miss Fancelli, he didn't have to flirt with me.'

'He flirts with everyone.' Susan's eyes were on the road, but her tone held an odd quiver and Vicky watched her, frowning.

'With you, too?' she asked lightly, and heard the involuntary, half-stifled sigh her cousin gave.

'Oh, well . . . yes . . . I'd just laugh if only . . .'

'If only what?' Vicky had known her since they were both in their prams; they had grown up together, living in the same small village five minutes' walk from each other's houses. She could always tell when Susan had something on her mind, and she sensed now that the something currently weighing heavily with her cousin was a six-foot-tall Italian called Riccardo Salvatore. It didn't enter Vicky's head for an instant that Susan might be in love with him. She had seen her cousin's face light up when she talked about her husband. Susan was still passionately in love with David, so what was bothering her? Was Riccardo Salvatore being rather too pressing? Had he been trying to seduce Susan? Vicky remembered the sensual, cynical curve of his mouth, the mocking blue eyes, and could easily imagine it. Susan's blushes, shyness, obvious uneasiness might have given him the idea that she fancied him, was giving him a green light. Ricco Salvatore might be sophisticated; Susan wasn't.

Vicky kept her eyes on her cousin's averted profile. 'Oh, nothing,' Susan said, very pink. 'By the way, this is a Roman road, the old road from Pisa to Florence. We'll be turning on to the autostrada in a minute. We should arrive by three-thirty. That will give you plenty of time to see the villa, have a bath and a rest on your bed if you like before David gets home. He's promised to take us out to dinner tonight if you aren't too tired.' Susan turned a brighter face to her, smiling. 'I hope you aren't! We haven't been out to dinner for ages. I'm looking forward to it.'

Vicky laughed. 'Oh, I'll manage to stagger out. I've been dieting but I don't see why I shouldn't gorge myself on some delicious Italian food once in a while.' Her eyes wandered over the flat landscape, dotted with little houses and vineyards and orchards, half veiled at the moment in a gentle, misty light. Spring was touching the trees with green, the first new leaves. Their colour seemed to run through the valley like green smoke, indefinite, drifting, hard to pin down. Vicky's eyes lifted to the skyline, where a range of hills rose, blue and hazy.

'Those are the Carrara mountains, where the marble comes from, you know? All the sculptors used Carrara marble, they still do if they can afford it, but it's very expensive now. David is going to drag you around to see everything Michelangelo did, so I hope you like sculpture.'

'I'm not in love with it,' Vicky said drily. 'A little culture goes a long way with me, you know that.'

Susan turned to grin at her. 'Well, I told David you used to have to be dragged round art galleries kicking and screaming, but he loves to spread the gospel. That only whetted his appetite. He thinks he'll convert you.'

'Optimist!'

They slowed as they approached the toll which marked the beginning of the autostrada. As they passed through the barrier Vicky leaned back in her seat, watching the other cars. One roared past, sounding its horn. She started, just catching a glimpse of Ricco Salvatore at the wheel of the gleaming red Lamborghini which was already heading away from them at a speed that Susan's little Flat could not possibly match.

'Aren't you going to tell me what went wrong?' Susan asked quietly a moment later, and Vicky gave a long sigh.

'I had to get away, I couldn't take it any more,' she said after a pause. 'You have no idea what it was like, Susan—a nightmare! Yesterday I woke up, and I knew I had to get away, end it. It was the only way—a sharp break. But if anyone had known what was in my mind there would have been all hell to pay, and I simply couldn't face that, more press, more questions, more photographers and . . .' She stopped talking, her voice harsh. 'So I rang you, and then I booked my flight and kept my fingers crossed that nobody at Heathrow would recognise the name, that there wouldn't be any press around watching people board. You've no idea how much I sweated until I was on the plane and we were taking off!'

Susan took one hand off the wheel and touched her lightly. 'Poor Vicky, I must say I don't think I could have faced it either. Not my scene—all that publicity, being in the limelight all the time. But what about Miller? He must have been shattered when you told him.'

Vicky stiffened in her seat, her eyes on the silver birches and tall, dark cypresses on the slopes above the road. She didn't say anything, and Susan looked round at her, face appalled.

'Vicky! You did tell him! You didn't just go?'

'I wrote to him; posted it on my way to Heathrow.' Vicky felt guilty about doing it that way, but she hadn't dared risk talking to Miller beforehand. Any hint that she meant to run would have been disastrous; he wouldn't have understood and he would have tried to talk her out of it, but far more than that, he would have told Sunny, he told Sunny everything and Sunny, of course, would have picked up a phone and told the press. No, she could'nt have told Miller until she was safely out of the country.

Susan was staring at her with dismay and reproach. 'Oh, Vicky! Poor Miller, what a dreadful shock it will be when he reads your letter, he's going to be so hurt. Don't you think you should have told him to his face? At least talked it over with him! Just going away . . . it doesn't seem very kind.'

Vicky's face was pale and set. She had known how Susan would react; she understood Susan's feelings, and looking at the situation from the outside it was the way most people would react, but then only someone who had been through what she had been through for the last month would understand why she was running away like this.

'Please, Susan, can we change the subject? I had to do it that way and I don't want to talk about it. For the moment, I just want to forget the whole thing.' She sat up straight, her hands locked in her lap. They were very cold, although the sun was warm on her face. 'What are those trees along the centre of the road?' she asked.

'Oleanders,' Susan,said absently, giving them a quick glance. 'In high summer they're covered with the most gorgeous flowers, pink and red. It's quite a sight.' She slowed pace, the car doing a steady forty miles an hour. 'Vicky, didn't you love him?'

Vicky kept her eyes fixed on the passing landscape. Ignoring the question, she asked, 'Is that another airport? I thought Pisa was the nearest one to Florence?'

'It isn't a civil airport, that's a military base. Oh, look, that plane is dropping parachutists!'

As they watched, the sky suddenly filled with delicate, frilly-edged white flowers which floated downwards like petals on a warm wind. The dark doll-like figures hanging beneath the flowers gradually came into view as men in camouflage uniform, but by the time the car had done another few hundred yards the parachutists were out of sight behind some airport buildings.

'I've often thought I'd like to do some parachuting,' Vicky said reflectively. 'I'd like to learn to fly, too. It must give you a great kick, being up there all by yourself.'

Susan didn't seem to agree, her brow was furrowed. 'David's bound to want to know what's going on, Vicky—what am I to tell him?'

'What I just told you.' Vicky glanced at her, biting her lower lip. She hadn't considered how David might react. 'Look, if you think he might disapprove, might not want me around . . .'

'Oh, don't be silly! David likes you, and he's often said we ought to have you to stay with us some time. You're very welcome, you know that. It's just that . . .'

Susan was always starting sentences she didn't finish, a habit which had begun in childhood when she found it so hard to talk to her father. Until quite recently she had stammered whenever she was nervous. Perhaps she still did? Uncle George had a lot to answer for; yet when he died Susan and her mother had cried their eyes out and been in a state of grief for ages afterwards. Even now Aunt Lucy hadn't remarried; the last time Vicky saw her, her aunt had several times mentioned her dead husband, although he had died four years ago.

'Just that what?' probed Vicky, patiently, used to Susan's incoherent way of blurting out confidences.

'Well, he was just joking, Vicky, but he said he

hoped that having you here wouldn't mean that we'd have the *paparazzi* descending on us, too.' Susan gave a nervous, placatory laugh. 'But he was only joking. It's just that Signor Rossi might not like any sort of publicity, David being caught up in any sort of publicity, I mean.'

'Who is Signor Rossi?'

'His boss,' Susan said, sounding astonished that Vicky hadn't known that. 'He's a very kind man, he's always sending us things—fruit, game, that sort of thing. He has a large estate in the hills somewhere, right out in the country. He's very rich.'

'Obviously. And he doesn't like publicity?'

'Well, for the firm, he does, but . . .'

'Not for David? Not the sort of publicity I'd attract, anyway.' Vicky could see the man's point. She didn't like the sort of publicity she had been getting lately, either.

David Bruce had taken up a job in Italy just after his marriage. Until then he had worked for a large multi-national oil company. He was a brilliant engineer, and had gone straight from college to work on oil rigs in the North Sea, but now he was confined to a desk in an office in Florence, having become a white-collar engineer. He was highly paid and had had promotion since joining the Anglo-Italian firm he worked for, but from Susan's letters Vicky had sensed that he had a lingering regret for the days when he worked in the field, getting himself dirty, taking risks, living a more exciting life than he did now when he was just a consultant.

'You did tell David not to mention that I was coming? To anyone at all?' she asked Susan, who nodded.

'Then there's no reason why anyone should ever find out,' said Vicky, staring out of the window as they climbed a tree-shaded hill. 'How much further is it to Florence?'

'You'll see it any minute now; it's just in front of us.'

They cruised along the narrow, winding road and emerged on to an open plateau, and there Vicky caught her first glimpse of Florence. The city was veiled in mist through which floated domes and spires, the warm yellow walls glowing softly in that diffused light, their colours so natural that they looked as if they had grown up from the earth they stood on rather than having been built by the hand of man. They clustered so close together that you could not see the streets.

Vicky leaned forward, mouth parted on a breath of enchantment. 'All the houses seem to be the same colour.' The yellow plaster was close to the colour of pale mustard, and the wavy ancient tiles on the roofs were all rose-red terracotta.

'They call that colour sienna, it means earth,' said Susan, parking the car close to a stone balustrade round a vast square which had been built above the city, looking through the trees, shrubs and flowers of a terraced garden tumbling down into the city itself.

'And that's the Uffizi—down there near the Arno. We'll take you there one day this week. That's where you'll see what David calls *le monstre sacré* of Italian art—Botticelli! If you can get near the paintings, that is—there's usually a crowd six deep round them all. Do you want to get out and take a closer look now, or are you tired? David did say he'd be home early to welcome you to Florence.'

Vicky would have liked to get out and stand there for a long time, gazing down on the city, but she picked up the reluctant note in Susan's voice and knew her cousin wanted to get back home, so she shook her head.

'I can see I'm going to have a strenuous visit, tramping around Florence from art gallery to art gallery, so I'd better conserve my energy for the moment. Anyway, I'm dying to see your little villa.'

Susan laughed, starting the car again, and drove on. 'I'm afraid it is little—we only have two bedrooms and a sitting-room and kitchen. But it's modern. Ricco only had it built two years ago.'

'Ricco?' Vicky was startled.

Susan turned to look at her. 'Yes, didn't you realise that he was our landlord? He lives in an enormous house, it's very old, thirteenth-century. It used to be a convent or monastery or something, but Ricco's family bought it in the seventeenth century and they've lived there ever since. They were in banking.' Susan laughed. 'Banking practically began in Florence, you know, it's the biggest local trade.'

'He's a banker?' Vicky was incredulous, and Susan laughed again.

'Ricco? No, of course not, although that's where all his family money came from—anyway, he had a lot of land with his house, and he wasn't using it, so he built two small villas at the far end of the gardens, and we live in one.'

She slowed to turn into a driveway through a pair of high ironwork gates. Stone lions sat primly, paws together, on top of two tall stone pillars; Vicky just caught sight of them as the car swept past, between rows of cypress trees. 'This is it,' said Susan. 'The Villa Giglio—that means lily, by the way, nothing to do with the famous singer. That's what I thought when we first came.'

'Is that the name of your villa, or of Ricco's?'

'Oh, his—our place is called Villa l'Arancia.'

'Which means?'

'House of the orange tree, or actually trees—there's a little cluster of them but the winter was pretty hard on them, we don't know if they survived it yet.' Susan turned right as she emerged from the rows of cypress. 'If you're quick you can just see Ricco's house through the trees there.'

She slowed, and Vicky peered through drooping branches, seeing sunlight on smooth, warm columns supporting a loggia on the upper floor of a long, two-storey building with the same terracotta tiles and sienna walls that she had seen a few minutes ago in Florence. The brief glimpse was enough to make her realise how old the house must be; it had a shabby beauty in the sunlight, yet even at this distance she could see the flaking paint on woodwork, the cracks in the plaster, the air of decay the whole place wore, even if it wore it with grace and charm.

'Did you say thirteenth-century?'

'That's the legend. It has a maze of rooms, some of them tiny—they look just like the cells of a monastery, very bare and austere. Ricco keeps them whitewashed and mostly empty. He sometimes talks of turning the place into a hotel, but he never gets around to it.'

'He must be rich, having all this land and that

enormous house.'

'I suppose he must,' Susan said uncertainly. 'He never gives the impression of being rich; he wears jeans most of the time, and his clothes are mostly pretty comfortable and shabby.'

'He's rich! They're always keen to look poor. It's people like us, without money, who want to look as if we've got it.'

'Don't be such a cynic!' Susan had threaded her way along another row of cypress and was parking right outside a small, modern, whitewashed villa, of the familiar Mediterranean type you could see everywhere—two-storied, boxlike, built like a dolls' house. This one was given more charm by a pair of small orange trees in high earthenware pots which stood on either side of the front door.

Susan watched her cousin's face as Vicky gazed out at it. 'What do you think?' she asked, anxious for Vicky to like it.

'It's very pretty. Were the orange trees your idea?'

'Ricco's.'

They got out of the car and Susan unlocked the front door while Vicky carried her case. It was obvious at once that the house had been designed for a small family; it was built on the open plan with one area downstairs divided by low half-walls into three separate spaces—a living-room area, a kichen area and a dining area. The walls had been lined with bookshelves and were topped with marble tiles on which stood house plants, giving the place a garden air, spacious, full of light.

'Ricco designed this, too, I suppose?' Vicky was really beginning to dislike him; he seemed omnipresent in her cousin's life.

Susan nodded. 'I think it's terrific, don't you?' She was on the defensive, conscious of Vicky's unspoken reservations.

'Charming,' Vicky agreed, and followed her cousin up the open staircase, built in a warm varnished pinewood, into the smaller of the two bedrooms.

Sunlight flooding in through a wide window showed her a pastel-painted room, one wall fitted with pinewood wardrobes, the décor modern and restrained. A dark blue bowl of some lustrous pottery stood on the window-sill, hyacinths growing in it, giving the air a heady scent.

'It isn't very big, but I think you'll be comfortable,' said Susan, going over to open the window. 'You're our first guest, apart from my mum and David's parents. Mum loves it here, she came for a month last summer. David's mum and dad have only been once, but then we had to cram another bed in here, which didn't leave much space. I'm afraid David's mother was rather disappointed.'

'You still don't get on too well with her?' Vicky was opening her case as she and Susan talked, and together they hung up the dresses and put away lingerie in the thoughtfully designed wardrobes which had a set of drawers built at one side.

Grimacing, Susan shook her head. 'She thought David could have done better for himself than me. She's very ambitious for him.'

'I think David couldn't have done better,' Vicky said firmly, smiling.

Susan went down to make some tea when they had emptied the case, and Vicky had a quick shower and changed into a silky yellow cotton dress with a scooped neckline and tight waist. The skirt swirled around her calves as she walked over to the window to stare at the terracotta roof of Ricco Salvatore's house, which she could just see through the trees. Was he there now, with his excitable lady-friend? Perhaps they were making up their quarrel. Vicky could easily imagine how—Bianca Fancelli had such sultry, inviting eyes, and Vicky didn't see Ricco Salvatore turning their invitation down.

A swallow darted past, a flash of blue and black, the forked tail quivering. She had a brief glimpse of its beak, full of small twigs; it was nest-building, another omen of spring. She followed its flight absently. It vanished under the eaves of Ricco's house, and then she saw that a small colony of swallows had set up residence there in nests of clay and twigs, baked dry by the Italian sun.

Vicky sighed, her shoulders shuddering. Now that she was alone and no one could see her she found it hard to pretend to be cheerful.

By the time she left, she had realised that she was no longer in love with Miller. She had made a mistake; what she had taken for love had been infatuation, yet even now he still had some hold on her. If she let herself think about him she felt a little tremor of response. He and Ricco Salvatore had this much in common—they were both flirts. Had Miller not been an instinctive flirt they would never have met, because they hardly moved in the same worlds, their paths would never have crossed in the normal way.

Vicky had worked in the design department of a small fashion house, her days there long and crammed with work. She lived in a modest flat in a north London borough which still had some pretence of being in the country; trees lined the streets, there was a little river, now too often polluted with industrial waste, and several large parks. All the houses had gardens, and in summer it was a pleasant place to live. Vicky had had several boy-friends in the past, but when she met Miller she had been heartfree, perhaps even ready to fall in love, and the way in which they met was so romantic and unexpected that it had pushed her headlong into an affair before she knew what was happening.

She had been walking in Hyde Park, very early one autumn morning, under the burnished trees which had just begun to shed their leaves. She had heard the thud of hoofs behind her on a bridle track running alongside the grass she was walking over and had glanced round, smiling, a fresh wind blowing her brown hair across her face. She had been feeling happy; it was such a lovely morning and her walk had been invigorating. The sight of the tall man riding his gleaming black horse seemed the perfect finishing touch.

What she hadn't expected was that the rider should suddenly veer towards her, putting his mount at the gallop. Vicky stood stock still, mouth open in shock, thinking for one horrified second that he was going to knock her down. She should have run, of course, but it all happened too fast. One moment she was frozen there, staring; the next a long arm scooped her up, her feet left the ground and she was pulled across the saddle in front of the laughing rider, held too tightly to feel scared, cradled against him as he rode on under the trees.

Her heart had been beating like a drum, but she hadn't been frightened, she had started to laugh, and Miller had looked down at her then, laughing too.

That was when she had recognised him, and her jaw had dropped. Miller had seen that dazed expression and realised what it meant. His eyes danced with amusement.

'Yeah, it's me,' he said, as if she had asked a question.

She had seen a huge photograph of him in that morning's paper as she ate her breakfast. She had been working half the night on a rush job for her boss and had slept on a couch in the office, that was why she was up so early, before London was really awake. She had gone out to have breakfast at a small café and bought a morning paper to read while she ate. Miller had been on the front page. His latest film was opening in London that week and he was over from America to publicise it. Vicky had vaguely noticed his lean, dark-skinned features, skimmed over the story under the picture. She wasn't a particular fan of his, although she had seen some of his films and enjoyed them. The news that he was in London hadn't excited her, and she had certainly never imagined in her wildest dreams that she might ever meet him, let alone that he might snatch her up and gallop off with her.

It seemed too much like a scene from one of his films, and after the first disbelieving shock she looked around among the trees. The park was almost empty; a few early morning joggers ran along the paths and a squirrel was frisking up a russet-leaved oak, but otherwise they might have been alone in a wilderness.

'Is this some sort of publicity stunt?' she asked warily as he let his horse slow to a walk, the reins loose in his fingers.

'See any press around?' he had drawled, grinning wickedly.

He had a natural charm, and even if he had not been so good-looking he would probably have been irresistible to her that morning. Although she did not know it then, Miller had been in much the same mood, euphoric and reckless, wide open to what hit them both as they looked into each other's eyes.

Oh, yes, it had been wildly romantic at the start, but it had left her with a sour aftertaste which she was sure would take a long time to wear off.

CHAPTER TWO

'WHAT about your job? Has your boss given you time off or did you just walk out on him, too?'

'David!' Susan's voice was appalled, but Vicky gave David a dry little smile, accepting the justice of the question.

'I was fired a month ago.'

David stared at her, frowning, but Susan's mouth opened in a gasp of dismay and sympathy.

'Fired? Did the firm get into trouble? You mean you were made redundant?'

'I mean I was fired. My boss had had enough. His patience ran out. He'd had enough of his clients being unable to get into the building through a solid wall of media people, he'd had enough of me vanishing for half the day after Sunny had whisked me off for lunch which turned out to be being eaten in Paris or Madrid or wherever Miller happened to be doing publicity. I think the final straw was when my boss sent me out to buy him a hot dog and I didn't show up again for four hours. When he'd stopped shouting I put on my coat and left. There seemed little point in telling him that Sunny had literally kidnapped me, dragged me into the car in spite of my protests and driven me to Sussex to see Miller sailing his damn yacht!'

They had both listened to her furious, gunfire recital in stupefied silence. Susan got up from the couch where she was sitting beside her husband and ran over to kneel down next to Vicky, hugging her.

'How awful, you poor darling! Why didn't you say it had been that bad?' She turned to eye her husband accusingly. 'Say you're sorry to Vicky, she's been through a tough time.'

'Sorry, Vicky,' David said obediently. He was a large, rugged man a good ten years older than his wife, with rough wiry brown hair and dark eyes, a sallow complexion which had taken the sun far more than Susan's skin had done,and shoulders and a deep chest which rippled with muscles. Vicky had been delighted when her cousin married someone so stable and easy-going. Susan was a vulnerable girl, insecure and uncertain about herself after her difficult childhood. Vicky had believed that David would give her cousin the secure affection she needed, and since the marriage, Susan had certainly blossomed. Her letters had been lively and cheerful and she looked well, but, tanned and healthy though she was, Vicky still sensed that something was wrong between husband and wife. They were far too polite with each other, far too careful. Vicky suspected that they were putting on an act for her benefit.

Looking at his watch, David said he must go and change and then they'd go out to dinner in Florence. Giving Vicky and Susan a placatory smile, he added, 'I've managed to book a table at Pinchiorri's.'

'Pinchiorri's!' Susan sounded taken aback, her eyes widening. 'Can we . . .' She broke off whatever she had been about to say, looking hurriedly at Vicky and forcing a smile. 'Well, that's a lovely idea, David. Vicky, you're in for a treat. Pinchiorri's is the best restaurant in Florence; their menu is supposed to be fabulous, and I've been told that their wine cellar is out of this world—not that we've ever been there yet. I've been dying to eat there, but we couldn't . . . well, hadn't you better hurry, David? It's a quarter to seven already.'

'Give me ten minutes,' said David, sprinting to the hall. They heard his feet thudding on the wooden stairs. Susan had got to her feet too. She drifted towards the kitchen with the tea tray.

'You keep talking about Sunny—I'm not sure who he is . . .'

'Miller's agent, or manager, I'm not sure what to call him. He runs Miller's life.' Vicky's voice was cold and hostile. 'And he wanted to run mine.' Her lip curled in distaste at things she had no intention of telling Susan; her cousin would only have been upset if she knew how much of an interest in her Sunny had taken. Susan knew nothing of the sort of world Sunny and Miller inhabited, and she was better off not knowing.

Susan looked up at the ceiling, through which they could hear David wandering around the bedroom above. He was pulling out drawers and slamming cupboards. 'He's looking for his tie and socks,' Susan said. 'I'd better go and help before he starts shouting.'

A moment later, Vicky heard Susan and David talking in the room above. They were obviously trying to keep their voices down, but this little house was not built for privacy; the walls were too thin, the spaces too open. Vicky couldn't pick out their actual words, but one thing was obvious: they were quarrelling.

She frowned. Susan sounded anxious—about what? Vicky had noticed the expression on her cousin's face when David said he had booked a table at Pinchiorri's. It was obviously a very expensive restaurant, and Susan felt David couldn't afford to take them there. Was that what they were arguing about now? Vicky bit down on her lower lip, forehead creased, then picked up her purse and checked that she had the folder of traveller's cheques she had got from the bank the afternoon before she left London. She wasn't going to let David bankrupt himself on her account. She would have to be tactful, choose exactly the right moment, then insist on paying the bill herself.

She had left in such a hurry that she hadn't had time to make arrangements for having money transferred from her bank to Florence, but in a way that might be just as well. Nobody could trace her through her bank; she had taken the precaution of having the cheques made out in dollars, which could be cashed in any country.

She had asked the post office to readdress all her incoming mail to her aunt, Susan's mother, who could then forward it to Florence. Vicky hadn't wanted to leave any loose ends for Sunny to follow.

Above her head, David's voice was raised a few decibels. 'I don't approve of any of this! She should have talked to him, face to face. No, okay, Susan, it isn't my business, but if you ask me this guy is well out of it. Vicky was never a serious type, now was she?'

Vicky swung away and walked to the french windows, suppressing a smile. Absolutely right, David, she thought, staring out at the roses, which were showing tight, tiny green buds. I was never the serious type.

Odd to think of oneself as a type. It lessened the feeling of being an individual, a person, making private decisions about private matters. Types acted all in one way, like computers, didn't they? They were programmed, fed instructions which they must follow. How did you decide which type you were? How did David see himself?

The serious type, she felt, yes, definitely—David would see himself as the serious type. Miller? He had been the glamorous type, no question of that. And Sunny?

She clenched her hands at her side, her mouth twisting with distaste. She didn't even want to consider what type he was—a rogue that had escaped from the factory with half the programming uncompleted. Why did Miller let Sunny run his life? He didn't do a thing until Sunny had given the okay; the man dominated Miller, his actions and thoughts as well as his career. If Vicky hadn't fled, Sunny would have tried to dominate her, too.

That prospect had made Vicky feel very serious indeed.

A few moments later Susan and David came down together, smiling too brightly, like people who have had a row but don't want you to know it. Vicky was sorry for David; he had obviously decided to take her to Pinchiorri's as a gesture of welcome which he couldn't really afford, simply to please his wife, and all he had got for his trouble was a row with Susan over the expense.

As they drove back into Florence down the hill Vicky wondered how much rent they had to pay

Ricco Salvatore. Far more than they could afford, she suspected, but then they hadn't had to furnish the house themselves. Susan had told her that Ricco had picked out all the furniture and was responsible for the upkeep and decoration of the house. His gardener came over once a week to do any heavy work in the garden for Susan, too, although she enjoyed looking after the flowers and shrubs herself.

The restaurant was situated on the ground floor of a fifteenth-century palace right in the heart of the city in the Via Ghibellina, close to the Piazza Santa Croce. David dropped them on the Lungarno, the road running along beside the River Arno, and drove off to find somewhere to park before walking back to join them at the restaurant. Florence was a city being strangled by traffic; the narrow medieval streets were unsuitable for cars, and the area round the Piazza della Signoria, where tourists most tended to cluster to see the Uffizi and the Palazzo Vecchio, had been made a pedestrian precinct, but there were cars everywhere on the streets where Vicky and Susan walked that evening, and parking was obviously impossible.

The air was cooler now; Vicky was glad of the white wool jacket which she had had to discard when she first arrived. Her eyes roamed curiously over the old buildings which they passed in the narrow streets. There were plenty of people about, crowding the pavements, forcing her and Susan to step off into the road at risk to life and limb from passing cars because the pavements were so narrow that two people could not walk abreast, but when they crossed the Piazza Santa Croce there was certainly space enough. It was a vast, open square with the enormous Franciscan church at one side.

'Michelangelo and Galileo are buried there,' Susan told her as she paused to stare at the façade.

'It's hideous,' said Vicky, and Susan laughed.

'Well, it isn't the most beautiful church in the world, but it has some wonderful art in it. David's going to take you there, so beware!'

'Michelangelo probably died of shock after seeing the place for the first time!'

'Oh, it didn't look like this when he was alive. I'm afraid an Englishman is responsible for the façade, as any self-respecting Italian would rush to tell you. The façade was added in the nineteenth century, so was the bell tower.'

'Gothic style—yes, I might have guessed it was Victorian. It's a nice big square, anyway.'

'They used to play football matches in it during the sixteenth century. Much nicer to watch out here than behind barbed wire fences the way they do today, don't you think?'

The sun was setting as they strolled towards the Ciofi-Iacometti palace, the ground floor of which had been turned into a restaurant. Vicky looked up, her eyes dazed by the roseate light running across the sky. Half blind, she walked beside Susan, not seeing where she was going, so that it was Susan who first noticed the man in the pale lightweight suit standing outside the palace entrance.

'Ricco!'

Startled, Vicky stared, seeing his lean face through a dazzle of gold.

'*Ciao*, Susan. Are you eating here tonight, too?' His deep voice was becoming familiar already. Vicky focused on him, her instincts warily picking up her cousin's barely disguised anxiety and Ricco Salvatore's mockery. He was smiling at Susan, but there was an odd glint in his eye. What went on between Susan and this man? Vicky knew there was something between them, something her cousin tried to hide from her, did not want her to guess.

'You're dining here?' Susan's face went pale and then blushed. 'Oh.'

Ricco flicked a look at Vicky, his black lashes touched with gilt in the fading sunlight. He looked very elegant; a tall, lean-hipped man whose clothes had a panache which to Vicky suggested very expensive tailoring.

'Are you alone, you two?' His eyes were skimming over her from her short blonde hair to her feet. 'Did you have a rest this afternoon, Miss Lloyd? Flying can be very tiring. Bed is the best place when you're so tense.' It was polite small talk—but how did he manage to invest it with an undercurrent of other meaning?

'Yes, thank you,' she said, and at the same time Susan stammered, 'No, we aren't alone—I mean, David will be joining us any minute.'

'And Miss Lloyd is playing gooseberry? A threesome is always awkward, isn't it? I'm eating alone, would you mind if I joined you?'

Susan took a gulp of air, pink to her hairline. She couldn't have looked more horrified if Ricco Salvatore had announced that he ate roast mice on toast, but while she floundered trying to think of a polite way of rejecting his suggestion Ricco took matters out of her hand and calmly seized Vicky's elbow, steering her into the building.

'Shall we go in and have an aperitif while we wait

for David?' he murmured.

Vicky threw her cousin a glance, wry and impatient, but there seemed little point in pulling herself out of the grip Ricco had on her arm, so she went with him and Susan unhappily followed them.

'What happened to Miss Fancelli?' Vicky asked as an attentive waiter showed them to a table, smiling as he greeted Ricco by name.

'She went to sleep as soon as she got to her hotel. She's a night bird; she'll wake up and feel hungry around midnight.'

'She isn't staying with you, then?'

He turned cool blue eyes on her. 'No, my house isn't big enough.'

Her brows shot up. 'It looks enormous.' She remembered the long, rambling building which Susan had described as a maze of rooms. What sort of house was Bianca Fancelli used to if Ricco's wasn't big enough for her? Was she very rich, or merely very demanding?

'Oh, it's large,' Ricco agreed drily. 'But if it had a hundred rooms it wouldn't be big enough to hold both myself and Bianca. Having her under the same roof is a little like living in the centre of a maelstrom. All singers have temperament; Bianca simply has twice as much as anyone else, but then her voice is twice as good, so we have to take her as she is. Have you ever heard her sing?'

'I've never heard of her,' Vicky admitted. 'What sort of singer is she?'

His blue eyes were incredulous. 'What sort of . . . my dear Miss Lloyd, I'm speechless! She is a mezzo-soprano, one of the best in the world, in my opinion; certainly one of the best in Italy, and we have a great many first-class mezzos.'

'Oh, opera?'

He regarded her ironically. 'You don't like opera?'

'I didn't say that.' She felt defensive, picking up the dryness of his voice. 'I just don't know much about it. I've seen a few operas, but I'm not particularly musical.'

'Vicky's a fashion designer,' Susan explained with pride, and Ricco's brows lifted.

'Really? A famous one?'

'No,' Vicky said stubbornly, lifting her chin. 'And I'm not the sort of designer Susan implied—I design the fabrics which are used by the man who designs the clothes,' She paused, her eyes regretful. 'I did, anyway.' Until Sunny saw to it that she lost her job!

'You did? Does that mean you've changed your job?'

She shrugged. She didn't want to tell him all the details of her private life. 'Yes.' The crisply succinct answer didn't stop him asking further questions; apparently a slammed door didn't register with Ricco Salvatore.

'So what do you do now?'

'At the moment, nothing. I'm on holiday.'

He studied her, his blue eyes narrow gleaming slits, but as his lips parted, no doubt to deliver yet another question, David loomed up beside their table looking at Ricco like someone discovering a tarantula in his bath.

Susan burst into nervous gabbling. 'Oh, there you are, darling—guess who we met on the doorstep outside here? Ricco was going to eat alone and so . . .' Her voice trailed into miserable silence as David turned his furious eyes on her.

'And so I wondered if you would all be my guests tonight?' Ricco stepped in smoothly with a sunny smile, ignoring David's glower. 'As there are three of you and one of me it seems a very sensible idea. Four's such a comfortable number, and as I've been offering to be Miss Lloyd's guide around Florence I can start right away by telling her about this place. The palace has a fascinating history.'

'Miss Lloyd?' David repeated, gazing round as if expecting to see someone else.

'Ann,' Ricco supplied, looking amused.

Susan's face was scarlet, and she was trying desperately to convey a message to David with her eyes, rolling them towards Vicky in a manner that merely baffled David even further.

Vicky decided it was time she intervened. 'Me, you idiot,' she said, managing quite a convincing laugh. 'I know it's two years since we last met, David, but surely you haven't forgotten me altogether?'

He caught on at last. 'Oh. Oh yes, silly of me—I had something else on my mind, sorry, V . . . er . . . Ann.'

'That's okay, I know how absentminded you are,' she said, wishing Ricco Salvatore wasn't listening with such keen attention. She had a feeling he hadn't missed David's second slip, and was no doubt wondering what David had been about to call her before he corrected the name. 'Do sit down, David,' she added to distract Ricco. 'You make me feel nervous, standing there like that!'

David sat down next to his wife and Ricco

clicked finger and thumb, softly summoning the wine waiter.

'Signor Salvatore?' the man enquired, bending towards him with a smile.

'What will you have to drink, David?'

'A Cinzano rosso, thanks.' When the waiter had moved away David said stiffly, 'Kind of you to suggest that we should be your guests, Ricco, but I insist that you must be ours. You're very welcome to join us, but . . .'

'I tell you what, David, this time you're my guests, and next time you and Susan can ask me to dinner, then honour will be satisfied.' Smiling coolly as though that settled the matter, Ricco looked around. 'Now, where are those menus? I don't know about you, but I'm starving. I've had a difficult day—Bianca is a wonderful creature, but she can be very exhausting.'

Vicky's brows rose. She could believe that. Ricco caught her eye, and a wicked comprehension flashed across his lean, tanned face.

'Naughty, Miss Lloyd . . .' he murmured. 'I can't go on calling you that when you're my guest—may I call you Ann?' His gaze wandered over her in her vivid yellow dress, lingering on the low scooped neckline with an appreciation which brought a faint wash of pink back into her face. The man had a sensuality which needed no words; Vicky felt his blue eyes as tangibly as caressing fingers, and stiffened.

David said irritably, 'We don't call her Ann, we call her Vicky.'

There was a silence during which Vicky and Susan looked at each other across the table and

Ricco glanced from one to the other of them with sharp interest.

'Really? Why?'

David floundered, and Vicky came to his rescue. 'It's my second name, and I prefer it.' The truth was the opposite; Ann was her second name, which was why she had invented her alias that morning when Ricco asked Susan what her name was.

Ricco considered her, head to one side. 'Vicky . . . Ann . . . mmm . . . yes, I think you're right—Ann is a little too simple for you.'

'I don't look simple?'

His smile was derisive. 'Oh, I don't think so.'

The head waiter arrived with the menu a second later, and for quite a while they were all preoccupied with choosing their meal. When the question of food had been settled Ricco and David began to discuss the wine list with the serious faces of men for whom wine is one of the more important elements of life.

Vicky kicked Susan under the table and when her cousin looked at her made an eloquently relieved face. Susan grinned. So far any real problem had been averted.

'I think Vicky should taste the best local wine,' Ricco was saying. 'They have some superb Chianti *riserva* in the cellar.'

While they waited for their first course to be served they talked lightly, largely discussing what Vicky should see while she was in Florence. Several times new arrivals walking past their table halted to greet Ricco. Each time the women in the party kissed him, each time he kissed the lady's hand. Vicky watched, her mouth wry. He had charm; no doubt about that. Well, Miller had been strong on charm too, but he had been as weak as water in most other ways. From now on charm was going to be right at the bottom of her list of desirable qualities in a man. Looks weren't important, either. She had learnt that character was the only thing that mattered. It would be a long time before she looked twice at any man, but when she did she knew what she would be looking for—and it wouldn't be either charm or good looks.

Over their *antipasto* Ricco asked Vicky how long she planned to stay.

'Until Susan and David throw me out,' she said, laughing. 'Well, for a couple of weeks, probably.'

'For as long as you like!' Susan insisted. 'Mustn't she, David? After all, she's practically my sister . . .' Her voice trailed off as Ricco's head lifted, and he stared at her.

'Your sister? I thought you said she was an old school friend?'

Poor Susan was scarlet again. She was not a good liar; lies embarrassed her, she forgot what she was supposed to have said, and sooner or later her tongue tripped her up.

'We were very close,' Vicky said. 'Best friends, just like sisters.' She wasn't going to let Ricco cross-examine Susan.

'How touching,' Ricco responded drily, and she felt like throwing something at him.

'This wine is delicious,' she said instead, changing the subject.

'You haven't got a sister, have you, Susan?' he asked, though, undistracted.

'No, I was an only child,' said Susan, happy in the

security of the absolute truth.

Vicky fished a morsel of something soft and white out of her *antipasto* and waved it at him on a fork. 'What's this?'

'Squid,' he said, and she dropped it.

'Squid? You mean, those things with all the tentacles?' Her face wrinkled in disgust, and Ricco laughed.

'Try it, you'll like it.'

'I don't think I'll bother, thanks.'

He leaned over, picked up the piece of squid with his fork and offered it to her. 'Try it.'

Vicky reluctantly parted her lips and he pushed the food into her mouth. She chewed while he watched her, then mimed surprised pleasure. 'It isn't bad either—you're right.'

The shrewd blue eyes held a spark of sarcasm or derision. 'I'm so glad you agree,' he drawled, as if he knew perfectly well that she had made all that fuss solely to get his mind off Susan's little slip.

The meal was eaten in a leisurely atmosphere in the elegant restaurant. It was obvious that they were expected to take their time and enjoy the extraordinarily good food and wine. Everyone else was doing the same; laughing and talking between courses, sipping wine, looking around, exchanging small talk with neighbours at another table. Vicky hadn't known a great deal about Italian cuisine before she came here; the only food she associated with Italy was pasta in rich sauces. Tonight she was eating a subtle meal, beautifully cooked and varied, more international than she had expected. To her amazement it was well past eleven before they had finished and were drinking their coffee, and she noticed David secretly looking at his watch. Susan noticed, too.

'We ought to be going soon, David has to be at work by eight. People over here don't have the same working hours that we have at home, Vicky. They take about three hours off in the middle of the day, for lunch and a siesta, then go back to work around three-thirty or four. In the summer it's far too hot to work between twelve and four. It can be a hundred in the shade here.'

'That must limit your leisure time,' said Vicky, doing her best to drink her very hot coffee but only getting her tongue burnt.

'I'm sorry to rush off like this, Vicky,' David said, smiling wearily. 'I can hardly keep my eyes open after ten o'clock these days.'

'Look, why don't you two go on and let me bring Vicky home later?' suggested Ricco. 'Give her a key, then you can go up to bed without waiting for her.'

Vicky had an immediate jab of alarm. 'Oh, that's okay, I'm ready to go now, this coffee's too hot to drink.' She began to get up, but Ricco caught her wrist.

'Nonsense! You don't want to leave so early.'

David was on his feet, his face visibly relieved. 'If you're sure you don't mind, Ricco? I don't want to spoil Vicky's first night in Florence, but I need a good night's sleep.'

'I'm delighted,' Ricco assured him. 'I won't keep her out too late.'

Susan handed Vicky a key and reluctantly she took it, realising that it was pointless to argue since both her cousin and David looked so pleased that the problem had been amicably settled. They had been guilty about breaking up the evening so early.

'Have fun,' they said, hurrying away, waving, and Vicky sank back into her seat, feeling trapped.

Ricco eyed her with amusement, reading that expression. 'I don't bite,' he promised.

'I wish I could be sure of that.' Her voice was cynical and his brows rose.

'Don't you trust me?' He looked round, summoning the waiter. 'A brandy for me.' He glanced at Vicky. 'Will you have a liqueur with your coffee?'

'No, thank you.'

The waiter moved off and Ricco gave her a dry smile. 'Want to keep all your wits about you, do you?'

'Am I going to need to?'

'Not on my account,' he said smoothly, but she wasn't very reassured.

'Florence is a beautiful city, isn't it?' she said politely. After all, it was his city, he was probably very proud of it.

'You haven't seen her at her best. By the time we walk back to my car the moon will be up; it's full tonight, and the city looks lovelier by moonlight than it ever does by day. You won't get a chance to see the streets so empty at any other time—too many tourists, too much traffic. I'm glad I don't live in the city itself, I think I'd have a problem with invasion of my space.'

She stared blankly. 'Parking space, you mean?'

He laughed. 'Personal space.' He moved his hand lazily, describing a circle around himself. 'Don't you know that we all feel we have a force-field around us, keeping other people at a distance, giving us a tiny strip of private territory to walk about in?'

'That's an interesting theory. Is it yours or did you borrow it?'

'I didn't invent it, no. I think it's generally accepted.' He leaned over and ran a hand down her bare arm. She stiffened, the tiny hairs on her pale skin bristling at the contact.

He smiled mockingly at the affronted stare she gave him. 'You didn't like that? I was invading your territory and you objected, you see.'

'My objections had nothing to do with territory, private or otherwise,' she said through her teeth. 'I'm like the fruit on the barrows in the street out there—you can look, but don't touch.'

His eyes wandered calmly. 'Oh, I've been looking,' he said. 'And I like what I see.' His eyes smiled, an invitation in them which she didn't need to know Italian to understand. 'You have skin like a peach; the English often do, it must be all that rain.'

'That's a myth; it doesn't rain every day in England. It's just that we have very changeable weather; we can have four seasons in one day.'

'Englishwomen seem to share the same tendency,' he drawled.

Vicky gave him a cool smile. 'If you're talking about me, I assure you you're wrong. I shan't change my opinion of you, so don't waste any time expecting that I will.'

'I hesitate to ask what your opinion is,' he said wryly, and she offered him another of her cool smiles.

'I shouldn't.'

There was a disturbance around the entrance,

someone had just arrived and was causing a sensation. People were craning their necks and buzzing like a hive full of bees. Vicky curiously looked that way, her mouth tightening as she saw who had walked into the restaurant.

'Well, this is lucky—Bianca's here, I'm sure you'll find her much more appreciative than I am. You can show her Florence by moonlight—she'll love it. I suppose I can get a taxi home if I ask the manager to find me one? I wouldn't want to drag you away just as Bianca arrives.' She stood up, smiling politely. 'Thanks for the gorgeous meal.'

'I promised Susan that I'd see you home safely,' he protested, getting up too.

Bianca was shedding a fur wrap and giving vent to the now familiar stream of excited complaint. Tonight she was in what she no doubt described as a simple little black evening dress. Satin and apparently cut to use the minimum of material, it left nothing of Bianca's luscious curves to the imagination. The bodice plunged at the front almost to her midriff, a modicum of decency preserved by the delicate fan of black lace stretched from one side to the other. Her full, smooth white breasts strained at the lace as she swept down on them, apparently not even seeing Vicky, but gesticulating excitedly as she kissed Ricco.

'*Caro, come stai? Vorrei un bicchiere di vino.*' She settled herself at the table with a rustle of skirts. A bemused waiter appeared with a glass, another bottle of wine, a menu card.

'Sit, sit, sit,' ordered Bianca, tugging at Ricco's arm.

He said something in Italian, gesturing to Vicky,

who was wondering whether to walk away or make some polite pretence of greeting the other woman. As Bianca had ignored her she felt like doing the same, but Ricco was obviously talking about her, so she stayed.

Bianca glanced at her, raised incredulous eyebrows, ran her gaze over Vicky, pouted those full red lips and shrugged. It was a brilliant performance. Vicky was inspected and dismissed with that final amused shrug. It was clear that Vicky was unimportant. She could find her own way home. Bianca brushed her off and sipped some of her wine, smiling at the waiter.

'*Bene*.'

He bowed reverentially, and melted away. Bianca put out a commanding hand to Ricco, giving him an imperious frown. 'Ricco, *caro*!' She patted the seat next to her, but he didn't obey.

Vicky decided she had had enough of the charade. She walked away, leaving them together. She hadn't particularly cared whether Bianca said hallo to her or not, but it had made her hackles rise to be inspected insolently, then dismissed with a shrug. Bianca might be a famous opera singer, but that didn't give her the right to act as though she owned the world. No doubt she did own Ricco, as much, that was, as any woman would ever do. He didn't look the faithful type—he reminded Vicky of Miller far too much. Men could be divided into types; Miller and Ricco had a great deal in common, not least their looks and their sublime self-confidence. Not to mention the way women fell for them like ninepins.

She saw the man she supposed to be the head

waiter, and tried to catch his eye to ask him to get her a taxi, but as he moved towards her Ricco's hand gripped her arm and she turned round, startled.

'I told you, I'm driving you home,' he said, looking impatient.

'I don't want to take you away from Bianca.'

'A very feline remark.' His mouth twisted mockingly.

'Was it? Sorry. I'll get a taxi, there's no problem.' She was irritated to be told that she sounded catty. Why should she care if he stayed here with Bianca? If he spent the whole night with her? She couldn't care less, and if he imagined for one second that she was jealous he could think again.

'You will come with me,' he said, sounding very Italian suddenly, and since several waiters were now hovering within hearing distance Vicky had no option but to let him steer her out of the restaurant.

As they walked in search of his car, she tried to correct the impression she appeared to have given him.

'I simply meant that I wouldn't want you to offend Bianca by leaving her alone there. After all, I suppose she was joining you.'

'She is meeting a number of friends, they will be arriving any minute,' he said coolly.

'I suppose you can always go back there when you've dropped me,' said Vicky, hurrying.

'Where's the fire?' Ricco asked drily, his long legs keeping pace without difficulty. 'You aren't even looking at the moon.'

She threw a glance upwards; the moon was certainly spectacular, and as they emerged on the

Lungarno she saw the silvery flakes of light rippling on the quiet surface of the river, turning the ancient buildings and bridges into a magic city floating like a dream under the moonlit sky.

She was so absorbed that she nearly fell over Ricco when he stopped to unlock his Lamborghini. He turned and steadied her, an arm going round her. Vicky stiffened and backed, and got a dry, ironic stare.

'Talking about myths——' he drawled.

'Were we?'

'Earlier, remember, you said that it was a myth that it always rained in England? Well, it's also a myth that Italian men make passes at every woman they meet.' He held the door of the car open and, flushing, she slid into the passenger seat. Ricco walked round to get behind the wheel.

'They only make passes at the ones they fancy,' he added as he started the engine.

Vicky laughed and he gave her a teasing smile. 'I'll remember that,' she said.

He switched on the tape player fitted into his elaborate Star Wars dashboard, and a voice floated out. Vicky was impressed by it, although she wasn't a great Verdi fan. She guessed who it was, of course, before Ricco said softly, 'Now you know why Florence adores Bianca. She has a voice that can steal the soul out of your body.'

Vicky watched his profile from behind the cover of lowered lashes as they drove away with a purr of enormous power. Had Bianca stolen his soul? Or just his heart?

CHAPTER THREE

OVER the next few days Vicky and Susan did a great deal of sightseeing, but as the weekend approached Vicky insisted that if she didn't have a day off from tramping around Florence she would scream, so they spent the Friday morning sunbathing, ate a picnic lunch al fresco on the lawn behind the villa, and relaxed.

At three o'clock Susan gave a sigh and looked at her watch. 'I ought to do some shopping, but you needn't come. Stay here and enjoy the sun while you can. The weather may change any minute—it's still only April.'

Vicky lifted her head sleepily. 'Are you sure?' Her ankles still ached from all the walking on Florence's narrow, hard pavements. She would much rather stay here idly, but Susan was her hostess, and she felt obliged to offer to go shopping with her.

'Certain.' Susan got up, smiling cheerfully. 'It will be much quicker and easier if I do the shopping on my own, and I expect you could do with some time to yourself. I won't be long, Vicky. Help yourself to a drink if you want one while I'm gone. Anything I can get you in town?'

Vicky shook her head, smiling back. 'I've got all I need, thanks.'

When Susan had gone Vicky drifted into sleep. The sun poured down, not hot enough to be uncomfortable, yet warm enough for her to have put on one of her bikinis. The cypress hedge round Susan's pocket-handkerchief garden stirred gently, whispering, in a faint breeze; birds sang and bees hummed somewhere among the shrubs and rose trees.

A soft clinking sound woke her, and she languidly opened her eyes to find Ricco Salvatore kneeling beside her, so close that for a second they were staring inches apart. Vicky got the distinct impression that he had been about to kiss her, and jerked upright, twisting her body out of reach.

'If you've come to see Susan, she's out.' Did he often drop over during the afternoon, when Susan was alone and David was at work? That would certainly explain Susan's uneasiness about him and the scowl that appeared on David's face every time he saw Ricco.

'I didn't come to see Susan. I came to see you.' He leaned over to pick up something which turned out to be an elegant glass pitcher of orange juice. Vicky realised that the ice in the pitcher had made the clinking noise which woke her.

'Where did that come from?' she asked, puzzled. Was Susan back? Or had Ricco gone into the villa and helped himself to the drink? Admittedly he was the landlord, but it seemed a little high-handed.

'I brought it with me.' He was pouring her a glass of juice; small squares of ice slid from the pitcher with a chink. 'I saw you out here from my house and thought you looked hot.'

'How thoughtful!'

Her dry tone made his mouth twist and the blue eyes gleam with impatience, but he handed her the glass without retorting.

She sipped, her brows lifting as she felt the tingle of champagne on her tongue. 'It's a Buck's Fizz!'

'Don't you like champagne?'

'Love it. I'm just not in the habit of drinking it in the middle of the afternoon.'

'Try living dangerously.' His eyes roamed and she stiffened on the red and white striped lounger, feeling that exploration as if caressing fingers were sliding over her bikini-clad body.

'I've tried it,' she said tersely, swivelling to take down a gauzy beach jacket from the back of the lounger. She had designed the material herself; a creamy background on which were splashed vivid summer flowers, scarlet poppies, purple anemones, dark blue irises. She slid into it while Ricco watched. It was too transparent to make much difference; he could still see the pale curve of her body through the fine material, but it was a gesture which made it clear that she did not like the way he was staring at her, and it made her feel slightly less exposed.

'I'm intrigued,' drawled Ricco, pouring himself a glass of Buck's Fizz and stretching out on the grass beside her as if he intended to stay for hours. 'Tell me more.'

She sat up, her knees drawn upwards and her chin resting on them, the glass in her hand. 'About what?'

'This dangerous living of yours—what went wrong?'

'I didn't say anything had gone wrong.'

'You didn't have to. I can read between the lines.'

'I'm afraid you're reading things that aren't there.'

He lazily shook his head. 'Oh no, you're on the defensive . . .'

'I am not!' She had flushed angrily at that, and his smile mocked her.

'Oh, you mask it as attack, but only because you believe that attack is the best form of self-defence!'

'You're too clever for me,' Vicky said bitingly, and drank some more to give herself time to think. He was shrewder than Miller had been, but he still reminded her of Miller; less good-looking and with a stronger bone structure, perhaps, but the two men had one quality in common, and they both had it in abundance—charm, a lighthearted, casual panache with which they faced life, certain it would give them whatever they wanted because it always had. Miller had been a star right from the first picture he had made in his early twenties. Ten years of stardom and everything that went with it—money, power, women—had spoilt him. He might have been a more admirable man if he hadn't had all the pleasures of life handed to him on a plate.

'I gather Susan's been showing you around Florence all week,' Ricco said, watching her frowning face intently. 'I came over several times, but you were both out.'

She looked at him, eyes narrowed. 'It must be nice being rich enough not to have to work.'

No wonder David resented and disliked him! While David was working long, hard hours in his office every day, Ricco had all the time in the world at his disposal to come over here with pitchers of Buck's Fizz, flirting with Susan and making the most of his opportunity, as her landlord, to take advantage of her isolation in a foreign city. Susan's only friends were the wives of men who worked with David, and the one thing the women had in common was their men. Vicky had already realised that Susan was lonely. Had Ricco discovered that months ago? Susan loved her husband, but she saw too little of him during the week. David didn't get home until late in the evening most weekdays. Susan was human and Ricco was a very attractive man; his attentions must be flattering. She might feel guilty, but even her guilt was revealing—she wouldn't feel it if she wasn't secretly attracted to Ricco.

'What makes you think I don't work?' His blue eyes were hard with anger, she suddenly realised; they watched her with hostility.

'Do you?' What did he do, then? Was he a director of some company, a sinecure job that took up little of his time?

'I couldn't afford not to!'

She glanced around her, smiling scornfully. 'You have plenty of land here and an enormous house, I assumed you had a private income to go with it.'

'I inherited the estate. I could sell it and raise a considerable sum, but it's been in my family for hundreds of years. I don't feel I have the right to let it go to strangers. That's why I built two villas in the gardens—the rent from them helps to pay for the upkeep of the rest. The house was in a terrible condition when I inherited. It needs a total modernisation—new roof, replastering, up-to-date plumbing—it will take years to get it all done, and it will eat up most of my income.'

'So what is your job?' She drained her Buck's Fizz and leaned down to place the glass on the tray he had brought over with the pitcher and glasses on it. Ricco's eyes watched the movement and she straightened hurriedly, realising that he had been staring.

'I run a recording company.'

Her eyes widened. 'Really? What's it called?'

'Musica Dolce.'

'Sweet music?' She had been picking up the odd Italian phrase during the week from Susan. 'That must be an interesting job—did you start the company or . . .?'

'I founded it, yes.' He stood up with the tray in his hand. 'Would you like to see my house? Come and look over it.'

'Now?' She looked down at herself, face wry. 'Like this?'

'Why not?' he teased, smiling.

'I'd rather change first.' She slid off the lounger, the gauzy robe flying open, and Ricco brushed a hand across her midriff, making her jump.

'You've caught the sun there—you had better put some lotion on it before you dress, or it will be very uncomfortable later. It isn't wise to underestimate the sun here—it may only be spring, but you can still get sunburn if you stay out in it too long.'

She turned away without answering and went into the empty villa, her skin tingling where Ricco's fingers had touched it. The little gesture had reminded her of something she would rather forget—the night when it had first dawned on her that Sunny fancied her and was going to make an embarrassing nuisance of himself unless she did something about it quickly.

Running upstairs, she tried to forget all about

that, but as she stripped off and put on a white vest top and a pair of pale blue cotton pants her mind was busy with unhappy memories.

She had been alone in the hotel suite in Paris where Miller was staying. Sunny had whisked her over for the weekend, but she had refused to stay in the suite he and Miller were sharing. She had insisted on a room of her own. Miller had been sweet-tempered about it at first, but Sunny had, as usual, been sneeringly sarcastic.

The following morning she had gone along to the suite to have breakfast with Miller, an arrangement they had made the previous night. She had found Sunny alone. He had told her that Miller was taking a shower and would be out in a minute, but Miller hadn't put in an appearance, and eventually Sunny had told her with one of his malicious smiles that Miller had left in the middle of the night to visit an old flame who was also in Paris.

Vicky had turned red and then white. 'I don't believe you! Miller wouldn't . . .'

Sunny had laughed and sat down next to her on the red plush couch on which she was uneasily perching. 'Grow up, sweetheart. Last night you said no to him. Miller doesn't like that, he isn't used to his ladies saying no.' He had been far too close and to her shock she felt his hand close over her leg, pushing aside her skirt, his moist fingers sliding upward and inward along her thigh. 'You aren't a virgin, are you, sweetheart? A lovely girl like you can't have got to twenty-three without going to bed with anyone.'

She had thrust his hand away and tried to get up, very flushed and upset. Sunny wouldn't let her go, he held her down by the shoulders, his body leaning over her, his mouth trying to close over her lips while she turned her head away, feeling literally sick. Sunny was not an attractive man; short and a little plump he was at least forty and going slightly bald. Vicky hated his liquid black eyes and sallow skin, the fleshy nose and even more fleshy lips. At that moment he was loathsome to her, and she gasped the truth out.

'I feel sick—let go, let go of me!'

Sunny had been surprised enough to release her, and she had fled. She had made it back to her own room, where she almost threw up before packing her case and going down to reception to check out and book a flight back to London. All the way to Charles de Gaulle airport she had shuddered, and the taxi driver had watched her in the mirror, obviously afraid she was going to be taken ill in his cab.

Miller had caught up with her at the terminal before she boarded the London plane. His concerned, alarmed face had made her burst into tears. Aware of being recognised, of the curious, fascinated stares of other passengers, Miller had put an arm round her and steered her out of the airport, and she had been in such a state that she had forgotten all about her luggage, already bumping along the conveyor belts towards the waiting plane. A limousine was waiting. Miller put her into it and they drove back to Paris.

'Darling, Sunny didn't mean to scare the life out of you—he was only playing around, he didn't mean what you thought he meant. Sunny's got a crazy sense of humour, and he isn't used to girls like you.

The sort of girls Sunny knows will go to bed with anyone at the drop of a hat, he isn't on your wavelength.' Miller had stroked her hair and kissed her wet face. 'He'll apologise on his knees for upsetting you, I promise you. He can't get used to the idea that I'm going to marry you, Vicky. Up until now we've always . . .' He broke off, giving her a quick glance. 'Well, things are different and Sunny will get the picture now.,

'He . . . he said you were with an old flame last night,' she had half said, half accused, watching him, while she pretended to be drying her eyes with his handkherchief.

Miller looked blank. 'He was just kidding. I was asleep in bed. He woke me up after you ran out of the suite and told me the two of you had had a row.'

'A row?' she had erupted. 'Is that what he called it? He had his hands all over me, he tried to . . .'

'I know, I know, he was out of order, but that's Sunny.' He sounded as if he might at any moment start to tell her that the whole episode had just been a joke and where was her sense of humour?

She hadn't been watching where they were going, and when the limousine stopped and she saw that they were back at the hotel she had turned pale again. 'I don't want to see him—take me back to the airport, Miller!'

He was already getting out of the car. He turned and pulled her out, too, protesting. Vicky hung back, shaking her head, her hair ruffled, her face smudged with tears. That was when the flashbulbs exploded, that was when the camera men and reporters dashed towards them. Miller had been all smiles; Vicky had been dazed.

'No, our engagement isn't off. No, there's no other woman, Vicky's the only girl for me. Okay, we had a little spat and she was on her way back to London, but we've made it up and everything's fine again now, isn't it, darling?'

In the background Sunny had lurked, watching, his cynical face and knowing eyes sending an icy tremor down her spine. Had his pass at her all been part of some publicity ploy? Had he wanted to stampede her into running so that he could blow it up into a major story? Or had he merely been an opportunist, in several ways, taking the opportunity of being alone with her in the suite, and when she turned him down making the most of that, too, by calling Miller and then the press?

Whichever was the true explanation, Vicky had never felt the same about Miller from that day, and she had hated Sunny. He had been perfectly aware of the fact, but that hadn't deterred him from making oblique advances to her later. She almost felt that it amused him to ask her to dance in public, knowing it would be hard for her to refuse every time, and realising just how much she hated to be in his arms, his hands touching her, his face deliberately pressed against her own. He took every chance he could, putting his arm around her as they walked into a restaurant, patting her behind in a pretence of humour, kissing her when they met—Sunny always took care never to go too far, yet he chose his moments shrewdly, and Vicky felt helpless about the way he manipulated Miller and herself. While she was working she could take refuge in her job, get away from Miller's travelling circus, but Sunny made sure he stopped that bolthole, and once she had no job Miller tried to persuade her to travel with him all the time. She knew what that meant, what it would mean. She would be with Sunny most of the day while Miller worked, and Sunny wouldn't leave her alone. She felt like a fly caught in a spider's web of treachery and intrigue, and the worst part of it was that some of her feeling for Miller still lingered. Away from Sunny he was a wonderful man. Sunny was a corrosive influence on him, she decided, but gradually she realised that she would never win against Sunny. He had been with Miller for too long, and Miller was blind to his real nature.

So she had taken the decision to go for good, and this time she had been secretive about it. Nothing would ever change her mind, but she hadn't wanted to face Miller and tell him so, because he would have called in Sunny, and Sunny would have told the press.

From the moment she met Miller, Sunny had made their love a public affair, although for a long time that hadn't dawned on her because she wasn't aware of all the publicity. She didn't read all the newspapers and magazines, didn't see the pictures of herself and Miller at nightclubs, dancing, kissing, jogging in the park, eating hot dogs in New York, swimming in Miami. When she did see the occasional photograph and story she thought it surprising that people should be interested, but she didn't guess how interested they were until she realised that little snippets of inside information about them both appeared regularly because that was Sunny's job, to make sure that Miller's face and name turned up as often as possible in the media.

Sunny had made that crystal clear to her,

eventually. The more intimate the gossip, the better—if she and Miller had a quarrel over another woman, terrific. If she broke their engagement, then was talked into putting on her ring again, wonderful. If she looked jealous when Miller danced with another girl, Sunny had the story in a gossip column the next morning.

It was distasteful, and Vicky couldn't take any more of it. One of the last straws was when she realised just how many women there had been in Miller's life before they met, and, even worse, that when Miller was tired of them Sunny was always waiting around to take up where he left off. That, at least, was what Sunny implied. She didn't know how much truth there was in it, but now and then Miller let fall unguarded remarks that made her believe Sunny's story.

Since she arrived in Florence she hadn't seen any English or American papers, and she couldn't read Italian ones, so she had no idea whether Sunny had told the press about her disappearance, but she imagined that if he had the story would have died by now. Miller had probably got a new girl-friend in tow; maybe the next one would be tougher and more able to cope with all the pressures of that life style—not to mention the problem of Sunny.

She ran a brush over her hair, staring at her reflection. Ricco was right, she had taken the sun, her nose was slightly pink and her throat was flushed. She hadn't thought that the spring sunshine would have much effect; she must treat it with more respect in future. Like love, it could be deceptive and dangerous.

She went downstairs and found Ricco stretched

out on the lounger, his long, slim body totally relaxed. He had his eyes shut as she walked up to him, but although she moved softly he opened his eyes and smiled up at her.

'You certainly took your time! I began to think you'd changed your mind and forgotten to tell me.'

'I'm sorry.' Vicky knew she sounded stiff.

He swung to his feet, smiling. 'You look very cool in that. Blue is your colour.'

'Thank you.' She couldn't hide the frostiness of her response; she didn't want him to flirt with her or use that charm he had on tap. She had had enough of men for the moment; she wanted a little peace and quiet, a space in which to be herself, unhampered by other people's demands or expectations. Her love affair with Miller had been too fast and furious, and it had gone wrong too badly. Her skin was tender to the touch, her nerves frayed.

She walked across the garden towards the little gate which she knew led into Ricco's villa gardens and he followed, carrying his tray like a well-trained butler, balanced on one hand. His shadow moved on the sunny grass and she watched it, her eyes cast downwards. He moved gracefully, she had to admit, teeth clenched. He had long, smooth hips, an athlete's body—muscled shoulders, deep chest, long legs and an easy, loping stride.

If she had met him a year ago she might have fallen for him hook, line and sinker, but she was a burnt child and she feared the fire.

'Does Bianca Fancelli record for your company?' she asked as they walked through the gate.

'Yes, she's one of our biggest stars.'

Vicky paused, delighted with what she saw in the

courtyard of his villa—rows of enormous terracotta pots containing orange trees, the burnt orange of the clay pots glowing in the sunlight, tapering dark cypresses, cherry trees in blossom and some very old statuettes placed here and there among the trees and shrubs; nude and pale nymphs with cupped hands pouring water into a deep basin in which they stood, Roman matrons in draped tunics, a leering satyr which reminded her at once of Sunny. The sun was lower in the sky now; it made soft dark pools of shadow on the grass and flowers and along the walls of the villa.

'Why do you grow your orange trees in pots?'

'Because we sometimes have severe winters, and the terracotta protects them from the worst frosts. Last year we got bushels of oranges from these, but it all depends on the weather, some years we hardly get any.'

They walked through the main door and Vicky's breath caught in disbelief at the long gallery stretching away in front of them. The walls were plastered, and hand-painted with country scenes and paintings of fruit; they must be very old, for their colours had faded into soft washes, but you could still see very clearly what the artist had intended—luscious cherries, red and ripe, round glowing peaches and green apples, and in the landscapes the familiar cypress and olive trees, the groves and vines of Italy, while cascades of delicately painted flowers hung from the high, arched ceiling some thirty feet above them. Vicky hadn't expected to see such a high ceiling; the gallery must be as high as the roof, she realised, and this must be one of the oldest parts of the house.

Ricco watched her entranced expression, smiling. 'In the Middle Ages, of course, this would have been a whitewashed refectory for the monks. The wall paintings were done during the seventeenth century, during the Arcadian period of Italian art.'

'It's wonderful, incredible—I've never seen anything like it!'

Chandeliers hung at each end of the gallery, the largest Vicky had ever seen, dripping with hundreds of glass pendants arranged in layers like the frills on a circular skirt, with separate swags of crystal at intervals around the globe and one long trail of them falling down below the main chandelier. The blaze of light they gave off when Ricco turned them on almost dazzled. In that radiance she picked out the sheen of gilt on antique brass-handled furniture, the colours of the paintings, the deep polish on the red-tiled floor. There were plants in pots everywhere; bushy fern, wide-leaved rubber plants, flowering African violet.

The whole effect was of a shabby beauty; this was a real home, not a museum—she saw books in piles on cupboards, little curios behind glass doors of cabinets, an umbrella left on a chair, a dog's lead hanging on a hook. The plaster was flaking, the gilt scratched, the furniture a little rickety, but someone had polished that floor until it shone like glass, someone had looked after those plants and cleaned the chandeliers.

'When I was small I used to ride my tricycle up and down here,' said Ricco, smiling nostalgically. 'When it rained, that is—otherwise my mother made me go out into the garden, but I loved it to rain so that I could play in the long gallery. It was much shabbier then; we didn't have much money, and the restoration of a place like this costs a fortune—especially the ceiling and walls. I had them cleaned and touched up a year ago. I won't tell you how much that cost.'

'You must have lots of help to keep the house in this condition.'

He smiled. 'Thank God, yes. I couldn't manage, otherwise.'

'Susan said something about a plan to turn the villa into a hotel?'

'I've played with the idea from time to time, but too much needs to be done to it first. A hotel needs bathrooms and modern public rooms—a bar, a dining-room. At the moment, I only use a fraction of the house. I live in three rooms, that's all I need. I'm having the rest of the place redecorated and modernised bit by bit.' He walked on along the gallery and she followed, skidding on the polished floor. Ricco turned and caught her with one arm, then put the tray down and took her by the hand. 'You'd better watch your step—Giulia believes in polishing until you can see your face, and I can't persuade her it's dangerous.'

Hand in hand they walked carefully until they came to a low arch in the wall through which Ricco led her into a square room furnished as a study, with a desk and bookcases and filing cabinets around the walls.

'I work here when I'm not at my office. I come here to get away from the telephone—my home number is private, and that helps to keep the calls to the minimum.'

He opened a door on the far side of the room and

she followed him into a spacious, open sitting-room with high, wide windows along the wall opposite. It was furnished with grey and red striped brocade-covered chairs and a matching sofa, something in the style of English Regency furniture, with highly polished acanthus-leaf decorations on the bow legs of the chairs. The walls were painted in the same fashion as the walls in the long gallery, landscapes in gentle greens and blues, giving her a strange feeling of not being in a room but in a grove. The sunlight through the windows moved across the painted trees and she almost felt them stir, smelt the flowers painted among the painted grass.

'It's so peaceful,' she murmured, looking around her. 'If I were you, I'd hate to turn it into a hotel, hordes of strangers trooping through these beautiful rooms—could you bear it?'

'I may have to, eventually. The upkeep is too much for my income. It's either turn it into a hotel or let it slowly disintegrate. You need a lot of money for a house like this.'

She walked over to look more closely at the brocade on the chairs, running an appreciative hand over them. 'Very classy material; this is original, isn't it?'

'Nineteenth-century,' he agreed. 'It was made for this room, for one of my ancestors, by one of the best Florentine workshops of the time. A year after it was installed here your Lord Nelson arrived in Italy, and there's a rumour that he visited my family, but there isn't a word of truth in it, we just tell the story to English tourists to amuse them.'

She laughed, catching the wicked gleam in his eyes. 'Don't you want to amuse me?'

'I'll think of something,' he promised, and she regretted her impulse to flirt with him and turned cool again, looking down at the chair.

'I've seen material like this in the V. & A. I spent a lot of time there, studying old material, when I was at college.'

'You were trained as a designer?'

'I did three years before I joined the firm.' A sigh escaped before she could stop it, and he picked up on that, of course.

'What made you leave them?'

Sunny, she thought, but aloud she said, 'We had a disagreement.'

'And you have no plans yet for another job?'

'When I've finished my holiday I'll start looking for one.'

'Will it be easy to find one? Are there plenty of jobs for designers of textiles?'

Her mouth wry, she shrugged. 'I might be lucky.'

He pushed his hands into his pockets and lounged there, watching her thoughtfully. The sunlight glinted on his dark hair and showed her the golden tan on his throat, that warm deep colour which seemed imprinted in his skin.

'Ever thought of designing record sleeves?'

Vicky stared at him, startled. 'No,' she said frankly, laughing. 'That's a very different branch of design; I'm into textiles, and . . .'

'Don't you ever take risks, impulse decisions?' Ricco asked with a sardonic little smile. 'I think you might come up with some interesting sleeves. While you're in Florence anyway, why not come along to my offices and see the sort of designs we use, get the idea of how we decide what image we want to get over? I know you've been doing something rather different, but that doesn't mean you can't try something new. I've a feeling you might bring a new approach to it, add a new dimension—if I'm ready to risk it, why shouldn't you?'

CHAPTER FOUR

'Do you think he was serious?' asked Susan eagerly later that evening.

'Well, he suggested I should visit his office and see the sort of work I'd be doing, so I suppose he must have been.' Vicky was dubious, though. She wasn't sure she trusted Ricco Salvatore, he might have an ulterior motive for offering her a job. It might be interesting to get involved in the music business, though. She was very tempted to accept the offer, so next morning Susan drove her into Florence to keep the appointment Ricco had made with her.

His offices were in a narrow street off the Via Tornabuoni, the most prestigious shopping street in Florence, Susan told her. You could buy beautiful clothes, shoes, or some of the jewellery for which Florence was famous, and the area was crowded with people that Saturday morning. Vicky had never seen such traffic in such narrow streets. Internal combustion was murdering Florence. The weather had changed, as Susan had predicted; a cloudy sky sat right on top of the flat roofs and the air hardly moved; sultry and humid,it clung around the houses, loaded with the smell of petrol fumes.

'I'll have to let you off here because of the one-way system,' Susan said apologetically. 'Take a left turn, then a right.' She looked at Vicky uncertainly. 'Do you think you can find it? There's a brass plate on the door. Musica Dolce, can you remember that? The offices are halfway down on the left-hand side. Oh, maybe I should find somewhere to park and walk back to show you the way.'

They were causing a blockage, and the car behind them began to hoot loudly. Susan threw a look backwards, blushing. 'Oh, dear!'

'Don't worry, I'll find it,' said Vicky, getting out of the car. 'I can see what this traffic is like, I'm not helpless, and Ricco said he would drive me back, so I'll see you later.'

She turned to give a grin and a cheerful wave at the young man in the Lancia behind them who was ferociously hooting his outrage that Susan should be holding him up. He stood up in his open-top sports car and called to her in dulcet-tones, his gesture beckoning, but she laughed, shook her head and walked away.

'*Signorina, signorina, per favore!*' he called after her, suggesting a drive or something rather more intimate in his warm Italian voice, but Vicky kept on walking round the next corner and out of sight and his life.

She found Ricco's offices easily and pushed the door open. She could hear a typewriter somewhere, and followed the sound along a passage. The building was ancient, judging by the crumbling plaster, but when she tapped on a door at the end of the corridor and went into the room she found herself in a modern office, high-ceilinged, with windows along the facing wall, steel filing cabinets and a girl sitting at a desk typing.

When Vicky came into the room she lifted her hands from the keys and smiled, beginning to say something in Italian, too fast for Vicky's shaky grasp of a few phrases.

'*Mi dispiace, non parlo italiano*,' Vicky interrupted, smiling apologetically.

The girl's face cleared. 'You are Miss Lloyd, yes? Please to go upstairs, Signor Salvatore is in the main office. I will tell him you are coming.' She picked up a phone and Vicky turned away. On her way out she heard the girl talking in her own language and laughing at whatever the person on the other end of the line was saying.

Vicky sighed. It was shameful, the way everyone here seemed to speak such good English when she barely knew half a dozen words of Italian. The staircase was narrow and not too well lit, but as she reached the top of it Vicky saw Ricco coming towards her from an open door.

He was wearing a cream linen tailored suit, the shirt he wore with it made of a lustrous apricot silk. His tie was very plain, a dark brown silk, unpatterned. Vicky admired the panache which could carry off the combination; she distrusted the crooked little smile he also wore.

'You're very punctual. I was afraid you might have trouble finding us.'

'Susan gave me very precise instructions,' she answered politely, although she felt the odd little prickle on the back of her neck she always got whenever she saw him.

He ushered her through a door into a high-ceilinged, spacious room which was completely empty of people.

'Oh, nobody else here? Don't you work on

Saturdays?' she asked, looking around her with curiosity.

'Only when I have something important to deal with,' he said drily.

'Am I something important? How flattering.'

His eyes mocked her. 'What do you think of our main office?'

'Very impressive.' She glanced around again, admiring the impression of airy brightness the room gave, even on a day as misty as this; it was a working environment which she could imagine finding very pleasant. Air-conditioning made the long room cool; plants everywhere made it feel like a garden.

There were enormous windows at each end, stretching almost from ceiling to floor. Pale blue venetian blinds covered them, no doubt to shield the workers from the worst heat of the day in summer. It had been designed on the same open plan as Susan's house, divided by low shelving topped with troughs of plants into separate areas, some containing desks and filing cabinets, others with racks of records and stereo equipment with headphones so that one could listen without annoying everyone else.

'I designed it myself.'

'I thought you might have done,' she said drily, and got a wry smile.

'Would you like some coffee? I have some already made,' He walked over to a broad shelf on which stood coffee-making equipment, lifted the pot and poured two cups. 'Milk? Sugar?'

'No, thank you, I like mine black.'

He brought the cups over to a wide, round table in

one of the alcoves and gestured for her to sit down. On the table lay a large portfolio. Ricco handed her a cup of coffee and then flipped open the portfolio.

'Take a look through here, before we talk.'

Vicky pulled the portfolio closer and began to glance through it at the paintings it held, each of them framed in a square of white paper. They differed widely: landscapes, faces, city streets, abstracts. The lettering on them differed just as much; small or enormous, splashed diagonally or written from top to bottom—the artists had gone to great trouble to ring the changes. The concept was, of course, similar to magazine drawing or any other form of commercial art—each drawing tried to illustrate the theme of the record and at the same time catch the eye, surprise, intrigue.

'Fascinating,' she commented when she had turned the last page. 'The technique is simple enough, nothing new to me, but I'm not that sort of designer, Signor Salvatore . . .'

'Ricco,' he interrupted, and she shrugged.

'Ricco, I can see that you have some brilliant artists working for you already, far better than I could ever hope to be. Some of those illustrations are inspired.'

He nodded, pulling the portfolio towards him and opening it again. 'Agreed. This guy, for instance . . .' He showed her one of the best in the collection. 'He's brilliant, yes, but that means he's very much in demand and costs the earth. We can't afford him unless the record is a sure-fire bestseller.,

Vicky gave him a cool stare. 'And you think I'd come cheaper?'

His mouth curled up. 'You're very direct. Yes, I

suppose that's partly it—but it's more than that. It occurred to me that it might be interesting to have sleeves illustrating the typical fashions of the period for a new series of chamber music we're producing—Renaissance music, for instance; you'd have an enormous choice of styles and materials to use there. The series covers five centuries of Italian music. We plan to issue several discs for each century, so we'd probably be talking about ten or a dozen covers in total. As you see, the actual illustration would be drawn much larger, since we need to see the details very clearly and it will be reduced in production.'

She was interested, in spite of her reluctance to have anything to do with him and his scheme. 'It would involve a lot of research in costume museums and libraries, picture galleries, of course . . . and I'm no expert on Italian costume. I might know where to start in England—I studied costume at college, naturally, that was part of my course.'

'I thought it probably had been,' he said smoothly.

She laughed, her mouth tightening with irritated amusement. 'Clever of you. You had it all worked out, just like that, in a flash?'

'That's why I said it was a hunch. I had already had the idea of using costumes of the period for the series, but I'd meant to use famous paintings, not get a modern artist to reproduce the clothes people wore. When I heard that you designed textiles it seemed like an omen. There you were, and there was my project; you clicked together magically.' His blue eyes held a wicked sensuality; he picked up her hand before she knew what he was going to do and entwined their fingers firmly. 'Like that,' he added softly.

Vicky pulled her hand free, her face cold. 'Ah, which brings me to the real reason why I came this morning,' she said, sitting up straight on the other side of the table. 'Susan.'

Ricco looked blank. 'Susan?'

'Have you any idea what sort of trouble you've been making for her?'

'I have? What do you mean? Susan's in trouble?' His tanned face wasn't smiling now, his eyes were fixed on her, frowning.

'You've been flirting with her . . .'

'What?' he interrupted, brows a black, angry line above eyes like blue ice. 'I've never . . .'

'Kissed her hand? Gazed into her eyes and told her how lovely she looked? Smiled at her across rooms, taken her flowers, called on her in the afternoons while David was at work?'

She had to admit he did the stupefied innocence well. His lean cheeks had taken on an angry wash of red and his mouth was a straight, tense line.

'I'm not in the habit of making passes at young married women,' he said brusquely, barely parting his teeth to let the words out. 'Did she tell you that I'd made advances to her?'

'No, Susan said you couldn't help it, you flirted instinctively with every woman you met.'

For a moment he just sat there, breathing heavily while he eyed her with what appeared to be homicidal intentions, then he gave a snarling sound and said, 'You believe in coming to the point, don't you? *Va bene*. Okay, let's be frank. If Susan got the idea that I've been flirting with her and meant anything by it, please assure her that my intentions towards her were . . .'

'Oh, please!' Vicky couldn't help the laughter which broke out of her. 'Not honourable, surely? And your English is usually so good.'

'My English is perfect,' he said through his teeth. 'I spent three years in your country, after leaving Milan University—a year at Cambridge and then two years working in London with record companies. So don't patronise me, Miss Lloyd.'

She looked down demurely. 'Sorry. But anyway, it isn't Susan who has the wrong impression—it's David, and their marriage is under quite a strain because of you. Susan doesn't have the right sort of temperament to handle a situation like this—David is ten years older than her, and she's a nervous girl at the best of times. She hasn't a clue how to make David realise that he has no cause to be jealous of you.'

Ricco got up and walked away, prowling restlessly, his hands in the pockets of his cream pants. She heard him muttering to himself in Italian; the words sounded fiery, and she was glad she didn't know what they meant.

He stood at one of the wide plate-glass windows staring out, his black head haloed with morning light. 'This is absurd,' he said in English. 'I'd no idea. Oh, I knew David wasn't very friendly to me, but it didn't dawn on me that he was actually jealous, or that there was anything behind Susan's shyness whenever I saw her. Of course, she always blushes and stammers, but I thought that that was her character, that she was simply a very sensitive girl.'

'She is—and with good reason.' Vicky began to tell him about Uncle George's icy sarcasm and the way he flayed Susan with his comments on her looks, behaviour, intelligence. 'So you see, when David flies into a jealous rage she simply dissolves into tears or runs away—she can't face him or discuss it as any sensible woman would. They don't talk to each other like two adults. David makes all the decisions, he's very much master of that house. Susan can't cope with his jealousy of you, she can't convince him she doesn't secretly fancy you because the very subject makes her fly into one of her tizzies.'

He swivelled and leaned against the window-frame, staring at her down the long room, his lean body poised and dangerous, vibrating with anger.

'So you decided to interfere?'

Vicky lifted her chin defiantly. 'I decided to make you see the sort of problem you had caused. Maybe you didn't mean it, maybe you can't help flirting . . .'

'Maybe I ought to throw you out of here before I lose my temper!'

She got up. 'Okay, I'm going, I've said what I came to say.'

He crossed the room in long-limbed strides and caught her before she got to the door, his hands descending on her shoulders and whirling her round to face him.

'Not so fast! I've got a few things to say to *you* now. I'm none too pleased to hear that you and Susan have been talking about me behind my back and deciding that I'm just a shallow flirt who can't keep his eyes off any woman he meets.'

'I didn't put it like that!' His fingers were biting into her flesh, but she didn't dare to struggle; it might inflame his temper further.

'That was what you meant! You made me sound like a conceited fool.'

Their eyes met and his face tightened into rigid, hostile lines. 'That *is* what you think of me, isn't it?' he demanded, shaking her.

'My opinion of you isn't important. It's David and Susan I'm concerned about. I'm very fond of Susan, I want her to be happy, and at the moment she isn't, although she should be. Just stop flirting with her and David will get over this.' She tried to break out of his grip, but it tightened on her.

'I haven't been flirting with her! When I see her I'm polite and friendly, she's pretty and charming and I wanted to make her feel at home here.' He paused, seeing the glint of derision in Vicky's eyes. 'Damn you! Don't you know the difference between a natural courtesy to a woman and making a pass at her?' His blue eyes were glacial, but she could see hot red glints in them and his voice had a metallic ring to it. 'There's more to communication than language. Let's try another way of making the point.'

His head swooped before she could back or turn her face away. His mouth hurt as it took her lips by force; the insistent pressure bruised and burnt, and while she was struggling to escape Ricco's arms encircled her and held her so tightly that she could hardly breathe, let alone break free. She backed a step, but that was no help; she found herself against the end of one of the partitions, and Ricco's body crushed her backwards until she was trapped between him and the solid wood. His muscled thighs leaned on her, holding her immobile, and one hand slid up her back and moved over her short blonde hair, tangling with it until his fingers suddenly closed over her nape, massaging it softly, his other hand caressing her spine, curving her body inwards towards him.

Vicky had kept her eyes angrily open; she had no intention of letting him get to her. What did he think he was doing? The kiss was too painful to be enjoyable, even for him—what did he get out of inflicting it on her other than some balm for his bruised ego?

The movements of his hands gradually undermined her, though. Their warm, firm caress was hypnotic, she found herself growing heavy-eyed, almost drowsy. The power of his mouth softened, he kissed her more as if he wanted to, as if it gave him pleasure, and her lids finally closed as her body arched obediently, her hands closing ovcr his shoulders and clinging there. The sunlight bathed them warmly, the silent room enclosed them, all she could hear was the beating of her heart and his, all she could see was the golden glow beneath her lids.

Ricco reluctantly released her lips and lifted his head. She opened her eyes and looked dazedly at him.

'*That* was a pass,' he said huskily, and she thought she saw mockery in his blue eyes.

That acted like a douche of cold water. She finally managed to break away, twisting her body and moving several feet off, breathing far too fast, her face much too flushed.

She was angry with him—but far angrier with

herself for letting down her defences. What had happened to her determination never to let him get any closer? Hadn't she learnt her lesson over Miller? Ricco was charming and attractive and sexually exciting—which made him all the more forbidden to her. Next time she let herself care about a man he was going to be a very different type, quiet, stable, reliable. Ricco Salvatore didn't fit the bill.

Moving to the door, she flung over her shoulder, 'Don't ever try that again or you'll be sorry!'

She heard his laughter with fury. How dared he laugh at her? She meant it, every word, and she wished she could think of some way of wiping the amusement out of his face, but short of actual violence there was little she could do about Ricco at the moment.

'You enjoyed it as much as I did,' he drawled.

'Like hell!' She turned at the door to glare at him. He was sitting on the edge of a desk, watching her with wicked eyes.

He made a horrified face. 'What shocking language! An innocent young girl like you!'

She fumed helplessly under his mocking gaze. 'I don't think you're funny! Keep your hands to yourself in future, that's all!' She swung round to march out, and he called her back.

'Haven't you forgotten something?'

'What?' she asked shortly, halting in spite of a feeling that she ought to go now while they were a room apart. Those long legs of his could cover far too much ground far too fast.

'When will you start?'

'What?'

'The job—when does your holiday end? How soon can you start work here?'

'You have to be kidding!' Vicky spat out furiously. 'You don't think I'm going to take a job with you when . . .'

'If you want David to believe I'm not interested in his wife, what better way of convincing him than by making him think I'm interested in you?' Ricco asked calmly.

She stared at him, dumbfounded.

'Take a few days to think it over, anyway,' he drawled. 'You can let me know on Monday. If you aren't taking the job I'll have to think of an alternative, so don't take too long.'

Vicky began to walk towards the door, nodding. 'Very well, I'll let you know.' She wanted to get away from him fast.

He followed her. 'I'm giving you a lift back, remember?'

She had forgotten completely, and he saw it in her face and laughed. Vicky set her teeth. She wasn't going to be able to get away from him just yet. She hoped she had done the right thing in tackling him about Susan. Sometimes interference could do more harm than good. When she had gone back to London, Susan would still be here. She hoped she hadn't put any ideas into Ricco's head that hadn't been there before. Even worse, she hoped she hadn't made him hostile to Susan and David. He was their landlord, after all. They enjoyed living in that little villa.

As they drove out of Florence the mist lifted and the sun shone through the clouds. Ricco glanced up at the sky. 'It looks as if it's going to be a fine weekend, after all. What are you planning to do? More sightseeing?'

'David said something about seeing the Tuscan hills.'

'You'll enjoy that. Get him to take you to Fiesole, one of my favourite places.'

'Etruscan, wasn't it?'

'Oh, Tuscany is saturated with the past—but even if you aren't interested in history, Fiesole is delightful. The views are quite incredible,' He glanced at her sideways and she took a deep breath.

'Keep your eyes on the road!'

The Lamborghini flashed along like a rocket now that they were out of the thick chains of Florence traffic, and it made Vicky nervous to have him looking at her instead of at the road.

'Don't be nervous,' he said, smiling, and patted her knee.

She brushed his hand off angrily. 'Will you stop touching me! Wasn't it you who told me that it was a myth that Italian men made passes at every woman they meet?'

His eyes slanted, dark and provocative. 'I said they only made passes at women they fancied, and that's true.' His hand was back on her knee, but he had removed it before she could hit him again, and he was laughing. 'Have you got a hang-up about men? You're very aggressive.'

'Not normally,' she retorted through her teeth. 'Only when I meet a man who makes me lose my temper.'

'Or a man who finds you attractive?' he queried, lifting his brows, and she was furious to feel herself flushing. He watched her, his eyes mocking. 'Now I wonder why you should find that so annoying?' he asked.

'I might be more flattered if I didn't suspect that you find a lot of women attractive,' she snapped. 'There's no particular thrill in being one of a crowd.'

'What makes you think you are?'

She laughed shortly. 'Oh, come on! Every time I see you, the evidence is pretty conclusive. I didn't need Susan to tell me you're a flirt, and I doubt if Bianca is the only other woman in your life.'

'Are you jealous of Bianca?' he asked, sounding amused, and her colour turned scarlet.

'No, I am not! I don't care who you go around with—I'm just telling you why I don't take you seriously.'

'Yet,' he said softly, his mouth curling in a complacent smile.

She turned icy. 'Ever,' she promised.

They were turning in at the gates of the villa now. Ricco slowed the purring monster and smoothly turned towards the front door of the little villa. He braked and switched off the engine and turned to survey her speculatively.

'It's dangerous to issue challenges of that sort,' he pointed out. 'No man likes to back off from a dare.'

'It wasn't a dare. It was a statement of fact.' She opened the car door and got out, and Ricco watched her with narrowed eyes. 'Thank you for the lift back here. I'll let you know about the job on Monday,' she said remotely.

That afternoon David and Susan took her on a drive around the countryside surrounding Florence, passing through Pistoia and into the tiny, remote villages in the hills. Spring covered everything with a vivid green glaze, the sun was warm and the hills beautiful. It was a lovely drive, and Vicky began to get some idea of the landscape surrounding her. They drove back through Lucca to get on to the autostrada, and were back at the villa in time to have dinner at home.

On the Sunday they all slept late, but after they had had a light breakfast of rolls and coffee David drove Vicky into Florence to visit the Uffizi, which was open until one o'clock. Susan preferred to stay at home to prepare lunch. One picture which Vicky found really striking was an Uccello, a Renaissance battle scene crowded with life and incident. It wasn't the people that made her eyes open; it was the fact that one of the horses was blue, strangely prefiguring modern painting. She had seen reproductions of most of the famous paintings in the Uffizi, but this was new to her, and she stood in front of it for a long time.

'What do you like so much about it?' David asked, studying it.

'It surprises me.'

'Is that good?'

'Art should always surprise. Most of us tend to go around with our eyes shut, metaphorically. We don't see what's right under our noses. The job of the artist is to shake us into looking, perhaps for the first time, at the familiar things we pass every day.'

'Like blue horses?' a voice drawled behind them, and she turned with an impatient expression to face Ricco Salvatore.

'What are you doing here?'

'Being shaken by the sight of a blue horse!'

David seemed amused. 'What do you think of the

painting, Ricco?'

'Ask me what I think of Vicky and I'll be more eloquent,' Ricco said, letting his eyes wander over her with cool sexual interest.

'Do you often spend your Sunday mornings in art galleries?' Vicky enquired with scepticism.

'No, I called at the villa and Susan told me you were here,' he admitted shamelessly.

David laughed. Vicky had never seen him look so friendly towards Ricco. Obviously he was far from displeased to see his landlord pursuing Vicky, and Ricco's eyes mockingly underlined the fact as he glanced from David's smiling face to Vicky's hostile one.

'Have you seen the Boboli Gardens yet?' he asked her.

Before she could answer, David said, 'I was just going to take her there—why don't you do the honours? You know them better than I do. Vicky couldn't have a better guide.'

'You're a very good guide,' Vicky said hastily, but Ricco talked over her.

'I'd be happy to. Come along, Vicky. The Gardens are a very popular place to walk on fine Sundays, but people usually crowd in there after lunch.'

'Are you coming, David?' asked Vicky, finding herself being towed away by Ricco's commanding grip.

'I'll catch up with you later,' he said, wandering away to admire some more pictures.

'Enjoyed your morning?' Ricco asked as they went down the wide stone staircase.

'Very much,' she said shortly. He made her feel

hunted. Why had he followed them here?

'Why did you go in for textile design instead of painting?'

She laughed angrily. 'What a question! Because that's what excites me, I suppose—texture, shape, colour. When I see someone wearing a dress made with material I've designed it gives me a kick. It's only when the material is worn that it really exists, flowing with the body moving under it. Then it's a living creation instead of just a design on paper.'

He listened with real interest, watching her excited face. They crossed the Ponte Vecchio and turned in through the gates behind the Pitti Palace, and Vicky looked up with some apprehension at the steepest public park she had ever seen.

'Who had the brilliant notion of making a park on the side of a cliff?'

'You have to be fit to stroll along these paths,' Ricco admitted drily. He led her through the green groves, past statues hidden in niches, the rain having made faint green tearstains down their marble faces; then turned upwards at an incline that took all their energy and left them none for conversation, along a beautiful cypress alley lined with sculptures from many different periods.

At the Neptune fountain he watched with amusement as she caught a few glittering drops of spray in her hand. 'Don't drink it,' he warned, and she gave him a dry look.

'I wasn't intending to. Can we sit down? My muscles are protesting like crazy. If I don't sit down soon my legs may go on strike!'

They found a green bench behind a low box hedge and sat down. Vicky stared at the tender blue sky; below it the flat roofs of Florence massed, and from up here you could see across the city to where the dark blue hills rose like the backcloth of some Renaissance play.

'I wonder where David's got to,' she mused, wishing Ricco wouldn't watch her, he made her self-conscious. She wondered what went on inside his head—why did she have the distinct impression he was plotting something? Or was she being cynical? If she had never met Miller, she wouldn't have been so suspicious of every man she met. She would probably have been a pushover for Ricco Salvatore. She couldn't deny he was sexy. Apart from Miller, he was probably the best-looking man she had ever met, and a year ago she might have given him a firm green light if he made a pass at her instead of angrily brushing him off every time he appeared.

'I expect he'll wait for us at the gate. You could hunt for someone for hours in the Gardens, there are so many different paths up to the top.'

She looked ruefully upwards. 'I hope you don't expect me to walk all that way!'

He grinned. 'No, we'll walk down again when you've got your breath.' He crossed one long leg over the other, turning towards her, his arm going along the bench. 'Thought hard about the job? Made up your mind?'

She shifted slightly so that his hand no longer lay against her nape, and felt his quizzical smile although she wasn't looking at him. 'I'm tempted,' she began, then stopped, making the mistake of glancing uneasily at him.

'Good,' he answered silkily, well aware of what

had just crossed her mind.

'That wasn't an intentional double meaning!' she snapped.

'Don't they call it a Freudian slip?' he enquired.

Her flushed face tightened. 'Look, can we get one thing straight? I'm not interested in you, Mr Salvatore. I might be interested in a job with your firm, but only on my own merits. I don't want you to make one for me with the idea that I might be available for more private duties outside working hours.'

'I could lose my temper with you any minute, Miss Lloyd,' he snapped, suddenly grim-faced. 'Do you really think I need to go to such lengths to get a woman? Or do you merely think that you're so ultra-desirable that every man you meet is going to crumble to his knees at the first sight of you?'

She got up and began marching back downhill to the park gates. Ricco caught up with her at the next bend, but he seemed to have nothing more to say. A few moments later they saw David waiting at the park gates.

'Did you have a good time?' he asked Vicky, then did a double take at the look she gave him. David threw Ricco a bewildered look, and found his profile just as rigid.

'*Ciao*,' he said, bestowing the word between both of them in icy indifference, and walked away. David stared after him.

'Did something happen?' he asked Vicky uneasily.

'Every time I meet that man something happens,' she snapped, and it was only later as they drove back to the villa and Susan that it occurred to her that those words, too, had a double meaning. Her clashes with Ricco were fuelled by more than mere irritation over his disturbing manner. Each time she saw him she reluctantly felt the lure of his attraction. You couldn't disguise that immediate chemical reaction, even from yourself. It was meaningless, of course. She didn't know him well enough for her awareness of him to be more than instinctive and physical. All the same, every time they met something certainly happened, both between them and inside herself. That was what annoyed her so much.

CHAPTER FIVE

VICKY was awake until very late on the Sunday night, making lists of pros and cons, but she still hadn't decided about Ricco's offer of a job when she came down to breakfast on the Monday morning. She kept veering between a strong desire to accept the challenge of an entirely new sort of artwork—and an equally strong uneasiness about the sexual challenge Ricco presented.

David had left for work before she got up, but she found Susan in the kitchen drinking some fresh coffee and reading the latest issues of the English newspaper which Susan's mother sent out in a bundle once a week to keep her daughter up to date with home news.

'Anything interesting happening back home?' Vicky asked, sitting down and pouring herself a cup of coffee. There was a wicker basket of rolls on the table; she took one and spread it with cherry jam. It was home-made local produce, thick and rich with dark fruit, very sweet.

'Strikes, murders and a train crash—oh, and a picture of the Princess of Wales in her latest hat,' said Susan, offering her the newspaper. 'Don't worry, there's nothing in it about you, I looked.'

Vicky didn't want to read the paper. She pushed it away, grimacing. 'I can't believe that I once used to read gossip columns myself, enjoying all those fascinating titbits about jet set life. It always seemed like real life soap opera. I don't think I actually believed any of the gossip, but I had no compunction about reading it.'

'Well, famous film stars don't seem to have real emotions, do they?' Susan said. 'Some of them get married four or five times. No wonder people stop believing they can get hurt like anybody else!'

'Those like Miller can't,' Vicky said tersely. 'Their lives aren't normal. All the money in the world can't make up for turning into a bit of flotsam floating on top of very murky waters.'

Susan looked horrified. 'Oh, poor Miller! You're very hard on him.'

'Don't be so soft-hearted. He's chronically incapable of being faithful to one woman, and he's as weak as water.' Vicky got up impatiently. 'Didn't we decide to go to Fiesole today?'

'Yes, of course. I'll be ready in two minutes,' Susan agreed, clearing the table. Vicky helped to load the dish-washer, admiring the compact way in which the kitchen had been designed. Ricco was really very clever. He must have a very clear, tidy mind. She found that slightly worrying, somehow.

Fiesole lay on the crest of a conical hill, looking down towards Florence and the river valley. Driving up towards it Vicky got a glimpse of some of the beautiful landscape she had been gazing towards from Susan's garden, those misty backdrops so like the distant perspectives of a Renaissance painting, green and grey, with cypress trees making dark exclamation points against a blue sky.

'It's a very old city,' Susan told her in between taking the curling bends in the steep road. 'Etruscan—much older than Florence. They had a war, actually, in the Middle Ages some time—twelfth century, I think. Florence won and sacked Fiesole, and after that it was Florence which dominated Tuscany, but I love Fiesole because it's small and gives a feeling of being open and spacious, because it's on a hill, I suppose. You get the feeling you're up in the sky.'

'*I* get the feeling we're going too fast!' said Vicky, clutching the door as Susan swerved round another bend.

'Sorry,' said Susan, slowing.

Vicky stared out of the window at the villas one could see on each side of the road, appearing and vanishing behind trees just breaking into blossom. They seemed to be built of the same stone as the houses in Florence, and were often the same colour, their paintwork faded by the hot Italian sun, their roofs the typical orange-red.

'What a super place to live! The views must be terrific.'

'They are. Lots of famous people have lived up here, it's a favourite place for the rich and powerful to settle down. Even the Medicis had a villa, just outside Fiesole. It isn't open to the public, it's privately owned, but it's gorgeous, so I'm told.'

They parked quite close to the small town centre and walked around the main square, the Piazza Mino da Fiesole, which they found from their guidebook had been the site of a Roman forum. It was lined with trees, the pavements crowded with street cafés and tourists like themselves. Vicky bought a few Etruscan reproductions, a small bronze owl and a tiny greeny-blue horse. She let Susan talk her into visiting the Roman theatre and walking up the steep hill to see the Duomo, a thirteenth-century church. When they walked down again Susan wanted to shop around for a set of fruit dishes, modern versions of a Roman model. The shops seemed to vary in price and it paid to check on them, but Vicky's feet were aching again, so she sat down at a café on the very edge of the hillside, looking downwards over the terraces and fields to the Arno valley, while Susan went to do her shopping.

A boy brought her an iced citrus drink, fresh squeezed lemon which was refreshingly tart on the palate. She leaned back in her chair in the sunlight, sipping her drink and watching the crowds, the lovers hand in hand, the pink cherry blossom on a nearby tree, a cloud passing over the busy square.

A woman at the next table was reading an English paper. Vicky glanced at the front page idly—and then froze. A picture of Miller covered half the page, and under it ran a black headline followed by a column of print. It was the headline that hit Vicky: MILLER OSBORNE CAR CRASH. She leaned forward to try to read the opening words of the story, but the woman holding the paper shifted, giving her an indignant glare, so that Vicky could no longer see that page.

Tense and disturbed, she took another sip of her lemon drink, looking round to see if she could catch sight of Susan. She wanted to get back to Florence as soon as possible now. She must get hold of a copy of that edition of the paper., and they were unlikely to find one in Fiesole. The kiosks in Florence sold English papers, however. The papers Susan's mother had sent had been days out of date.

'You look very grim on such a lovely day!'

She stiffened at the sound of that increasingly familiar voice, looking up in disbelief. 'Are you following me about?'

He leaned over, his hand on the back of her chair. 'Not this time. It's sheer coincidence.'

'Oh, of course!'

His eyes laughed. 'Fate meant us to meet.'

'Fate can mind its own business!'

He bent closer, and she ducked her head under his arm and out of reach. Ricco shrugged and moved away, dropping into the chair opposite her. She didn't like the calmly patient expression in his face, the look of the fisherman whose fish has ignored the bait, but who is prepared to sit there all day waiting for it to come and be caught.

'I came up here to see one of our studio engineers who was taken ill during the night. It wasn't serious, but he has a weak heart and I was worried when I heard he was ill. He ought to retire, but Giorgio is a stubborn man and doesn't want to give up working.' The cherry tree behind Vicky's chair cast a dancing shadow across his face as he gestured, for once very serious. 'We don't want to lose him, either, but I keep a close eye on him to make sure he doesn't overdo things. If it's his job or his health, his health has to win.'

'Is he better this morning?' she asked sympathetically.

He shrugged. 'If you believe him, yes. His wife looked very tired. I think she has to carry a lot of the worry. Giorgio isn't the worrying type.' He looked at her glass. 'What are you drinking?'

'Iced fresh lemon. It's delicious.'

The waiter had been hovering for a few seconds. Ricco ordered two more of the same and leaned back in his chair, crossing his long legs. The woman at the next table was unashamedly staring at him over the top of her newspaper. Vicky felt like telling her to keep her eyes to herself; it was infuriating the way women stared at him. Men had never watched her the way women seemed to watch Ricco. No wonder he was so conceited and sure of himself! All his adult life women must have been tumbling into his arms at the slightest encouragement.

'Are you up here alone?' Ricco asked

'No, Susan's with me but she went shopping. She should be back any minute.'

'Did you tell her that you'd spoken to me about her?' he asked drily, and she flushed.

'No, it would have sent her into a tizzy.'

'It didn't exactly make my day, either,' he drawled. 'I've thought over what you said, and although I don't accept that you were right . . .'

'I didn't expect you would,' she said bitingly.

'Although I don't accept your version of my behaviour,' he growled through his teeth, frowning, 'I'll make very sure in future not to give her the wrong impression.'

'Thank you,' she said, and looked away, down at the valley, her eyes absently tracing the undulations of the landscape. The colours here were so gentle, and yet so vivid; the leaves had a newly minted clarity against that soft, misty blue sky.

The waiter brought their drinks and Vicky glanced back at Ricco. He was looking around the open-air café thoughtfully. She saw his eyes meet those of the woman at the next table, who immediately smiled at him. Ricco smiled back, a faint, wry little smile. He knew, of course, that the woman had been staring at him for some time. How could he help knowing?

The woman got up and came over to the table. Incredulously, Vicky watched her smiling at Ricco again. 'Would you like to borrow my paper? It's yesterday's, but I heard you speaking English and thought you might like to catch up with the news from home.'

Vicky's heart missed a beat. If Ricco saw that story about Miller, he might put two and two together. She hadn't told him her real surname, but simply reading about a girl called Vicky who had disappeared might make him start to think, and he was clever. She knew he hadn't missed her occasional slip, that he was curious about her and her odd reticence about herself.

'That's very kind of you,' he replied, giving the woman a charming smile and accepting the newspaper. 'My wife and I will enjoy reading it.'

He put the paper on the table and Vicky discreetly pulled it towards her and pretended to glance at it. In fact she was watching Ricco and the other woman, who had begun to back, rather pink, obviously taken aback by Ricco's lie about having a wife.

'Well, nice to meet you,' she mumbled, and fled. Vicky's cold gaze followed her. Talk about being obvious! She didn't see herself scraping acquaintance with a good-looking man in that shameless way.

Pushing the newspaper hastily into her shoulder bag, she met Ricco's ironic eyes.

'It must be your fatal charm,' she told him.

'To which you're impervious?'

She smiled sweetly and didn't answer.

'Give it time,' he said coolly, then looked over the table. 'What happened to the newspaper?'

Vicky's eyes shifted away, and at that second she caught sight of Susan on the other side of the road, just going into a shop. Vicky stood up and made a big performance out of waving, but Susan wasn't looking that way.

'That's odd,' muttered Ricco, glancing down around the table. 'What on earth happened to it? Did it blow off the table? I'd swear I put it down right there in the middle.' Obviously he had been too busy watching his departing admirer to notice Vicky concealing the paper in her bag.

Vicky thought desperately of some way of distracting him. 'About that job,' she said and he looked at her attentively.

'You'll take it?'

'I'm not sure—Susan tells me it isn't easy to find a flat here. And then there's the problem of getting a work permit.'

'No problem, I can handle that. As to somewhere to live, I have a suggestion to make.'

Vicky couldn't help the cynical smile. It annoyed him.

'Don't jump to conclusions!'

'I'll try not to.'

'I could easily learn to dislike you,' Ricco said impatiently.

'Start now,' she invited.

His eyes held a flicker of aggressive hostility, but he smiled tightly. 'If you'll let me explain? My house is enormous, as you know, and I only live in part of it. There are many rooms which are empty although they're perfectly habitable. One wing could be used as a separate apartment. The rooms are small. They were the monks' cells originally; they're pretty basic, whitewashed walls, stone floors. At the moment they're empty, there's no furniture in them, but I have plenty of that. The house is crammed with old furniture, so you can take your pick. You'd have your own front door, too. The wing is quite self-contained.'

She stared at him, taken aback. The problem of where she would live if she did take the job had been one of her main reasons for hesitating. She certainly couldn't impose on Susan and David for ever. The house was too small, and they had a right to privacy in their own home.

'You and Susan would be neighbours, you could see her quite often,' Ricco coaxed. 'She seems to be rather lonely here, she'd like to have you living near by.'

'You've thought of everything,' she said drily.

His smile was complacent. 'Have I convinced you that this is an opportunity you shouldn't miss?'

'Whose opportunity, though?' she enquired.

His eyes held intimate mockery, and she felt the back of her neck prickle with sharp awareness of him. He was a man whose sexual impact was immediate and inescapable, even on women who weren't exposed to his deliberate charm. Vicky didn't want to make the mistake of getting involved with him. She had only just escaped a similar trap. Angrily, she wondered why she kept meeting men like Miller and Ricco. She must give off the wrong vibrations. Did Ricco think he was getting some sort of signal from her, and was that why he kept pursuing her? Some women did play a tricky game, on the surface indifferent while underneath they were inviting male interest. How was she to convince Ricco she wasn't one of them, that she wasn't pretending to run while constantly looking back to make sure he was following?

'Stay in Florence, Vicky,' he said suddenly, his eyes holding hers, and she stiffened, her mouth going dry. He was far too attractive; she ought to get away while she could.

Susan arrived breathlessly while they were staring at each other in silence. She fell into a chair, clutching her parcels.

'Oh, I'm so thirsty!' Only then did she realise Ricco was sitting opposite her cousin and a flush invaded her face. 'Oh, Ricco—hallo, I didn't see you there.'

'Hallo, Susan,' he said politely.

Vicky pulled herself together. 'Did you get what you were looking for?' she asked her cousin.

Susan nodded and began to talk about the items she had bought. Ricco called the waiter and ordered Susan a glass of mineral water.

A few minutes later Vicky looked at her watch. 'Shouldn't we be going, Susan?'

Susan nodded, getting up, and Ricco rose, too. 'Let me know your decision before tonight,' he said, calling the waiter over to pay the bill.

Vicky nodded. 'See you later, then,' she agreed. 'I'll come over to give you a final decision this evening.'

As they walked away, Susan asked, 'Is he talking

about the job?'

Vicky nodded, her face wry. 'Yes, and he's offered me a place to live, too. Guess where?'

Susan paused beside her car, looking enquiringly at her.

'In his house!' Vicky said drily.

'No!' Shocked, Susan stood there, the door half open. 'He didn't make a proposition, Vicky? What a nerve! He's only met you a couple of times. I'm surprised you didn't smack his face!'

'He put it very discreetly—said there was an empty wing in his villa I could use, old monks' cells, he said, and I could pick out my own furniture from other rooms. I'd have my own front door and be very private.' Vicky got into the car and laughed angrily. 'He must think I was born yesterday. I'd move into his house one day and he'd move into my bed the next. He can think again!'

Susan slid in beside her. 'There is an empty wing, mind you. The rooms are small, little stone boxes, in fact—he showed it to us once. In winter they're freezing, there's no heating in that part of the house, but in summer they must be beautifully cool—the walls are so thick.'

They drove down to Florence in a stream of other cars. Fiesole was a popular place for visitors and Florentines alike. Susan said that locally people believed it was cooler in Fiesole in summer than it was down in the closely packed, dense streets of the city. On summer days people headed out of Florence up into the cool hills, leaving the sweltering, dusty streets behind them for a few hours.

'Not to mention the traffic,' Vicky said wryly as they came nearer to Florence and the cars became a traffic jam, hooting, bumper to bumper, the air full of petrol fumes.

As soon as she could get away she went to her own room, sat down on the bed and got the crumpled newspaper out of her bag, hurriedly turning the pages until she found Miller's photograph. She read the story anxiously, on edge until she realised with enormous relief that the headline had been misleading. She should have known it would be—popular papers always tried to dramatise the trivial.

Miller had crashed his car while he was driving on a country road late at night. He had been drunk and run off the road into a tree. By some lucky fluke his injuries had been minor, a few cuts and abrasions, a bruised rib and possible concussion. His seat belt had saved him from going through the windscreen.

Sunny had talked to the press, brushing aside the questions about Miller's blood alcohol level. Yes, Miller had been drinking heavily, he had admitted, but only because he was distraught over losing Vicky. They had had a lovers' quarrel, she had walked out and Miller had been out of his mind with grief.

'My God,' Vicky muttered through her teeth, screwing up the paper, 'how can he lie like that?'

She walked angrily to the window and back again, tense as a caged animal. Only when she had begun to calm down did she start to think sensibly. Sunny's press release hadn't simply been aimed at blackening her; he had been getting Miller out of trouble, giving a believable explanation for the drunken driving, which otherwise might have serious consequences. If the police prosecuted,

Miller might be heavily fined—he might even be sent to prison.

Sunny was shrewd and knew how to manipulate the press and public opinion. He was making a fuss over Vicky's disappearance and Miller's alleged heartbreak in order to distract attention from the drunken driving. Of course, the press had leapt at the wider dimension of the story like hungry trout jumping at crumbs. It made a routine drunk driving into a headline story.

Thank God Ricco hadn't seen the paper. She stared through the trees at the roof of his house. The car crash would intensify press interest, keep the story alive. She couldn't go back to London while she ran the risk of being recognised.

She had to take that job. It was her only chance of staying away from England until Miller went back to the States and the story died down.

That evening Susan asked her if she was going over to see Ricco before dinner or afterwards.

David looked up from the newspaper he was reading. 'Are you dating Ricco?' he asked curiously, smiling.

'No, he's offered me a job, and I said I'd give him my answer tonight.'

'I thought you'd turned that down?'

'I'm having second thoughts,' she said evasively.

Susan told her husband about the apartment Ricco had offered Vicky in his villa, and David's eyes widened.

'He obviously fancies you,' he laughed, clearly relieved at the thought that Ricco Salvatore's amorous attention was straying from his wife. 'Well, I'm sure you can handle that,' he added.

'After coping with a Hollywood big shot surely an Italian businessman is no problem?'

'No problem at all,' Vicky agreed, her face rebellious. She wasn't going to admit that she found Ricco Salvatore any sort of threat.

'That wing of his house isn't super comfortable, though,' Susan pointed out. 'It's rather stark and basic.'

'That doesn't bother me,' Vicky protested. 'It sounds quite modern—simple living with a minimum of frills!'

'Then what have you got against the idea?' David asked reasonably, and she couldn't come up with an answer.

That evening, while David and Susan were watching *Dallas* on television—the famous faces talking in fast, hard-to-believe Italian—Vicky went across the garden to call on Ricco to discuss the idea of working with him. She was almost persuaded that it would be a good idea, but first she wanted to see the rooms in which she would be living. She wandered past the orange trees in their enormous terracotta pots and rang the bell on the main door. There was no answer for several minutes, and she was about to turn away when she heard the click of high heels along the red-tiled floor of the long gallery. Through the glass of the door she saw Bianca Fancelli, swaying languidly on her high-heeled white sandals, her lovely figure glittering in a scarlet and gold lamé dress, the impact of which was only heightened by the fact that some of it was missing. Bianca opened the door and regarded Vicky through smouldering eyes.

'*Si?*'

Vicky couldn't help staring at the smooth bare golden midriff, against which dangled swinging, gleaming tassels of gold suspended from Bianca's breasts.

'Er . . . *mi scusi*, Signor Salvatore, *per favore*?' she mumbled, lowering her eyes, but that didn't help much, because now she could see the long slits at the thigh which revealed more of Bianca's beautiful skin.

'Cosa vuole?' Bianca demanded, and went on to say a lot more in her furious Italian before Vicky got a chance to say it didn't matter.

'Non importa, grazie.'

There was little point in seeing Ricco Salvatore tonight. She couldn't compete with Bianca for his attention, especially not in that dress. Vicky turned away and walked back, telling herself that anyway Bianca had looked like a circus performer with all that glitter and nakedness. She and Ricco Salvatore suited each other!

CHAPTER SIX

VICKY was drinking a second cup of coffee at the breakfast table next morning when someone rang the door bell. Susan got up and went to answer it. Vicky heard her voice change, heard the deep warm voice which answered, and looked towards the hall with a frown. Ricco walked in and eyed her drily.

'*Buon giorno, come sta?*'

'*Sto bene, grazie,*' she said, tight-lipped,and his brow lifted.

'Did you get out on the wrong side of the bed?'

'Would you like some coffee, Ricco?' Susan intervened quickly.

'I'd love some, thank you,' He sat down at the table, without taking his eyes off Vicky. 'So, what did you want last night? Why did you go away again without seeing me?'

'How do you know I called?'

'I saw you from the loggia—we were drinking coffee up there. By the time I got downstairs you had walked off—Bianca said she'd told you she would fetch me.'

'In Italian, maybe, but I don't speak your language. And anyway, I thought you probably had your hands full.'

Her dry tone didn't go unnoticed. 'Bianca and I were working,' he said impatiently.

Her mouth curled. 'Oh, sure.'

'You have a very suspicious mind!'

'A mathematical one,' she said, drinking some more coffee. 'I put two and two together, that's all.'

'Or, in this case, one and one?' he enquired, his blue eyes very dark.

'Well, I didn't need a computer to work it out,' she agreed. 'I didn't want to interrupt anything, so I left again.'

'You wouldn't have been interrupting anything.' He glanced across at the kitchen area where Susan was making some fresh coffee. Raising his voice a little, he called to her, 'Oh, please, don't bother just for me, Susan!'

'It's no bother, I expect Vicky will want another cup, and the old pot was quite cold.' She came towards them with a clean cup and saucer and put them down on the table. 'It's a lovely morning, isn't it? It won't be long now before summer arrives.'

Through her lashes Vicky watched Ricco's uptilted black head, his skin lit by sunlight, the clear-cut profile striking. He smiled at Susan without any of the teasing he normally showed her, and Susan smiled and walked back into the kitchen.

Looking back at Vicky, he said, 'Last night, Bianca and I were . . .'

She cut in sharply. 'Look, what you do in your own home, in your own time, doesn't interest me! Your private life is entirely your affair.'

'We were working!' he insisted, his voice rising. 'And I didn't like the way you used the word affair.'

Vicky was irritated with herself. She was beginning to sound like a jealous woman, and Ricco wouldn't be slow to decide that that was just what she was. It wasn't true, of course; she wasn't jealous of Bianca. If any other woman had opened that door last night she wouldn't have been so annoyed, but there was something about Bianca Fancelli that infuriated her. The singer was too sure of herself. Too sexy, too beautiful—too everything! Vicky thought venomously. Bianca made her feel insignificant, mousy, dull.

Susan came back, face anxious, to pour his coffee, and Ricco gave her another of his careful smiles. At least he wasn't flirting with Susan any more.

'I'll start tidying the bedrooms, I think,' said Susan. 'Excuse me, Ricco.' She vanished discreetly upstairs. Ricco sipped his coffee, watching Vicky's expressive face.

'If you've stopped quarrelling with me, can we discuss the job?' he asked sarcastically.

'I've decided to accept the offer,' she replied stiffly, and saw his smile with resentment. He needn't look so pleased with himself. She wasn't taking it to be near him.

'Come over to the villa now and I'll show you the apartment,' he suggested.

She called up to Susan, who appeared at the top of the stairs, a duster in her hand.

'I'm going over to Ricco's villa to see the rooms,' Vicky told her and Susan nodded, looking relieved that they were in a more amicable mood. Argument always upset her.

As they walked across the gardens, Ricco asked mockingly, 'Do I get a prize?'

She stiffened. 'For what?'

'Treating Susan like a maiden aunt.'

'Virtue is its own reward.' She turned innocent eyes on him. 'Is Bianca still at your house?'

He opened his front door and stood back for her to enter. 'She and her manager had dinner with me last night, then they went back to their hotel.' He paused, eyes teasing. 'There's no need to be jealous.,

'I wasn't!' she snapped, taking an unwary step. She had forgotten how highly polished the floor was. Her feet slid from under her and she would have crashed to the floor if Ricco hadn't caught her.

She suddenly found herself lying across his arm, splayed like a rag doll. Off balance, she looked up dazedly at him.

'I've got you where I want you now, haven't I?' he murmured wickedly, his mouth curling in a smile of sheer mockery.

Vicky's eyes flickered restlessly and her colour rose, but she wouldn't let him know how disturbed she was by the way he was watching her.

'You won't get me anyhow, anywhere,' she assured him through tight lips. 'Let go of me at once.'

He made as if to do so, and at once her feet slid again and she gave a gasp of alarm, clutching at him.

'I thought you wanted to get away from me?' he said lazily, skimming his gaze over her flushed face until he was staring at her mouth. Stupidly, Vicky felt her heart skip a beat. It was shock; that was all, she told herself.

'Help me to stand up,' she ordered sharply, her hands moving up to his shoulders, while she tried to avoid looking at him.

His hands closed on her waist and lifted her upwards. She was furious with herself as she found she was watching his face in spite of her firm intention not to. His skin was so tanned and clear, a smooth, dark gold. The line of his mouth had a strangely hypnotic fascination. You could read his character in it; a strong will, humour, even, oddly, a certain detachment. He was not a man to treat lightly; he was a lot less obvious than she had thought, and, perhaps, far more likeable—but if he kissed her she would hit him.

He didn't. He dropped his arms and stood back, watching her through his lashes. Vicky was surprised—and it showed. She saw a quiver of amusement run through his face. Furious, she turned and walked off along the gallery. Ricco kept pace with her wary steps, halting at an arched door in the wall. He produced a key and unlocked the door.

'This is the only way through to the empty wing, so this would be your private front door,' he told her with a sideways smile of derision. 'So you could be sure of privacy.'

She made no comment, following him along a narrow whitewashed corridor off which opened a row of doors. Ricco opened them one after the other so that Vicky could see the rooms. They were just as he had described them—square, whitewashed, empty.

The final one was a bathroom, apparently from the Victorian era, with a vast white enamelled bath and a lavatory of the same period enclosed in polished mahogany.

'My grandfather had the bathroom installed,' he told her, turning on the taps in the bath. The water came out reluctantly and was rather rusty, but after it had run for a while it cleared.

'It's a museum piece, but it works,' he added, turning the taps off. 'I'm afraid there's no heating in these rooms, but I can get an electrician in to put some points in strategic places.'

'What about cooking?'

'I could have a simple kitchen installed within a week—an electric stove, a sink, a few cupboards.'

Her forehead creased. 'All this would be very expensive, surely?'

'I've been meaning to have something done with this wing for a long time. When you leave, I could let this place to someone else.'

'You said something about furniture,' she reminded him.

'Come and choose what you like.' He took her round the closed rooms of his villa, opening shutters to let the sunlight into dark, stuffy bedrooms often crammed with furniture from a strange mixture of periods. Vicky knew very little about antiques, but she could see that some of the pieces must be very valuable, whereas others were merely old.

It was rather fun, like shopping with a blank cheque, able to pick whatever you fancied without worrying about the cost. She didn't like to risk choosing anything that she suspected might be worth a lot of money, so she largely concentrated on Victorian and Edwardian pieces—a brass bed and a wardrobe and a tiny kidney-shaped dressing-table of polished oak for her bedroom, a pink-velvet-covered chaise-longue, and two matching chairs for the sitting-room. Ricco persuaded her to add a stained glass Tiffany lamp with a solid brass base, a nest of tables in black oak, a small bookcase and a few other items.

It was obvious that a large part of the villa hadn't been kept dusted and cleaned in the way that the rest of the house had been. Ricco showed her most of the rooms, some of them revealing signs of damp. The upper rooms had crumbling plasterwork, and their ceilings were cracked and dirty. The air in them was musty.

'It seems a shame to let these rooms decay like this,' she said to Ricco, who nodded agreement soberly.

'When I can afford it, I'll have the whole place modernised, but my company profits go back into the business at the moment.'

Some of the older pieces had been homes for mice; she saw stuffing leaking out of chairs, horsehair littered under a sofa. When she ran her hand over a sideboard her finger came away coated with pale dust. Yet she gained an impression of spacious elegance at times, a glimpse of an age long vanished, chandeliers glittering from stuccoed ceilings, deep-piled carpets and brocade and silk. Paintings hung on the walls—she had no idea if they were valuable or not, but some of them were of men and women with Ricco's features: high, arrogant noses, black hair, eyes that stared with his cool assurance, mouths shaped like his and jawlines full of Ricco's determination and insistence.

'My grandfather,' he told her when she stood and stared at one of them, a portrait of a typical Victorian, she decided—upright, dressed in sober dark clothes, a white shirt with a stiff collar rising against his throat. He had all the family characteristics except that his direct eyes were black, not blue, but she felt that his mouth was a little cruel, a thin upper lip and a lower one which combined sensuality with a certain fierceness, and gave his high-boned nose the look of a beak, the beak of a bird of prey.

'He looks rather daunting,' she observed.

'He was an old devil. My father was petrified of him when he was in a temper. He ran his household with a rod of iron, but then in those days I suppose men did.' He gave her a sideways glance, gleaming with mockery. 'The good old days!'

'Which you regret, of course!'

'The days when women knew their place and men ruled the world? Doesn't everyone?' He was laughing, but she frowned.

'I wish I thought it as funny as you do, but I get a little tired of masculine jokes about women's place being in the home and men being superior. In a way, I think I preferred it when it wasn't said as a joke, when men meant it seriously—at least that was honest. Now they make jokes about it to your face and secretly mean it, and that's worse.'

'You prefer honest tyranny to a secret hankering after it?'

'At least you know where you are with it when it's out in the open. You can fight it then.'

'Hasn't anyone told you—the fight was over long ago, the war's ended.'

'Then what was all that stuff about the good old days?'

'You have no sense of humour,' Ricco told her, and Vicky eyed him scornfully.

'I don't like black jokes, I admit, or sick ones. My sense of humour is limited to what's really funny.' She looked back at his grandfather.

'What was your grandmother like?'

'Small, frail, beautiful—even when she was eighty, which is when I remember her best. She was only four foot ten, but she had more spirit than a wild horse. I don't think my grandfather frightened her. In fact, my mother always told me it was the other way round—*he* was scared stiff of her.'

'Good!' Vicky said ferociously, and Ricco took her arm and steered her out of the room on to the wide loggia on the upper storey of the house. She had long ago lost count of the number of rooms there were or the number of staircases she had been up and down. The house was built in the most rambling, ramshackle way imaginable; Ricco said that there had been additions to it from time to time over the centuries. At one period it had been occupied not only by his family but by a dozen servants, with their wives and children. Now Ricco had two people working for him—a woman who did the housework and a man who looked after the gardens.

The loggia was just a wide terrace with a low wall topped with smooth plastered columns facing outwards. On the terracotta tiles stood pots of geraniums in flower, red and pink and white. The sun made patterns on the floor and whitewashed walls. There were half a dozen wicker chairs arranged along the loggia. They were a golden colour in the sunlight, their cushions a pale green weave.

'It's charming,' said Vicky, entranced, and wandered along to the other end, gazing out through the columns at the gardens and the other houses she could see through some clumps of pine trees and oleanders.

'I'll have all your furniture moved in there during this week. I should be able to get the electrician along over the next few days, then the place will be ready for you. When will you start work?'

'I'd like another week's holiday, if that's okay with you?'

'Va bene,' he said, joining her, his shoulder touching hers as they both leaned on the parapet of the loggia and stared at the blue spring sky.

'You have no family, Susan tells me.'

She looked round, sharply. 'Did she indeed?'

'You don't like to talk about your family?' Again he sounded faintly Italian.

'I don't like people discussing me behind my back.'

'I asked about your family and Susan told me,' He gave a wry Latin shrug. 'What's wrong with that?'

'When was this?' When had he seen Susan alone since she arrived? Her eyes darkened with suspicion as he watched her, and his mouth compressed impatiently.

'I rang her, early this morning, to find out if you had plans to go out today or whether I would find you in if I came over after breakfast. And you can stop looking at me like that—what am I being accused of now?'

'Oh, nothing,' she said, flushing. 'My parents are dead and I was an only child. Susan is my closest relative, except,of course, her mother—and she isn't a blood relation. My father was Susan's father's brother. They're both dead now. Susan and I practically grew up together, we're more like sisters than cousins.'

Ricco was staring at her oddly. 'I thought you were old school friends, not cousins.'

Vicky stared back at him, dumbstruck. She had completely forgotten lying to him, and now she had been caught out.

'What other lies have you told me?' Ricco asked, and she bit down nervously on her inner lip.

'None,' she managed in a whisper.

'Why lie to me about being Susan's cousin? I don't understand. Why couldn't you tell me the truth in the beginning? What was the point of making up that fairy tale about being at school together?'

She clung to the edge of the parapet, trying to think. What could she say to him? How could she talk her way out of this?

'I . . . I was irritated with you,' she said slowly. 'It was a silly joke, that's all.'

'Oh, that's the sort of humour that really amuses you, is it?' His tone was biting. 'Telling lies for no reason—an odd way to behave, isn't it? Or is this another lie? Is there more to this than I understand yet? Why did you come here? For a holiday or to get away from something? Are you in some sort of trouble? Is that it?'

She swallowed, and he caught hold of her arm and turned her back to face him, his cool fingers digging into her arm. She was wearing a short-sleeved blue tunic top and a pair of pink cotton pants. Suddenly she found herself shivering as though it had turned cold.

'Why did you leave your job in England? Were you dismissed? You might as well tell me—it won't take me long to find out anyway, you know. I can easily check on your last job—perhaps I should, to get a reference.'

At that she turned on him, her head flung back and her eyes angry. 'I'm not desperate for this job, you know. It was your idea, not mine. If you've changed your mind about it—well, that's fine with me.' She pulled free and began to walk away fast.

It was a full minute before he came after her, and by then she was at the foot of the stairs leading down to one end of the long gallery. As she began to walk towards the front door, she heard Ricco running down the stairs. She was afraid to move too quickly in case her feet skidded again on the polished floor, and Ricco rapidly gained on her, his long legs covering the ground at twice the speed of hers.

He caught up at the door. 'Don't turn temperamental on me! I didn't say I'd changed my mind, only that I was curious about your reasons for lying to me. Is that so odd? How would you feel in my place?'

'Maybe it wasn't such a good idea for me to take this job, though,' she evaded. 'I know nothing about this sort of artwork and I . . .'

'You've accepted the job. I'm holding you to that.' His voice was cool and hard; his face matched it. She looked up warily at him. Why was he so determined that she should work for him? And what if he did check up with her previous employer? That would really put the cat among the pigeons. She should have thought of that, but Florence seemed so far from London, this was another world, another life.

'I don't want you getting in touch with my last firm,' she insisted, and saw the tightening of his features, the hardness of his eyes.

'No? Why not?'

'I haven't done anything criminal, I'm not on the run from the police, but I don't want my old boss to know where I am, I don't want him to find me.'

Ricco's eyes narrowed, probing her face. 'I see.'

She looked down, sliding her hands into the pockets in her pants. 'He'd come to find me, and I don't want that. It's all over, but . . .'

'He won't accept that? You had an affair with him?'

Flushed, she shrugged.

'He's married, I suppose? Older than you?' Ricco's voice was icy and contemptuous. 'And you suddenly came to your senses and walked out, but he still wants you?'

She risked a glance at him through her lashes. 'You won't get in touch with him, will you? Please! I couldn't go through that again, you don't know what it was like.' The truth came into her shaky voice at that moment; she was talking about Miller and Sunny, although he didn't know it. 'Please, don't interfere—I don't want this job if it means getting in touch with him again.'

She heard Ricco breathing, a rough, ragged sound, as if he was bitterly angry. She was beginning to guess that he was old-fashioned in some ways—you could say more kindly that he was a traditionalist. He might flirt with a married woman, but he didn't approve of girls who had affairs with married men. Well, neither did Vicky, but she didn't have double standards—one standard for herself and another for everyone else. Ricco obviously did, and she despised him for that and resented the way he was staring at her, the distasteful twist of his mouth. It had thinned and tightened; suddenly it looked very much like his grandfather's—that cold, cruel mouth which had struck her so forcibly in the portrait upstairs. He had no right to look at her like that. Even if she had been telling the truth, she would have resented having judgement passed on her by a man who was almost a stranger.

'Do you still love him?' he asked harshly.

Vicky flung back her head and looked him in the eye. 'No.' She answered honestly. No, she no longer loved Miller, she knew she never had. There was a gulf between the sort of crazy, excited feeling she had had for Miller and real love. That was deeper, more fundamental, surely? It didn't grow like a mushroom at first sight and wither almost as fast.

Ricco held her gaze. She found the fixed lance of his stare slightly unnerving. What was he looking for in her face to stare like that? Some proof that she was telling the truth this time? Or was he trying to work her out? They barely knew each other, after all. He had acted on impulse, offering her this job and rooms in his own house. Was he beginning to regret leaping before he looked?

'But you were in love with him once?' he asked, his mouth hard.

She looked away. She wished she hadn't lied to him in the first place; it had been done on crazy impulse, a desire to hide her real identity. When they met at the airport, she hadn't known whether or not Susan had ever mentioned her to Ricco, talked about her cousin's engagement to Miller Osborne. It would have been quite natural if she had, Miller was famous, it would have been the sort of information one does mention in passing conversation.

'Answer me,' Ricco said tersely, and she reluctantly looked at him again.

'I suppose so, in the beginning.'

His eyes bored into her, making her even more nervous. 'So that explains your prickly mood ever since we met,' he said as if to himself. 'Once bitten, twice shy, is that it?'

She decided it would be wiser not to answer that; he was very close to the truth.

'I'm sorry I lied to you,' she said huskily. She did regret lying, but she knew that if the situation recurred she would have to behave in exactly the same way, because it was a choice of evils. Whatever happened she couldn't bear to have Miller, Sunny and the press on her trail again.

'I wish I understood you, Vicky Lloyd,' he said slowly. 'Is that even your name?' He watched the little start she gave, his mouth compressing. 'I see it isn't.'

'It is Vicky,' she muttered.

'Well, that's something, I suppose. Why can't I know your real name? Are you famous? Would I recognise your real name, is that it?'

She closed her eyes, giving a sigh. 'There's no reason why you should recognise my name,' she evaded. 'I simply didn't want to get involved with anyone in Florence. I was trying to forget.'

'Oh, you made it crystal clear that you didn't want to get involved,' he said through his teeth. 'And now

I understand why. You've just broken off an affair with another man, and don't want to risk any new relationship.'

'Something like that.' She was surprised by the strength of her own regret. Why should she feel so upset because Ricco looked at her with cold contempt and disappointment?

'I presume you really are a trained commercial artist?' Ricco asked drily. 'You can do this work I'm offering you?'

'Oh, I can do it,' she said in a low voice. 'If I can't you can always fire me.'

'I will,' he promised, almost as though he hoped he would get the chance.

CHAPTER SEVEN

A WEEK later she moved into the apartment, which looked quite different once it held furniture, warmer, smaller, more homely. The spring was in full flood now, and with all the windows open, soft air blew through the rooms and sunlight picked out the gleam of polished wood. Vicky invited Susan and David to Sunday lunch that weekend. She didn't cook, she served salad and cheese and fruit, but it was fun eating the food in those new surroundings.

Susan lay on the pink velvet chaise-longue, sighing. 'I feel like one of those languid Victorian ladies—where are my smelling salts?'

'You ought to have a house-warming party,' David suggested, inspecting the plumbing in the bathroom with incredulity a few minutes later. 'This is the oldest bath I've ever seen outside a museum! I must take some photographs of it, or people will never believe it!'

It was an enjoyable day, and when they had gone back to their villa Vicky sat by the open window looking into Ricco's garden feeling idle and contented. It was the last day of her holiday—next day she started work in Ricco's firm. She hadn't seen much of him over the last few days; he had been in Rome on business, but his housekeeper, Maria, had supervised the builders, and had helped Vicky to move in that weekend. Maria was fifty, plump and cheerful and sang off key as she worked.

She spoke English when she felt like it, which wasn't very often, but her broad smile said more than enough. She and Vicky got on at once. The kitchen wasn't yet completed, which was a snag. 'Lazy swine,' Maria told the men with a friendly smile. They didn't seem to take it amiss, promising fervently that it would be finished by the middle of the next week.

'Va bene,' said Vicky, and the men all laughed over their glasses of rough red local wine. They didn't take tea breaks; they took beer breaks or wine breaks, but they got the work done, and the kitchen was beginning to look very good.

Vicky had a strong feeling she was going to be very sorry to move out of this apartment. She could sit here by this window forever, looking into the garden and watching dusk falling over the orange trees and grass, listening to the poignant calls of the birds.

A new sound made her look upwards, startled. Bianca was leaning on the low wall of the loggia, talking over her shoulder in a throaty purr. She was wearing something black and off the shoulder; her bare skin gleamed like gold silk as she beckoned. Vicky eyed her with dissatisfaction; her magnificent body was tawny and dangerous in that dress—why did she always wear such daring clothes if not to show off that incredible figure?

A second later Ricco appeared beside Bianca and Vicky shot back from the window, her heart performing a strange acrobatic leap. She hadn't seen him for a few days, that was all; it was odd that at the sight of him she reeled back as if she'd had an electric shock.

Her nerves jangled violently; she sat down on a

chair, wondering what on earth was wrong with her. She could still see Ricco through the heavy cream lace curtains over her windows. His tanned face was in profile; the combination of gathering dusk and seeing him through the lace made him more than ever reminiscent of his Victorian grandfather, a long, arrogant nose, hard mouth and insistent jaw. He was wearing a black evening suit—obviously he and Bianca were going somewhere special.

Vicky felt a sharp little stab of emotion—annoyance, distaste, she told herself. It couldn't be jealousy. Why on earth should she be jealous? She hardly knew the man.

She stayed out of sight; she didn't want Ricco to think she was spying on his love life, or that she was interested in what he did. He had denied that there was anything but business between himself and Bianca, but Vicky didn't believe him. She knew what liars men were, and she couldn't believe that any man could be indifferent to that tigrish figure, those languorous, provocative eyes. Bianca reeked of sex; even her voice held the musk of sensuality.

She was murmuring in Italian to Ricco, her body half-turned his way, swaying invitingly towards him, her breasts visible above the black satin of her dress.

Vicky watched Ricco's expression, her mouth tight, teeth clenched together. So he wasn't Bianca's lover? Then why was she putting her arms round his neck? Vicky got up to walk away, she didn't want to see them kissing. She felt like a voyeur already. She should have turned her back on the window the minute she saw Bianca on the loggia.

She went to bed early that night because she had

to get up very early. Ricco had promised to drive her to work, and he would be picking her up at seven-thirty.

Waking in the pale dawn was something of a shock to her after the lazy days in the sun. She felt half asleep even after a cool shower. She dressed carefully in a cool blue linen dress with white shoes. Her mirror showed her the image she was after—a capable professionalism. She didn't want Ricco's staff to get the wrong impression. She wouldn't be surprised if they had jumped to the conclusion that she was Ricco's girl-friend—even Susan and David seemed to believe that his motives were purely personal.

Vicky eyed herself threateningly. If Ricco had given her this job because he hoped to have an affair with her, he could forget it. She had no intention of letting him lay a finger on her.

Do you hear that? she asked her reflection, but her mirrored eyes seemed to hold a knowledge which she found disturbing.

She turned away as she heard Ricco's tap on her outer door. He was precisely on time; it was seven-thirty, she saw when she looked at her watch.

She opened the door, feeling intensely nervous. Ricco's dark blue eyes flicked down over her slender figure and she saw his mouth twist.

'Very cool,' he mocked. 'Settled into your new home? Maria tells me the builders haven't finished the kitchen yet—I apologise, I'll see them about that later today and try to prod them into hurrying themselves.,

'No problem,' she said offhandedly. 'I won't be cooking while the weather is so fine.' She followed him out of the villa. 'How was Rome?'

'Hectic as ever. You need a course of vitamins before you can face the place these days. It gets more crowded every year.'

It was easier to talk to him than she had feared—but then Ricco didn't know she had seen him last night with Bianca, so *he* wasn't selfconscious with *her*.

He opened the door of his car and she slid into it, prickling as he watched her slim legs swing sideways. Sometimes he reminded her so much of Miller, as now, when he gave her that intimate, teasing smile, his eyes gleaming behind their thick black lashes. Why should she feel edgy just because she had seen him with another woman? If he had a dozen women it meant nothing to her.

Perhaps she was jealous because of the humiliation of discovering that Miller was dating other women while he was engaged to her? Her ego had taken quite a beating at Miller's hands. She was scared stiff of a repeat performance.

Ricco's gleaming Lamborghini made short work of the drive into Florence until it met the usual clogged traffic jam inching its way into the city.

Ricco had his window wound right down. He leaned out, his body graceful in a lightweight white suit, gesticulating impatiently, when the car in front hesitated about moving off from some traffic lights.

He sank back in his seat, muttering in fierce Italian, then caught her eye and grimaced. 'Traffic like treacle this morning—I wonder we put up with it. What sort of life is it when we spend so much time sitting in tin boxes screaming at each other on these hot, dusty roads?'

She laughed sympathetically. 'It does seem crazy, doesn't it?'

They arrived at his office a few minutes late. As they opened the door Vicky heard phones ringing, typewriters clacking, voices talking. The building which had been so quiet and empty on her last visit was now full of people hard at work.

Ricco took her straight up to the art department on the upper floor, above the room she had seen on her previous visit. She had wondered why he hadn't shown her the art department last time, but as soon as she met the art director she knew why—Ricco wouldn't have cared to risk offending Andrea Parigi, who might have resented having his own department invaded while he wasn't on the premises.

They found him sitting in front of an easel staring fixedly at a painting.

'Andrea, sorry to interrupt, but . . .' Ricco began, but Andrea threw up a silencing hand.

'Un momento!' He leaned forward, peering more closely, clicking his tongue and shaking his head.

Vicky watched him curiously. A broad, stocky man, he had dark hair turning grey, a rugged face and a pair of piercing black eyes which he suddenly turned on them.

'*Si*, Ricco?'

'Andrea, this is Vicky Lloyd—you remember, I talked to you about her?'

'The English girl? Yes, of course,' He held out his hand, smiling with great warmth. *'Piacere? Lieto di fare la sua conoscenza.'*

'She doesn't speak Italian,' Ricco told him, but Vicky had by now learnt enough to realise that Andrea was merely saying hallo, nice to meet you. She answered smilingly, *'Sto bene, grazie.'*

'Molto bene, signorina,' said Andrea, shaking

hands with a firm, warm grip.

'Don't count on her keeping that up for long,' Ricco said drily. 'I've got an appointment, Andrea. Can I leave Vicky with you? Vicky, I'll see you at seven o'clock tonight and drive you back to the villa.'

'Thank you,' she said as he walked to the door. It closed behind him and Vicky looked at Andrea uncertainly. 'I have no experience of this sort of work, you know.'

'So, okay, what experience do you have?' He swivelled in his chair and gestured to the chair on the other side of his desk. 'Tell me about yourself. Ricco told me a little, enough for me to know you have some sort of training.'

She gave him a brief run-down on her career and years at college. 'I brought some of my work to show you, to give you an idea,' she ended, opening her bag and bringing out the sketch pad in which she had been working. 'Pastels, largely; a few watercolours—I have a large portfolio of stuff, but it's back in London and won't be sent here for a week or so.'

Andrea took the sketch pad and began to turn the pages, looking at the work with the same thoughtful eye he had been giving the picture on the easel. Vicky's gaze drifted towards that now, and Andrea said without looking up, 'What do you think of that?'

'You certainly wouldn't miss it on a display shelf.' It was a modern abstract, zigzags of flame and purple cut through by wide splashes of yellow. Vicky liked it; it was her kind of painting.

'What sort of recording would you expect to find inside that sleeve?,

'Modern, jazz or heavy rock. Maybe even pop,

depending on the group.'

Andrea grunted, his spatulate fingers closing her sketch pad. 'You like it?'

'Yes,' she replied, a little defiantly. After all, he was a Florentine; to him art would mean a certain sort of painting and sculpture, classical work, not this brash, defiant modernism.

Andrea leaned back in his chair, his fingertips together, nibbling them ruminantly. 'Do you smoke?'

'No.'

'Good. I'm trying to give up and it's driving me crazy. I couldn't cope with someone else smoking in here,' He chewed his fingertips while he stared at her; she wondered if the habit had developed since he gave up smoking.

'You know what Ricco wants? The classical series? He told you exactly what he's looking for?'

'Yes, costumes in period with the music.'

'How are you on costume?'

'I was a fashion designer—fabrics, not actual clothes, but I . . .'

'Good, good. Up your street, then? That's the phrase? Up your street?' He grinned, a gold tooth displayed. 'My wife is English, miss. She makes me speak English one day a week at home. For the children, you know? They learn while they eat, very good, yes?'

'Marvellous—I wish I was bilingual. I'm afraid my Italian is pathetic.'

He laughed. 'Okay, I teach you Italian—you correct my English when it is going haywire. You start now. Tell me—what does that mean—haywire? My wife is always using phrases I don't know.'

'I've no idea,' Vicky said blankly. 'You used it correctly in context, but I've no idea where the word comes from.'

He shrugged. 'Okay.' He went to a large cupboard and produced a printed manual. 'Read this—no need to hurry, take it home. It will give you all the technical details you will need. First, look through all the books of earlier jacket sleeves, see what we did before. And you can start studying Italian costume; we have reference books on the bookshelves at the far end of the room.,

She glanced towards them, nodding, and Andrea smiled at her. 'Okay, old chap?'

She giggled, and he eyed her enquiringly. 'That is wrong?'

'A chap is a man, not a girl,' she explained.

'Then for a girl, what?'

'Old lady, I suppose,' she said hesitatingly. 'Although it . . .'

Andrea swept aside her rider. 'Old lady, please go away and start to learn what you can. I have too much work to do, okay? We will talk tomorrow when you are finding your feet here.'

She got up. 'Thank you, Mr Parigi.'

'Andrea,' he said cheerfully. 'And my wife and I will be very happy if you come to dinner soon.'

'Thank you, I'd love to,' she said, surprised but pleased.

'Saturday?'

'Yes, that's fine with me, I'll look forward to it.'

'You can speak English with my children. I think when they grow up they will associate English with eating—at every meal they have to talk in English.'

She laughed. 'Very probably.'

'They speak better than me; when I get words

wrong, they laugh at me. Very bad children.'

And a very nice father, Vicky thought, as she settled into the far corner of the room to study her manual and a pile of books on Italian costume. She became absorbed in her work at once, and was surprised when Andrea interrupted her to suggest that it was time she went to lunch.

He took her downstairs and introduced her to some of the staff in the administrative office which she had seen on her previous visit. They took Vicky to lunch in a small family *trattoria* a short walk from the office. They had a cheap and simple meal—a typical Tuscan meal, the other girls told her. *Passatelli in brodo*, a broth made with some sort of cheese dumplings, followed by veal served with spinach and boiled potatoes and a sweet which the other girls laughingly told her was called *zuppa inglese*.

'English soup?' she repeated, puzzled, but when the dish arrived it turned out to be trifle, and the other girls laughed a great deal at her surprised expression. She couldn't eat much of it, the meal had been too filling, but it was delicious.

Vicky was ashamed to discover how many of the girls spoke some English. A few were fluent, but all of them knew some words. She was determined to learn Italian while she was living here; it would be lazy and stupid not to, so she kept asking what phrases meant, and the other girls were quite happy to teach her a few necessary expressions.

One of them was distinctly unfriendly—a thin, olive-skinned girl with brown eyes and a pointed face.

'Is it true you're living with Ricco?' she asked spitefully as they drank their coffee.

'Lina!' one of the others exclaimed, looking embarrassed.

Vicky refused to look ashamed. She calmly explained that she had an apartment in Ricco's villa, but it was quite separate. How had they found out? she wondered.

'Andrea didn't want you, you know,' Lina told her, and there was an intake of breath around the table as the girls exchanged speaking glances.

'How do you know?' Vicky asked, trying to keep her temper.

'He always gets the artwork from an agency. He doesn't need a full-time artist working for him.' Lina's dark eyes held malice. 'Ricco pushed you on to him—no wonder Andrea was so furious!'

'Oh, take no notice of her,' the other girls interjected hurriedly. 'She's a cat!'

Vicky was disturbed, though. Her instincts had been right. Ricco had manufactured this job for her, and Andrea Parigi hadn't been very happy about it.

She was relieved to find that the office staff had all left when she and Ricco set out for the villa that evening. She didn't want to walk out of the building with him while Lina watched with those sharp, malicious eyes.

He looked sideways at her curiously as they drove away. 'How did you get on with Andrea?'

'I liked him very much.'

'And the work? Found it easy?'

'Did you manufacture this job for me?' she broke out angrily.

He kept his eyes on the road, his profile cool. 'What makes you think that?'

'I picked it up—Andrea didn't really want me, did he? I'm not accusing him of saying anything, or even giving me a hint—he was kind and pleasant—but he doesn't usually employ full-time artists, he commissions special work and otherwise just buys from an art agency.'

'So?'

'So why did you offer me this job?'

'I wanted to keep you in Florence,' he said, so casually and calmly that for a minute she didn't quite take it in, then she flung round to stare at him fixedly.

'Why?'

'I didn't want you to go back to London.'

'Why?' she persisted, knowing that although he was talking with such apparent frankness he was still being evasive.

His voice became impatient. 'Must you keep asking questions? What difference does it make? The job is there, you can do it—why I offered it to you doesn't matter.'

'It matters to me,' Vicky countered tartly. 'I like to know what I'm getting into.'

Ricco turned into the gates leading to the villa, his tyres swishing on the gravelled drive.

'You have a suspicious little mind. There are no strings attached, if that's what you mean.'

'That's what I mean!' she said, and Ricco shot her an angry stare.

'You can always lock your front door at night!'

'I will, don't worry. But how many spare keys are there?'

'You have both of them,' he said tersely. He pulled up outside the villa and got out of the car. Vicky clambered out the other side just in time to find him striding round to confront her.

He grabbed her shoulders and shook her furiously. 'If I wanted a woman I wouldn't have to buy myself one—with a job or anything else!'

'Don't manhandle me!' Vicky snapped, jerking away. 'Bianca Fancelli may like rough stuff, but I don't!'

His face altered, the dark blue eyes glittering with mockery. 'You seem obsessed with Bianca!'

Vicky's face burnt. She hadn't meant to say that, it had just slipped out.

'If anyone's obsessed with her, it's you, not me,' she said furiously, turning on her heel. She remembered the glassy floor, and slowed down once she was inside the long gallery. Every time she walked down the vaulted garden-like room she felt surprised by the strangeness of being here, living in a place as extraordinary and beautiful as this one.

Ricco loomed up behind her as she put her key into the ancient lock. 'Just because some man treated you badly, there's no need to slap me down all the time,' he said harshly.

Ricco was like this incredible gallery—he surprised and riveted your attention, but he was also dangerous if you let yourself walk unwarily. One false step, and your feet would slide from under you.

She opened her door and was about to walk into the apartment, when he caught her waist, his hand firm and inexorable.

'I'm talking to you!'

'Really? I thought you were shouting,' She tried to pull away, but his hand gripped her more tightly.

'Was he much older than you? A married man, you said—a father figure, was he? Your own father died years ago, I gather. You must have been very young at the time. It probably had a traumatic effect on you, left you vulnerable to older men . . .'

'What absolute rubbish,' Vicky snarled, turning on him. 'Don't you try to analyse me! That cuts both ways, you know. What are *you* looking for in a woman? Didn't you say your mother was dead? Well, I suppose that would explain why you're so fascinated by Bianca!'

He stared down at her, apparently stupefied, then began to laugh. 'You wicked little cat! Bianca's years younger than I am.'

She opened her eyes wide at him. 'I'd never have guessed! And before you start casting yourself in the role of my next father figure, I am definitely not into older men!'

She pulled herself away while he was taking that in and managed to slam the door, leaving him on the other side.

She was very tired that evening and went to bed early again. An owl hooted somewhere in the gardens just as she was drifting off to sleep, and she got up to close the shutters over her bedroom windows to shut out the mournful cry. It was a very dark night, but as she was reaching up to fasten the shutters she caught a tiny red glow in the darkness, and then the scent of a cigar. Vicky stood there, hearing a slow footstep on the gravel path, the grate of a heel. Ricco was walking in the garden, smoking a cigar. His face was a pale blur between the leaves of a lilac tree and she stared towards it, wondering why he wasn't asleep. He had to get up early too.

He took another step, and at that instant glanced towards her window. She knew he had seen her, for he turned that way, the cigar in his hand making a small red arc as he gestured.

'Can't you sleep either?' He walked over to the window and stood on the other side of the glass, staring at her.

It was a cool spring night, a little wind stirring the branches in the garden, but suddenly Vicky was hot; she felt beads of sweat break out on her temples, and her legs turned to rubber.

Without a word she hurriedly pulled the shutters together and bolted them, almost running to bed to climb in under the sheet. She was shaking. Under Ricco's stare she had become conscious of wearing a short, thin nightshirt of fine cotton which hid very little of her body. There had been glass between them, yet his eyes had had an impact almost as violent as if he had been touching her instead of merely staring.

She curled up and tried to get to sleep; it wasn't easy. Next morning when Ricco picked her up she felt tense and uneasy long before he tapped on the door. Living here, so close to him, was going to be more of a problem than she had feared. She had told herself that she could handle him—she hadn't reckoned with having to handle her own instincts too.

Ricco gave her a dry look when she opened the door. 'Speaking to me today?'

'Of course,' she said as coolly as she could.

'Well, that's nice,' he said. 'If it bothers you to have me looking at you when you're only wearing your nightdress, you'd better not stand at the window like that in future.'

'Oh, shut up!' snapped Vicky, getting into his car.

She saw very little of him over the next few days, except in the morning and evening when he drove her to and from the office. She was totally occupied in what she was doing in the art department, and time seemed to flash past. To her relief she found

Andrea very helpful; whenever he had time he would give her tips on how to conceive ideas for the jackets, show her earlier artwork, discuss why he had picked it and how successful it had been. Vicky felt she was learning all the time, and by the end of the week she was much more hopeful about being able to do this job.

On the Friday afternoon she was alone in the art department when Ricco walked into the room. She looked up, startled, her eyes immediately wary.

'Andrea isn't here.'

'I didn't want Andrea, I wanted you.'

Her eyes flickered at the phrasing and his mouth twitched impatiently.

'That wasn't a double meaning.'

'I didn't think it was!'

'No? You looked as if you did.'

'Oh, really, stop picking me up on everything I say and do!' she burst out, and Ricco put a finger on her lips to silence her, his face quizzical. He smiled, and Vicky muttered, 'Sorry I got mad.'

As her lips moved under his finger, the words breathed out on his skin, Ricco bent towards her. Vicky froze, her eyes restlessly skating over his face. She didn't want to feel that stab of sharp attraction, but she couldn't deny, even to herself, that she did feel it.

'Did Andrea tell you that he's invited me to dinner this Saturday too?' he murmured, staring at her mouth and still tracing the curve of it with that long index finger.

'No,' she said breathlessly, mind racing. Andrea had invited him to make up the party? Why would he do that unless he believed that she and Ricco were intimately involved? Andrea knew by now that she was living in Ricco's house; no doubt he had drawn his own conclusions, and Vicky flushed deeper at the realisation of what that would mean. Andrea was sophisticated and knew Ricco very well. Had other women lived in the villa before her? Susan hadn't mentioned that she wasn't the first, but then Susan might not have known, or might be reluctant to repeat gossip of that sort.

'We're supposed to be there by eight—I'll drive you there. He lives on the outskirts of the city. It's going to take us half an hour, so we'll leave at seven-thirty.'

They were so absorbed in each other that they hadn't noticed the click of the door opening, but they both heard the sharp intake of breath and the tap-tap of heels on the floor. Vicky's nostrils quivered at the powerful scent of a woman's perfume as she turned her head to stare at Bianca Fancelli.

The high-pitched spate of Italian made no sense to her, of course, but she didn't need a translation. Bianca's rage vibrated in her voice, her black eyes burned, darting from Vicky's flushed face to Ricco's wary one. At every stabbing word she gestured, a rolled-up magazine clutched in one hand. Vicky got the feeling that at any minute Bianca might beat Ricco over the head with it, but Bianca suddenly threw it on to the desk, dropped her purse next to it, unbuttoned the short fantailed white mink she was wearing and stalked close to Ricco, continuing her monologue eye to eye with him, ignoring Vicky.

Vicky would have left the room if she could have got up and exited without attracting Bianca's unwanted attention. She lowered her eyes and kept very still, letting Ricco cope with his lady-friend.

The magazine Bianca had flung down was slowly unrolling; Vicky watched it absently from the corner of her eye.

With a wild shock of disbelief she saw her own face appear, a photograph in colour, blown up too large, a distorted image she only just recognised. Her head swung quickly and she looked up at Ricco, eyes wide in alarm.

What was Bianca saying to him? Had she recognised Vicky on the cover of the magazine? Was she telling Ricco that he was now employing Miller Osborne's missing fiancée?

Ricco must have sensed the sharp movement, and he slid a sideways glance at her. Hurriedly she looked down, her face burning.

Bianca stopped, mid-spate, flung round to glare at Vicky and spat out two words that made Vicky stiffen with affront. She was pretty sure she knew what that meant, and she didn't like the job description.

'*Zitta!*' snapped Ricco, and that, too, Vicky understood. Be quiet, he had said, in a tone that Bianca did not like at all.

Grabbing her purse, Bianca made for the door. Vicky picked up the magazine as Ricco followed the other woman; she was about to drop it into the wastepaper basket when Bianca stalked back and snatched it away from her. The cover ripped—Vicky had been holding the magazine too tightly. Bianca made noises like a kettle boiling. She waved the magazine at Vicky, pouring out more Italian, then her eyes narrowed and she stopped talking to stare, closely, frowningly.

Vicky somehow held her stare, but she was very

cold and pale. Bianca looked down at the photograph on the cover, looked at Vicky again, staring at her short blonde hair. The girl on the cover had dark hair, of course, smooth and straight, brushed down over her shoulders. That made the face seem thinner, and Vicky's make-up had been different.

'Come si chiama Lei?' demanded Bianca.

Vicky knew perfectly well that the other woman was asking her name, but she didn't admit she understood, she simply gave a blank shrug.

'Bianca, che cosa c'è, ora?'

Ricco's voice from the door made Bianca turn her head, the sloe-black eyes intent, a spark of malice in them—or was that Vicky's imagination? Nervously she tried to read the other woman's face. Had she recognised her? Or had she merely picked up a resemblance, a similarity, and begun to wonder?

Giving Vicky one last hostile look, Bianca walked towards the door, taking the magazine with her, clenched in her hand again. Vicky heard the sound of the footsteps receding down the stairs. She collapsed into a chair with her hands over her face.

What had the article in the magazine been about? She wished she read Italian, but the splash headline on the cover had made no sense to her. All she had picked out was her own name and Miller's, his in much larger type, coming first.

She must somehow get hold of a copy of the magazine and ask Susan to translate it for her. She wished she had noted what it was called, but in her anxiety over seeing her own face on the cover she hadn't thought of looking at the name of the magazine.

Had Bianca recognised her? If she had, would she tell Ricco? Vicky began to wish she had told him herself. She should have warned him about the sort of publicity that might blow up in her face if Miller and Sunny ever found out where she was, but when they first met she had been desperate not to be recognised, and by the time she knew him and was pretty sure he would never betray her it had been too late. She had been unwilling to talk about Miller to him. She had been unwilling to talk about Miller to anyone. The whole subject made her sick. It had been such a revelation to her of the depths of corruption which existed; she had been so naïve and blind until she walked into that spider's web. She had escaped, but she knew she would never be the same again, and she hated talking about it.

Ricco wasn't going to like it when he found out how much she had lied to him. He had been angry enough when he discovered that she had lied about her name, but this was much worse.

It was only then she admitted how much it mattered to her what Ricco thought, and the admission shook her. In a few weeks he had become important; she didn't know how she could have been so stupid as to let another good-looking man get to her like that, but it was too late to re-erect her shattered barriers. Ricco had got through them.

CHAPTER EIGHT

VICKY spent the Saturday morning shopping with Susan and had lunch with her cousin and David in their villa. They were intrigued to discover that she was having dinner with Ricco. David teased her about it; Susan was faintly worried.

'I can handle him,' Vicky assured her, with a confidence she was far from feeling. 'And anyway, we're having dinner with the Parigi family—with children to chaperon us, Ricco hasn't a chance of trying anything.'

'During dinner, maybe not, but what about later, when you're driving back alone?' David teased. 'In the moonlight, by the river? Very romantic! That Lamborghini has a sex appeal that turns girls' heads.'

'Which is more than its owner does,' retorted Vicky, and got an incredulous look from Susan, who clearly didn't believe that. Nor did David, who hooted derisively.

'Go on! You know you fancy him.'

'I'm not arguing with you any more,' Vicky said with dignity. 'Can I have some more coffee, Susan?'

'You do like the job, though, don't you?' Susan asked as she refilled Vicky's cup.

'It's fascinating—next week Andrea may be taking me to watch a recording session in the studios.'

'Have you come up with any ideas for a cover yet?' David asked, relaxing in a chair with a sigh.

'Not yet,' said Vicky, uncertainty in her eyes. She now had a pretty good idea of the techniques involved—what was required was inspiration, and so far that hadn't struck. 'It'll come,' she said, whistling in the dark. At least, she hoped it would.

That evening she had a hard time trying to make up her mind what to wear. Her own uncertainty irritated her to the point where she felt like screaming. She was only going to dinner with a pleasant family—it wasn't a world-shaking event. Why was she so screwed up about it?

What if Ricco was taking her? Was that any reason for dithering about like an idiot? She firmly took down a dress made from a fabric she had designed herself, a warm rose-red printed with faint white spirals that looked from a distance like tiny roses. It had been designed for her by a friend from art college who had helped her to sew it. It had a tight waist, a full skirt that swirled as she moved and a delicate lace collar on a low, round neckline.

Every time Vicky wore it she had poignant memories of her last year at college. Her best friend had planned to join a good fashion house and from there launch into designing for herself, but she had married and become pregnant, so her career had gone out of the window as soon as she left college. Vicky had occasionally heard from her since—they had always talked of starting up in business together. Vicky would design fabrics, Annie would design the clothes. They would be famous and make their fortune.

It hadn't turned out like that. Fate had taken a hand. Vicky made a face, sighing. It would have been fun.

Ricco arrived promptly and leaned on her front

door, looking her up and down, whistling.

She flushed. 'Thank you.' She ran her eyes over him in deliberate imitation and whistled back. He deserved it, casual in pale blue cotton slacks and a blue-and-white shirt, a cotton jacket matching the slacks over that. The fashion was Italian, striking, very elegant. Vicky loved the flowing lines and cool colours.

His eyes mocked. 'Am I supposed to be taken aback? I'm glad you approve.'

She looked into the dark blue eyes, smiling. Bianca hadn't said anything to him, she was sure of that. It made her feel relaxed, happy. Her smile seemed to run through her whole body.

'A pity we're not going dancing,' said Ricco, watching her lock her door. 'That dress was meant to be danced in—maybe on the way back from Andrea's, if it isn't too late, we might stop somewhere?'

They emerged into the soft dusk of an Italian evening, the air heavy with scents of late spring. Ricco unlocked his car and watched her slide into it, then walked round to join her. Vicky was silent, her head cloudy with a languor she couldn't explain, watching him through her lashes, her head back against the seat, her pulses beating slowly and sleepily. She didn't feel like having dinner with strangers, making polite small talk. Ricco was right—it was a night for dancing. She wondered what it would feel like, being held in his arms, moving with him to music. Her pulses picked up and beat faster.

'Music?' He turned on a tape player and a guitar began throbbing; gypsy music, Spanish, she thought vaguely.

'One of yours?'

'Of course.' He turned his head, smiling, his teeth a white flash against brown skin. 'Andrea suggests you might like to sit in at the studio one day next week. I'll fix it.'

'Thank you.' The deep passionate beat of the music sounded inside her, in her bloodstream, in her body.

The city was crammed with traffic, as usual, those narrow streets hot and stuffy with petrol fumes and noisy with the sound of engines roaring. Ricco drove without speaking, his tanned hands resting on the wheel, his body poised patiently, and she watched him drowsily, beginning to admit that she wanted to touch him, to trace the hard contours of that face, learn the feel of his body under her hands. The gypsy music beat higher, she could hardly breathe.

Ricco turned into a less busy road and picked up speed. He shot her a look that gleamed with awareness, and her eyes quickly dropped. He knew she had been staring; had he picked up what she was feeling?

Oh, God, I hope not, she thought, very hot. A moment later he had parked and shut off the music, and Vicky stumbled out of the car without waiting for him to move first.

It was a pleasant evening, after all. Andrea's wife, Lucy, was a calm, friendly woman at least ten years older than Vicky, perhaps more. Their children were lively and easy with adults, used to having grown-up conversations, interested in what went on around the table, able to enter into discussions about music and books and television. The food was very good; Lucy had made a fruit cocktail to start with, and then served a dish of green and white tagliatelle with a meat sauce which was quite delicious. 'Straw and hay,' Lucy told her when Vicky asked what the dish was called.

The children laughed. Vicky looked at them, glanced at Ricco.

'No, really? What is it called?'

'Paglia e fieno,' said Ricco, grinning.

'And what does that mean?'

'Straw and hay,' they all chorused, laughing, and when she refused to believe them Lucy went off to find a dictionary and proved that they weren't making it up.

Lucy didn't look particularly English, her skin was so brown and her eyes were even darker. At a glance she would certainly pass for an Italian, but her accent betrayed her when she opened her mouth, and she had curly brown hair with a streak of red in it.

She and Vicky washed up together after the meal. Vicky had to insist; she wanted a chance to get to know Lucy better without the men around. As they worked she told Lucy about Susan and David.

'Susan's made some friends, with the wives of men who work with David, but her Italian isn't very good yet and she feels a bit lonely here. That's partly why I'm staying on—I know Susan likes having me near her.'

'It isn't easy, when you first move to Italy, but once you can speak the language it gets easier. You have to make the effort to find friends, but that applies anywhere. If you moved to a strange town in England you'd have the same problem.'

'I'm planning to have a small housewarming party soon—mostly people from the office. I hope you'll come. I'd like you to meet Susan.'

'I'd love to,' said Lucy, putting away plates in a wall cupboard. 'Andrea tells me you're living in part of Ricco's house.' She glanced round. 'The empty wing, isn't it?'

'That's right,' Vicky said guardedly, wondering what Lucy thought of that.

'I like Ricco, he's been very good to us. When my eldest boy, Piero, was knocked down by a car Ricco insisted on paying for a specialist from Milan, the best man in the country. I think if he hadn't done that Piero might have lost his sight. He had to have a very difficult operation immediately. Even a delay of a few days might have meant his chances were remote, but thanks to Ricco the operation was performed almost at once and was a hundred per cent successful. I'll never be able to forget what he did for us. Neither will Andrea.' Lucy turned, wiping her hands on a tea towel. 'He's a nice man.' She smiled. 'Far too nice to get caught by someone like Bianca Fancelli!'

Vicky carefully put down the coffee cup she was drying. 'You think he may marry her?' she asked, hoping she sounded casual.

Lucy grimaced. 'I hope not.'

Vicky's stomach was clenched as if someone had just hit her there. She listened as Lucy talked, trying to look calm.

'Bianca's a singer—first and last a singer! Everything else in her life has to fit her work, she doesn't care twopence for anyone but Bianca Fancelli and her career.' Lucy's face was ironic. 'If she does marry Ricco it will be because he's useful to her, and she'll give him hell. She's ruthless, spoilt, selfish—a typical star.'

Vicky felt a cold jab of comprehension, recognising the description—Bianca and Miller were two of a kind, their careers were what mattered, and the people who got involved with them were unimportant and expendable. Their amorality was instinctive, a defence against the many people who tried to use them. They made sure that they were the users, and in a way that was understandable, but it made them poor risks for anyone stupid enough to love them.

'Do you think he's in love with her?' she asked huskily, and Lucy shot her an odd look.

'I wouldn't like to guess—Ricco plays his cards close to his chest, but he has seen a lot of her over the past couple of years, although he couldn't really avoid doing so considering she's such a major recording star.'

'She's good, isn't she?' said Vicky, grimly determined to face facts.

'Good?' Lucy looked at her drily. 'She's fabulous, and she knows it.'

'Does Andrea talk about his work much?'

'Endlessly.'

'Do you go to the opera often?'

'Whenever we can get a baby-sitter. We have all our favourite operas on disc, but however good the recording it can't compare with a stage performance, that's a feast for the eye as well as the ear, and the singers get more of a buzz from having an audience, their performances are often better. Bianca, in particular, comes over the footlights like a typhoon. She has tremendous stage presence; when she's on, even if she has her mouth shut, you can't take your eyes off her.'

Vicky's teeth set like concrete; she went on

smiling, but it hurt. Why should she imagine that Ricco was interested in her when Bianca had ten times her sex appeal, plus all that talent, beauty, sheer knockout presence? She should have remembered her first impression of him—like Miller, he was a flirt.

Lucy opened the kitchen window wider. The dark night sky was cloudy, the air heavy and humid. 'I've got a hunch it may rain overnight. We haven't had any rain for days, so it will do the gardens good.' She turned, smiling. 'Shall we see what the men are up to?'

The children were in bed and asleep by now. The men were talking shop, but when Lucy and Vicky came in Ricco got up, stretching his long body with a smothered yawn.

'I'm afraid we must be going, Lucy. I think a storm is on the way, don't you? I'd like to get home before it breaks. Thanks for a wonderful evening.'

Vicky added her own thanks. 'And don't forget my party—I'll let Andrea know when I've fixed the date.'

Andrea and his wife waved goodbye from their door, their arms around each other. Vicky looked back, waving. 'I like them very much,' she said to Ricco.

'So do I.' He threw her a smile. 'And what was all that about a party?'

'A housewarming, it seemed a good idea.' She made a mock face at him. 'I'd forgotten you were my landlord—do I need permission?'

'Am I invited?'

'Is that the price of permission?' She laughed. 'Yes, of course you are.'

'Then I agree, a housewarming is a good idea.'

The streets were far less empty now, and they drove back faster than they had come.

'Who else are you asking?' he queried.

'Some of the girls from the office—if that's okay with you?'

'Why ask me? You're the one giving the party.'

Vicky watched him through her lashes; his face seemed abstracted, brooding.

'You're welcome to bring someone,' she said huskily. 'Bianca.' She stopped short as his head swung towards her, his dark blue eyes intent. 'Or anyone you like,' she added hurriedly under that probing stare. The last thing she wanted was to have Bianca Fancelli at her party, in her apartment, in the same room with her; especially if Ricco was there too, and she had to watch them together. It had been bad enough the other night, seeing them up there on the loggia, knowing that they were going out to dinner, might well come back to Ricco's villa afterwards and make love. It would be ten times worse if they were in the same room, but she had made herself suggest that he brought Bianca. Perhaps she was a masochist, she thought, but her only way of dealing with those sharp stabs of jealousy was to grit her teeth and pretend she didn't care.

His face had an odd, ironic cast in the stormy light. 'You want me to bring Bianca to your party?'

'If you want to,' she muttered through clenched teeth.

'But you don't mind if I do?' Ricco enquired.

She made an acquiescing noise. She couldn't actually speak.

His expression was bland. 'You're very tolerant—after what she calllled you yesterday!'

Vicky went red. 'You know I don't speak Italian very well.'

'You didn't understand? Well, it was a very colloquial phrase—shall I translate?'

'No, thank you!' she said furiously. 'I got the general drift from the way she said it.'

'I suspected you had,' he drawled, amused. 'Bianca doesn't much care for you, it seems.'

'What have I ever done to her? Until yesterday she has always pretended I didn't exist.'

'You have a very convenient memory,' he murmured, and she looked quickly at his profile. He was watching the road as he drove and smiling to himself. Vicky did not like that smile; it held far too much complacency.

'What does that mean?' she asked.

'You've apparently forgotten that when Bianca walked into the office she found us having what she felt was a very intimate conversation.'

Vicky stiffened. Had it given his ego a boost to know that he had made Bianca jealous? Was that why he was paying her so much attention? She was so furious she felt like hitting him.

'Well, she needn't be jealous of me,' she snapped. 'Because I'm not in the least interested in you!' After that there was a long silence between them as Ricco drove with his foot down, frowning. As they turned into the lion-topped gates, Vicky threw a look towards her cousin's house and saw that the windows were all dark. Susan and David must be in bed now; it was gone eleven. She yawned. She felt very tired herself.

'Well, we beat the storm,' said Ricco as he parked in the garage at the back of the house. They walked round to the main entrance and said goodnight by

Vicky's private entrance.

'See you at crack of dawn,' Ricco teased as she let herself in, and she made a face at him over her shoulder.

She had just undressed when all the lights went off. For a moment she just froze there, in the darkness, startled, then she saw the night split with a silver flash and ten seconds later there was a deafening crash of thunder. The storm had arrived and, it appeared, knocked out the electricity supply. Ricco had warned her that that sometimes happened. The wiring in the house wasn't all it might be. She groped blindly for a dressing-gown, hoping fervently that Ricco had a lightning conductor on the roof of the house. The storm was raging violently just overhead, and she kept starting as lightning crashed downwards outside followed almost at once by peals of thunder.

Vicky couldn't remember ever being through a storm like it. The noise was deafening, the flashes of lightning made her eyes hurt.

She almost didn't hear the knocking on her outer door, through the clashing of thunder, but at last she realised that Ricco was checking that she was okay. Still shaky with nerves, she groped her way to the door and opened it. Ricco stood there with a flashlight. He shone it on her face and she blinked, putting up a hand.

'Hey, I can't see a thing with that shining right into my eyes!'

'Have you got any candles?'

'No, have you?'

'Yes, plenty—I brought some round for you—the power may not be restored for quite a while.' He had lowered the flashlight's beam and now she could see him. He had undressed, too; she saw his bare legs below the edge of a black towelling bathrobe.

'I was in the bath,' he said drily. 'I almost cracked my skull open, slipping on the soap when I stood up as the lights went out.' He raised the flashlight a little; she saw his face and gave an exclamation of concern.

'Your forehead's bleeding—I think you did hit your head.' She leaned forward to see the cut better. 'You'd better come in and let me put a plaster on that.'

He came inside, shutting the door, and they went to the bathroom. Vicky found some cotton wool, moistened it and cleaned the small cut. It wasn't as bad as it had looked at first, more blood than wound. She gently dried it, very conscious now of Ricco's nearness, her mouth suddenly dry as she touched his skin. He had put down the flashlight and was perching on the edge of the vast bath. Vicky was standing close to him, too close, she felt, sensing his eyes on the deep lapels of her dressing-gown.

Could he see that she had nothing on beneath it? Her fingers trembled as she applied the small plaster, pressing it down over the cut.

'There,' she said huskily, trying to step back. Ricco's hand snaked round her waist and held her. His other hand cupped the nape of her neck before she could break away, pulling her head down. 'Thanks,' he whispered just before he kissed her, ignoring the resistance of her tense body.

Vicky tried to resist that kiss, but his mouth softly teased with a sensuous, lazy movement until her lips parted. For a moment they kissed, her eyes shut but aware of the flash of lightning outside—or was that wild white light part of her own reaction to Ricco's caress?

She mustn't let things get out of hand, she thought dazedly, putting her hands up to push him away. Her palms flattened on his wide shoulders, then one slid helplessly, of its own volition, and she felt his warm skin as she gripped the side of his throat.

'Let go, please,' she muttered, struggling. She should never have invited him into the flat; what had she let loose now?

He suddenly pulled her downwards across his lap, her head cradled on his shoulder and her feet right off the ground, and without taking his mouth from hers coolly slid one hand inside her dressing gown . If he hadn't guessed that she was naked underneath it, he knew now. His mouth was still for a second—in surprise?

Before she could lift her head to demand that he let go of her, the kiss deepened, his tongue warm and intrusive, but it wasn't his mouth that was worrying her now, it was what his hands were doing. Their slow, seductive caress made her head swim. She knew she had to do something at once, before it was too late, so she struggled to get up with a frightened violence that sent them both tumbling backwards.

Vicky gave a cry of shock as she realised they were falling, and the next second they landed with a thud in the deep bath. She lay sprawled across Ricco, who wasn't moving. Vicky breathlessly tried to scramble up, only to come against the rigid bar of his arm across her back. Lightning split the sky again, showing her his face, the eyes wide open, showing her his body also, the dark robe thrown open in the fall. Ricco was naked too, and he was staring at her, breathing thickly. Arched back as far as his arm would permit her, her breasts pale in the darkness, her thighs tangled with his, she stared down at him, trembling.

For a space of time the sexual tension between them dragged like a taut wire, and then Ricco deliberately broke it.

His voice husky, he said, 'Now I've got a bang on the other side of my head. This is obviously one of those nights!'

Vicky felt his arm fall and knew she was free to get up. Her scramble out of the bath was undignified. With trembling fingers she retied her belt as Ricco stepped out of the bath too.

Vicky looked shyly at him. His face was full of amusement, and suddenly she began to laugh wildly, staggering across the room. The laughter was a release and it was safer. She had never in her life felt such powerful electric tension between herself and a man. Her body still ached with a desire she hadn't expected, her breasts were hot and heavy with it.

'I'd better go before I collect any more cuts and bruises,' Ricco said drily, moving to the door as he tied his belt. 'You're a lethal lady in a bathroom! Remind me never to kiss you when there's a bath around for you to hit me with.'

She followed him to the door, still shuddering with laughter. He held his flashlight down, making yellow circles on the stone floor. He had given her a pile of candles which she clutched in her hand, but they needed neither flashlight nor candles to see by while the storm raged overhead, a new flash of lightning ripping through the sky every moment or so.

'Good night,' he said, his eyes gleaming at her as he turned to walk away, and she watched him for a second or two before she shut the door. She only had to call him back and he would stay. Her senses cried out for the satisfaction they had begun to expect, but Vicky firmly closed the door and leaned her hot face on it. She didn't know how she was going to be able to walk back to her bedroom.

And how was she going to face Ricco tomorrow morning? Then as she tumbled into bed she remembered—tomorrow was Sunday, she wouldn't have to get up at crack of dawn, neither would Ricco. It was almost one by the time she got to sleep, torn between wishing she hadn't sent him away and feeling glad that she hadn't given in to those crazy impulses.

When she woke up in the morning, the storm had blown itself out and the air was calm and still in the sunlit gardens, but her own emotional storm hadn't quietened down in the same way. She thought of Ricco the instant she opened her eyes and groaned, hurriedly shutting them again.

That didn't make the memory of last night disappear. It brooded over her as she lay in bed listening to the call of the birds in the garden. She had told him angrily as they drove back from Andrea's house that she wasn't in the least interested in him. Just an hour later she had been in his arms,lost to all common sense, making it very clear that she was violently attracted to him.

No wonder he had smiled with that maddening complacency last night! She had made a fool of herself.

She spent that Sunday quietly with Susan and David, driving through the Tuscany hills, watching the misty blue lights of further hills recede and advance, looking back towards the Arno valley to see the green fields, olive groves, orchards and swathes of pine and evergreen trees.

When they got back it was dusk, and the lights were on in the big villa. She let herself into her own apartment without running into Ricco. Was he alone? she wondered. Or was Bianca there again tonight? If he was playing out some strategic game, using Vicky to make Bianca jealous, he was obviously succeeding. There had been no doubt about her jealousy on Friday in the art department—she had raged like a tiger snapping at prey which is out of reach.

Vicky stayed awake for hours brooding over being used in that ruthless fashion. When would she start believing her own first instincts? Ricco wasn't in the film world, but his business dealt in the same debased coin. This was just another part of the same jungle; the animals were all as sharp in tooth and claw and as hungry for prey. She had picked that up the minute she met him, but she kept forgetting. Ricco made her forget, with his mocking, intimate smiles and those seductive hands. When he began to kiss her, her rational self had flown out of the window; the submerged desire she didn't want to give in to had taken over and she had lost her head.

From now on she was going to keep him at a distance, he wasn't getting another chance to do that to her.

CHAPTER NINE

WHEN she joined Ricco next morning his eyes were bright and intimate, but one look at her face and his expression changed.

'What's wrong?'

'Nothing. Why should anything be wrong?' Vicky walked on with a fixed smile. It felt as though her teeth were set in concrete, but her pride demanded that she shouldn't let him think she was vulnerable to him. She had to look cheerful at all costs.

As they drove out of the gates Susan was cleaning the upper windows of her house; she waved and Vicky waved back.

'How is Susan?' asked Ricco. 'I haven't seen her for a few days. Everything okay now between her and David?'

'Back to normal, thank God.'

'Thanks to me, don't you mean?' he said teasingly.

'Oh, you confuse yourself with the deity, do you?'

'I thought you might,' he murmured, watching her averted face quizzically. 'You seem very sharp this morning. Did you have a bad night?'

She shrugged. 'I've had better.'

'What was keeping you awake? Or should I ask who?'

She violently objected to the light, teasing manner. He was so pleased with himself; he really thought he had her fooled. She felt the vicious instincts of someone with a pin eying a balloon they are about to puncture.

'It wasn't you,' she snapped. 'You'll never keep me awake.'

He took his eyes off the road to stare in maddening surprise. 'You *are* bad-tempered this morning!'

'Are you trying to drive into the back of that lorry?' Vicky asked, checking that her seatbelt was clipped in case he actually did crash into something.

He paid more attention to his driving for a few moments, then said quietly, 'Do you ever think about the guy you left behind in England?'

'As rarely as possible!'

'He must have hit you badly to make you this angry.' She felt him watching her sideways again as they drew up at some traffic lights.

'It isn't him I get angry about,' Vicky said tensely. 'It's my own stupidity for ever falling for him in the first place.'

He put out his hand and patted one of hers. 'We all make mistakes, Vicky. We just have to learn from them, and then forget them.'

She gave him a cynical smile. 'That's exactly what I plan to do.'

'All men aren't like him!'

'I didn't say *all* men are.'

He watched her, frowning. 'I'm not, for a start.'

'No?'

'No!' he insisted, starting to sound irritated. 'Look, I resent being classed with a man like that. I'm trying to be patient with you . . .'

'How gracious of you, remind me to feel grateful.' She bitterly resented his condescending tone. Who did he think he was, being patient with her? What mountain did he think he lived on?

'Maybe it's the time of the month,' he began through his teeth.

'Leave my anatomy out of this!'

'Don't you mean biology?' Ricco snarled.

'To you, I wouldn't use the word—it immediately makes you think of sex, but then every word in the dictionary seems to make you think of sex.'

It wasn't until he had pulled up outside the office that he turned a normal colour again. Before she got out of the Lamborghini he clamped an angrily detaining hand on her arm, turning on her with bared teeth.

'If I had a suspicious mind, I'd wonder if you're so angry because I didn't stay on Saturday night,' he said icily.

She would have hit him if he wasn't grasping her right hand. Instead she said a word in Italian which she had sometimes heard Andrea say when he was in a temper.

The effect on Ricco was electrifying. He looked at her as if he couldn't believe his ears. Vicky took the opportunity to escape while he was still reeling. As she ran up the stairs to the art department she wondered what the word meant, and decided it might be wiser not to ask Andrea.

She was in an irritable, edgy mood all morning, but after a good lunch and some local wine she felt faintly ashamed of her bad temper. Ricco couldn't realise it, but most of her anger had been aimed at herself for making the same mistake twice. She had known he would be dangerous to her peace of mind the minute she set eyes on him. He attracted her the way nectar attracts humming birds. She'd told herself she wouldn't let him matter, but her willpower was practically nil. On Saturday it had vanished altogether. He was right—she was in a temper because if he *had* decided to stay all night she wouldn't have tried to stop him.

She imagined he'd keep out of her way for the rest of the day, but to her surprise he showed up in the art department that afternoon, eying her frowningly.

'Want to come to the studio to watch a recording session?'

'*Bene,*' Andrea said at once, nodding vehemently. 'Go, go, Vicky. You will learn a lot about the business and I will get some peace and quiet.' He grinned at Ricco. 'She is being a bear with a sore head today—I don't know why. Maybe it's love, love makes you bad-tempered.'

Vicky was cross and pink. 'Don't be silly,' she muttered, collecting her handbag while the two men watched, their expressions amused.

'It couldn't be love,' Ricco told Andrea mockingly. 'Her heart's impervious.'

'I don't believe it,' Andrea denied, shaking his head. 'A nice girl like her!'

'Cold, though,' Ricco murmured, watching her walk towards the door. 'Cold as the Alps in winter.'

'But even ice thaws,' Andrea reminded him. 'A little sunshine, a little fire.'

'Any man brave enough would need a blowtorch to melt that ice,' Ricco shrugged.

'Oh, do stop it!' snapped Vicky, turning on them. 'If you two have had enough fun, can we get going? At this rate, by the time we get to the studio they'll have finished recording and gone home.'

Ricco drove them the half-mile to a narrow back street in a less busy part of Florence. As he parked he gave Vicky a wry look.

'Got it out of your system yet?'

She grimaced. 'Sorry I was edgy.'

'We all get days like that,' he said, and she looked up to find him smiling at her in a way that made her heart turn over.

'I wish I didn't like you so much,' she said before she could stop herself, and Ricco's brows rose, his blue eyes laughing.

'Is that a backhanded compliment?'

'More of a heartfelt prayer,' she said, getting out of the car.

The studio was in a draughty old building which reminded Vicky of a barn. The studio itself had a strange, lunar atmosphere because of the soundproofing of the high walls. There were no windows, the walls were padded with quilted polystyrene tiles which were vaguely like thick eggboxes, the ceiling was similarly soundproofed, and the floors were tiled with rubber so that footsteps made no noise.

Ricco pulled open a heavy swing door with a porthole in the centre of it and waved Vicky through. She found herself in a brilliantly lit little room; two men wearing headphones sat at a bank of electrical equipment in front of a glass wall. They turned to stare at her, frowning, then recognised Ricco as he came in behind her, letting the heavy door swing shut softly.

'Ciao,' they said, smiling.

Vicky saw that below them lay a large rectangular studio. There were several high mikes set up in front of stools on which sat some young men with guitars propped between their knees and cups of coffee in their hands.

'Coffee break?' Ricco asked drily, and one of the

engineers took off his headphones and swivelled in his chair to nod.

'This is Vicky Lloyd, she's working in our art department now,' said Ricco, and the man leaned over to shake hands. 'Vicky, this is Giorgio, our best sound engineer. He's been with me since I set up the studio.'

Giorgio was in his fifties, heavily built with receding hair and piercing black eyes. His tan seemed to be permanent; she had the feeling he was always this deep, dark brown.

'Hi, Vicky,' he said, and again she thought how stupid it was that she shouldn't speak their language, while they all seemed so fluent in hers. 'You've come to sit in on a session, Ricco tells me. Pull up a chair.'

'You all speak such good English,' she said, and he smiled.

'We need to—we record so many American and English artists.'

Ricco drew a chair over to the bank of instruments and Vicky sat down, murmuring, 'Thanks.' Ricco took a chair on her left. Giorgio was on her right, and he began explaining the layout of his instruments.

The young men in the studio were laughing and playing the fool, throwing their empty coffee cups at each other.

'High spirits,' Ricco said drily. 'Is it going well, Giorgio?'

Giorgio looked at his watch. 'Five minutes, and we'll try for a recording. They've been rehearsing for a couple of hours while we juggle with the electronics.' He glanced at Vicky sideways. 'I have quite an array here—an orchestra at my fingertips.'

He ran his hand lightly over the equipment. 'Electronic drums, keyboard, woodwind section, echo chamber—I can make any sound you want just by pressing one of these switches.'

'Modern recording equipment practically does away with the need for live musicians,' Ricco said drily. 'Of course, the musicians' union would kick up murder if we tried to do that, and I wouldn't want to, anyway. Electronic music can't replace the live musician in my book, but it certainly helps with the cost of recordings and the time spent in the studio if you can tape a bass player, for instance, and use him to back a group like this—Giorgio can fade him out, bring him back in, at any level, just by touching a button. Having the man here for hours would waste his time and ours, and he might not get on with the group, might not be able to synchronise his free time with theirs. Anything can go wrong if everything's live.'

'Who are this group?' asked Vicky, watching the young men picking up their guitars and tuning them.

Giorgio told her an Italian name she'd never heard before.

'You wouldn't know them,' Ricco said. 'They're very popular here, but they don't play outside Italy yet.'

They were skinny young men with dark hair and eyes, all wearing T-shirts and faded blue jeans.

Giorgio depressed his mike key and said something. The boys in the studio looked up, waving, then caught sight of Vicky and at once whistled and grinned at her, shouting something.

She laughed, and Giorgio asked, 'You speak some Italian?'

She shook her head. 'I'm afraid I only know a few phrases yet, but I'm working on it.'

'They said you were very sexy,' Ricco told her with a cool intonation. 'And what are you doing tonight?'

'Oh,' she said, laughing again. That was what she had thought they said, but she didn't admit it.

'Tell them she isn't available,' Ricco told Giorgio with sardonic emphasis and a sideways glance at her. 'Tell them she's English and as cool as a cucumber sandwich.'

Giorgio grinned and talked into the mike. The musicians made caterwauling noises, waving their arms at Vicky in disgust.

'Okay, we try a recording now,' Giorgio said to Ricco.

Vicky loved the music; it was fast and modern with a good beat to it. One of the young men sang in Italian. She didn't understand the words but she picked up the feeling, her body swaying with the music. She began to notice when Giorgio was introducing some of his electronic wizardry, the rhythmic note of the bass, the drums, the echo. It was fascinating to see how the sound was mixed; the men working the electronic equipment had sensitive, quick-moving hands, and they operated their switches with as much skill as the young musicians in the studio.

When the group stopped playing Giorgio wound back the tape and played it for them. They sat on their stools, listening, faces intent.

Giorgio talked to them in Italian and they answered; Vicky didn't know what was being said. She looked at Ricco, who gave her a wry smile and translated.

'Giorgio thinks they weren't playing tightly enough. They weren't coming in on exactly the right beat at the right moment all together, as they should. The lead guitar is saying they'll be tighter next take.'

He kept his voice very low so as not to disturb Giorgio and his assistant. After a few minutes the group played again, and again Giorgio wound back the tape and played it for them before they had another of their earnest discussions.

Ricco glanced at his watch. 'I'm afraid we'll have to go,' he told her. 'I have an appointment at six and I can't miss it.'

He stood up and drew back her chair as she got to her feet. Giorgio took off his headphones, swivelling to smile and say goodbye.

'Drop in at the fish tank any time, as long as you give me notice you're coming.'

'The fish tank?' she asked, puzzled, and he nodded to the glass wall.

'That's what it looks like from down there in the studio—a big fish tank in the wall. That's what the boys call it.'

'Thank you very much for letting me eavesdrop, I enjoyed it enormously.'

'Good, nice to meet you. *Ciao*, Ricco.'

Giorgio was totally absorbed in his work again before they had left the room. Vicky looked back through the porthole and saw him with his headphones on, leaning forward to talk to the studio.

'*Did* you enjoy it?' Ricco asked as they made their way back to the Lamborghini. 'I know you told Giorgio you did, but you English are so polite. You don't always mean what you say—that's what gives your nation the reputation of being hypocrites.'

'I'm not a hypocrite,' Vicky retorted indignantly. 'And I meant what I said, it was really fascinating. I could have stayed there all day.'

'I'll try to make sure you have another chance to watch a session, then,' said Ricco, opening the car door for her to get in.

As they were driving back to the office a lorry backed out of a narrow alley, without warning, right into their path, and Ricco braked with such force that Vicky almost went through the windscreen.

Ricco yelled furious Italian at the lorry driver, who yelled back before driving off, making an insulting gesture through his window at them.

'Are you okay?' Ricco asked, turning to look anxiously at her.

'I think so.' She had been shocked more than hurt.

He leaned over and kissed her lightly. 'You're shaking! Thank heavens you had your seatbelt on.'

She couldn't think of anything to say; his gentle kiss had undermined her again. Had what happened with Miller and Sunny made her too cynical, too suspicious? Was she wrong about Ricco? She felt confused and disturbed as they drove on—she wished she knew for certain what sort of man he was, and at the same time she had a sinking feeling that it was too late to find out. She watched his profile secretly, brooding over him.

She had been too sure of herself when she met Miller. She had thought she knew her feelings, she had been ready to leap into love without knowing Miller at all. This time she had been determined not to let Ricco get to her. At least she had known the dangers, she hadn't just charged straight ahead into disaster, but her wariness hadn't saved her. She had known on Saturday night that it was a little more than physical attraction between herself and Ricco. Her emotions were involved again, and she had a premonition that she was going to wish she had never met him.

I don't want to fall in love again, she thought grimly. Or is that the wrong tense? Am I in love already? What else explains the odd effect he has on me every time I see him? The frayed temper, the crazy excitement, the sudden happiness and a moment later the stupid misery? Being in love was like a spring day—sunshine one minute, showers the next, and an awareness of being alive that was sharper than at any other time.

She didn't want to be in love; it hurt too much. She might be called a coward, but she wasn't going to be called a fool again.

When she and Ricco walked into the art department they found Andrea standing in front of a line of advertising posters which he had pinned up on the wall. He looked round, grimacing at them.

'Look at these—would you believe it? They printed the wrong colours, transposed the yellow and purple—look!'

Vicky and Ricco looked, faces blank.

'They look fine to me,' said Ricco.

'I like them,' Vicky agreed.

'I didn't say they weren't okay, I said the colours had been switched,' Andrea grunted impatiently. 'As it happens, it works, but I want you to talk to those crazy printers, Ricco. Kick them around, get it home that if they do this again we'll take our work elsewhere.'

'The artwork is really stunning, isn't it?' Vicky

said, sighing. Whoever had done the poster had been a genius. It was spectacular—a wild crash of colours which immediately made itself noticed.

Andrea shrugged. 'It's passable.'

They began to talk about the artwork while Ricco perched on the side of a desk and listened, his face amused. It must have been half an hour later that the door opened and Bianca swept into the room in one of her lush minks, her ears glittering with diamonds in a swinging cascade.

'Ciao, caro,' she said to Ricco, kissing him and purring like a cat in that long white throat.

Vicky watched, her teeth tight with jealousy. She hadn't liked Bianca on sight, but she hated her at that moment, watching the other woman curve an arm round Ricco's neck, gazing up into his eyes.

'What are you doing here, Bianca?' Ricco asked, smiling.

Bianca spun, her diamond earrings flashing. She threw Vicky a malicious smile and Vicky tensed in alarm. Had Bianca recognised her on the cover of that magazine? Why was she staring like that, an odd smile curving her red mouth?

'I bring a surprise for *her*,' Bianca said in thickly accented English.

She walked to the door and opened it, and Vicky went white as she saw Miller in the doorway.

CHAPTER TEN

VICKY'S feet seemed to be rooted to the spot. She had had nightmares about this happening and woken up to find that they had been just that—a nightmare. This wasn't something she would wake up from; this was real, it was happening.

'Vicky!' Miller was acting—that much she took in at a glance. He would have done well in silent films, he had a real talent for sweeping mime. He came towards her with outstretched arms, radiating bittersweet reproach, love, forgiveness.

Vicky felt like kicking him in the shins.

Andrea was chewing his pencil. 'He looks like someone. Who is it? I know that face, I never forget a face.' He opened his mouth, his jaw dropped and so did the pencil. It rolled across the floor. Andrea exclaimed with bated breath: 'My God! It's Miller Osborne. I'd swear he's Miller Osborne—or his double. Ricco, isn't he Miller Osborne?'

'What the hell is going on?' demanded Ricco in a voice that almost made the windows shake.

Bianca told him in cooing Italian. Vicky was rather glad suddenly that she hadn't yet learnt enough of the language to know what Bianca was saying about her. Whatever it was, it made Ricco look as if he could eat nails.

Miller tried to kiss Vicky. She jerked her head away and all he kissed was her cheek.

'How could you do it? I nearly went out of my mind with worry, I thought you'd been kidnapped,' said Miller.

Over his shoulder Vicky saw Sunny and her stomach clenched. Just the sight of him made her feel sick. He had a pack of photographers with him, they must have been waiting outside to give Miller time to get her in his arms. Miller smiled down at her as if he hadn't noticed she was as stiff as a jointed wooden doll in his embrace. He swung her deftly so that the photographers would snap his best side. It wasn't just that he was acting; he had a script to work to, and it was obvious who had written it—Sunny, the master of the set-up, the magician of the publicity release. Miller even had his moves chalked out for him.

'Get out of my office!' snarled Ricco, leaping between them and the photographers just as the flashbulbs went off.

'Hey, what do you think you're doing, mister?' Miller complained, scowling at him. 'Get out of the way—you ruined the picture! Sorry about that, guys—we'll do it again. Hey, Sunny, get this jerk out of here, will you?'

That was when Ricco hit him. Miller went down like a tree, mowing Sunny down on the way. The photographers got their picture and Miller's best side was camera forward. Vicky didn't care how she looked, or whether she was in the picture at all. She was staring at Ricco and he was staring back as if he meant to hit her next. She had never seen him look so angry.

'Is it true?' he asked through his teeth.

Miller was scrambling foggily to his knees, holding his jaw and making an incredulous noise. It was the stunt man who did all that stuff in his pictures, not the star. Getting a punch on the jaw was not written into his contract. His insurance company weren't going to like this.

'Sunny!' he yelled.

'Answer me,' Ricco told Vicky, his hands screwed into fists at his side. 'Were you going to marry him?'

'I . . .' Vicky couldn't get the words out. She had a form of emotional lockjaw; everything inside her had frozen. So she ran. It had become a habit, perhaps. Running was the easiest way out and at that moment the wisest, because the longer she stayed around the more pictures the photographers were going to get.

Miller had forgotten her; he was picking Sunny up from the floor and anxiously dusting him down. He couldn't operate without Sunny there to feed him his lines, tell him what to do and think. Vicky still found Sunny terrifying, but she wasn't running away from him this time—she was running away from Ricco. The look in his blue eyes had made her knees give. He hated her. She felt so miserable as she saw that look on his face that she couldn't bear to see it any more.

She hadn't quite got away yet, though. She heard the following feet, the shouted questions, the pleas for her to stop. The reporters like bloodhounds poured down the stairs, shoving each other in their attempts to be the first to reach her. Vicky ran through the front door of the building with the pack on her heels, thinking wildly: How am I to get away from them? She had no car, there were no buses around here. She simply put on more speed, and saw ahead of her on a corner a lady in a large blue picture hat getting out of a taxi. Vicky put on another spurt, breathless by now, her chest heaving.

A man was running from the opposite direction towards the taxi, his hand held up. Vicky pushed past the lady in the picture hat, who was just paying the driver, and threw herself into the back of the taxi.

'*Signore, per favore, rapidemente! La stazione*!'

'*Centrale*?' he asked, tucking the money his last fare had given him into a wallet.

'*Si, si, grazie*.'

They moved off a second or two before the pack caught up with them. Vicky peered back and saw them engulfing the lady in the picture hat and the man who had run to catch the taxi, too. She saw the reporters talking to them. Demanding where she had asked to be taken?

Vicky bit her lip, wondering what to do. Go to Susan's house? But the reporters might find out about her cousin from Bianca and descend on the house in droves, giving poor Susan the scare of her life.

She dared not go back to Ricco's villa, that was too obvious, and anyway, she was in no hurry to face Ricco either. Where could she go? Suddenly she had a brainwave and leaned forward.

'*Signore*?'

'*Si*?'

She told him to take her to Andrea's house. Nobody would think of looking for her there; she would have a breathing space in which to think and work out what to do next, and she wouldn't be giving Susan any trouble. Vicky knew how much her cousin would hate having a herd of reporters trampling through the garden, shouting through the letterbox, peering in at the windows.

The first thing she must do when she reached

Andrea's was ask if she could use the phone. She must ring Susan and warn her.

Lucy opened the door, her expression taken aback. 'Oh, hallo.' She noted Vicky's flushed and dishevelled state, frowning. 'Is something wrong?'

'Lucy, can I come in? I need your help, I'm sorry to be a nuisance, but I'm in bad trouble.'

Lucy wordlessly waved her into the house and Vicky collapsed into a chair, her mind in a state of utter disarray. Lucy looked hard at her.

'You need a cup of tea.'

Vicky laughed, well-nigh hysterical by then. Lucy paused on her way to the kitchen.

'On second thoughts, we'll make that a stiff brandy.'

'I'm sorry to be a . . .'

'Don't say it again, you're not a nuisance,' Lucy produced a bottle of brandy, uncorked it, held it over a glass. 'Say when.'

'Oh, please, that's more than enough,' Vicky said breathlessly. Her eye fell on the telephone on a table near the window. 'Lucy, may I use your phone? It's urgent.'

'Be my guest.' Lucy poured herself a brandy too. 'Am I going to need this? Yes, I think so,' she said, sipping. 'Oh . . . Andrea is okay, isn't he?'

Vicky was lifting the phone. 'What? Oh, yes, yes, he's fine. I was just with him in the office, but . . .' She swallowed and stopped talking until she had got Susan on the phone. 'Susan, listen, it's me, Vicky—no, don't panic. Listen, just listen—Miller is here. Yes, in Florence. No, don't scream! I've got away from them and I'm quite safe, but the press may come to your place. Look, get David on the phone, tell him what's happened, then drive to his office and stay with him at all costs. Don't go back home until you've checked that the press aren't around.' She listened to Susan's aghast exclamations. 'I'm sorry, Susan, very sorry to have dropped all this on you. No, I wouldn't just stay put if I were you, because I know those people, they'll camp out all round the house if they think you're in there, and they'll keep on ringing the bell and trying to get in until doomsday.'

When she put the phone down Lucy was sitting staring at her, her brandy glass already empty. 'I think,' said Lucy, 'I'm going to need another brandy. A bigger one this time.'

Vicky came back towards her and sat down, nursing her brandy glass. 'I owe you an explanation.'

'Let me make myself comfortable—I get the feeling this is going to take a while.' Lucy curled up in her chair like a child about to hear a bedtime story. 'Right, fire away—no, wait—do you want some more of this?' She gestured to the brandy bottle.

Vicky shook her head and plunged into her explanation. Lucy didn't interrupt once, listening with fascination while she sipped her second glass of brandy.

Only when Vicky stopped talking did Lucy comment. 'I must say, it's better than *Dallas*. I wish I'd been there. You say Ricco hit Miller Obsborne? Miller Osborne—good heavens, it's amazing just to talk to someone who actually knows him!' Her eyes skated over Vicky in her powder-blue top and white pleated skirt. 'And you were engaged to him! I don't know how you could walk out on a man like Miller Osborne. He's so gorgeous!'

Vicky smiled weakly. 'Well, you know the saying . . . one woman's man is another woman's poison.'

Lucy laughed. 'I suppose he can't be as terrific as he seems in his films, he wouldn't be human if he was. All I can say is you must have great strength of character. I'd guess that a lot of women would put up with the odd flaw in him simply for all that lovely money—he must be terrifically rich. He's been making films for years, hasn't he? Is he forty or so?'

'Oh, no, he's only in his thirties.'

'He seems to have been around much longer than that.'

'He was a hit in his first film, and his career has been very well stage-managed.'

'By this agent of his?'

'Sunny—yes, I think he was the master-mind.' It certainly hadn't been Miller. He was no fool, but he was more concerned with how he looked in films than in choosing the right parts. It had undoubtedly been Sunny who made the clever decisions. Was that why Miller relied implicitly on him? Probably.

Lucy watched her curiously. 'Is *he* still in love with *you*? I read about all this, a week ago, in the last pop paper I saw from England. My old mum sends a batch to me every month, to keep me in touch with home news. I don't know why I didn't recognise you, there was a big picture of you in the paper, but it didn't ring any bells—well, I'd never met you then, so it wouldn't, and when we did meet I suppose I didn't connect you with the missing Vicky . . .' she paused, knitted her forehead. 'See? I can't even remember your surname.'

'Gavin.'

'Oh, yes. Gavin. Vicky's not that unusual, of course, and anyway, Andrea had been talking about you for a couple of weeks and calling you Ricco's girl-friend, so . . .'

'What?' Vicky sat up, very flushed. 'Calling me what?'

'Well, Andrea has a simple mind,' Lucy said apologetically, 'Ricco talked him into taking you on, and Andrea just leapt to the obvious conclusion—obvious for a man, that is,' She grinned, but Vicky wasn't laughing.

'Well, please tell your husband that I'm not Ricco's girlfriend.' Vicky was very much on her dignity.

'Even if Ricco did knock your ex-fiancé down,' Lucy supplied drily, and Vicky's flush deepened.

'Miller called him a jerk, that's why he did that.'

'Yes, I can see that that would get under Ricco's skin. And he has got a hot temper at times, although he can be a positive lamb,' Lucy smiled at Vicky. 'So what are you going to do now? You can't keep hiding, you know. Sooner or later you're going to have to face Miller and talk it out with him.'

'Not with the press for an audience,' Vicky got up and prowled impatiently round the room like a caged tiger. 'That's why I went away without seeing him, I knew Sunny would pull a trick like this on me. Miller can't even sneeze without the media there to commemorate it. If I had married Miller, I might have found myself going on honeymoon with TV cameras and a busload of pressmen for company. And I began to think Miller himself might not show up.' She swallowed, grimacing. 'Just Sunny.'

Lucy's face grew grave. 'I see why you felt you had to get away. What's he like, this Sunny?'

'Loathsome.'

'That bad?'

'Worse. I'm being polite about him.'

Lucy laughed, then shook her head. 'It isn't funny, is it?'

'No. I'm scared of snakes too, but if I had a choice between being shut up in a room full of snakes or a room with Sunny, I'd try to learn to like snakes,' Vicky looked down at her bare forearms. 'Look, goose-pimples, at the mere idea of it. He makes my skin crawl.'

'Are you sure it wasn't because of him you left Miller—rather than because you fell out of love with Miller himself?'

'I'm certain. It was a mixture of both. Miller knew, you see; he knew Sunny had made a pass at me, I told him, and he didn't care. He laughed; he thought I was naïve for being so shocked. Sunny told me Miller and he often shared girls.'

'Shared them?' Lucy looked shocked now. 'Do you mean . . . shared them?'

'That's what I mean,' Vicky nodded, and Lucy took a deep breath.

'I think you were right to run away. What an awful let down, and I thought Miller Osborne seemed so genuine.' The phone rang, and Lucy went towards it at once.

'If it's Ricco, don't tell him I'm here!' Vicky burst out, stiffening.

'I won't,' Lucy picked up the phone and asked warily: 'Hallo?' Her face relaxed. 'Oh, hello, darling.' She looked at Vicky, smiling. 'Don't worry, it's Andrea.' Then into the phone she said: 'Yes, she's here—how did you guess?' then listened, smiling. 'Very shrewd of you. She thought she'd better not go back to the villa or her cousin's place in case the press turned up there. Yes, that's right. Her cousin knows, yes. She's gone to meet her husband, they're staying clear until the press leave,'

'Ask him not to tell Ricco,' whispered Vicky.

'Vicky doesn't want you to tell Ricco, Andrea,' Lucy said. 'She seems scared of what he may do—were you there when he hit Miller Osborne . . . really? No? I didn't hear that. What, all the way down the stairs? Was he hurt? From what Vicky has just been telling me, he deserved it.' She listened without speaking for a few minutes, then said: 'I'll see you later, then, darling. Goodbye.'

She hung up and looked round at Vicky. 'Ricco ran that agent out of the building after you'd gone, got hold of his jacket and threw him out bodily. Andrea says he threw him down the stairs but as he got up and walked off after that he can't have been hurt. Andrea was probably exaggerating. He seems to have enjoyed the whole thing.'

Vicky closed her eyes. 'Did the photographers get a picture of that, too?'

'Andrea didn't say. I hope so, I'd love to see it.' Lucy looked at her watch. 'Look, I'm starving after all this mad excitement, aren't you? Why don't I make some lunch? You stay here, have a rest—nobody will disturb you, the children are at school. I'll call you when lunch is ready.'

'You're being very kind, thank you, Lucy.' Vicky felt a strong tendency to cry, which was silly, but it had been a very emotional morning, and Lucy's kindness on top of all that seemed just too much.

'Nothing of the sort. I haven't had so much fun for ages; you've brought a splash of mad colour into my humdrum life.' Lucy gave her a smile and went out, closing the door. Vicky curled up in her chair, her head drooping sideways, and stared at the clock.

It had been two hours since she ran like a hunted hare from Ricco's office. Just two hours. It felt like a hundred years. What was she to do now? She couldn't ever go back there, people would stare. Ricco must hate her.

She had lied to him over and over again. He wouldn't forgive her for that. She closed her eyes, tears stinging under her lids. She hadn't meant to care, but somehow it had happened—she must be very weak-willed. She had known on Saturday that it was more than just a passing attraction she felt for Ricco. There had been intense passion between them,in the dark, with the storm raging outside, lightning showing them each other's faces. Perhaps that was how love always happened—you saw the other darkly, by brief flashes of illumination. That was how it had been with Miller, too, and when she saw him clearly she knew it was all illusion.

She was afraid it would be that way with Ricco. What did she know about him after all? She hadn't even met him much more than a month ago. She might know him a little better than she had got to know Miller before their engagement, but perhaps she was wrong about him too, perhaps he wasn't the man she thought he was, and she didn't think she could bear another crass mistake. When love goes wrong, nothing goes right—wasn't that a song title? It was spot on anyway, she had learnt that.

Suddenly she heard Lucy's voice rising outside. Lucy was almost shouting. Vicky sat up, rigid with shock.

'You can't see her! I promised her—please listen, I promised her I wouldn't let anybody in, she doesn't want to see you.'

It was Miller, Vicky thought, getting up and backing from the door. If she could have seen anywhere to hide she would have leapt into it. Lucy wasn't going to let him in here—was she? But Miller and Sunny might force their way past her, they weren't above that, and Lucy would be no match for both of them.

'But I promised her,' Lucy protested, very close to the door. Vicky knew that Lucy was trying to warn her, give her time to . . . to what?

She looked round the room. Where could she go? The window was the only exit, of course. She crept over to it and slid it up very carefully, making as little sound as possible. The window looked out into a narrow alley, and there was quite a short drop to the ground. Vicky climbed on to the sill and slid her legs through, but she was too late. She heard a movement behind her, looked upwards, backwards, expecting to see Miller or Sunny, but it was Ricco and he was striding towards her, his eyes hard and menacing.

'Oh, no, you don't!'

He caught hold of her waist and pulled. Vicky struggled to throw herself forward, outward. Her feet sank. Ricco dragged them upwards again. A small boy in a pair of red shorts stood with his thumb in his mouth, watching, in the centre of the alley.

Inch by wriggling inch, Vicky was drawn back into the room, feeling like an escaping worm hauled back to the surface by a much stronger bird. From upside down Ricco's nose did look rather like a beak, and there was no doubt about it, his feathers were distinctly ruffled. She made a last attempt, calling to the boy outside: 'Help!' Her last hope just stared, bolt-eyed.

Ricco dragged her into the room and dropped her unceremoniously on the floor while he shut the window. By the time he had turned round Vicky was on her feet again, slightly breathless, staggering a little, but making for the door as fast as she could.

Ricco got between her and her exit somehow. One minute she was within arms' reach of escape, the next she was slamming into Ricco's very solid body.

'Now!' he said, and she resisted a crazy temptation to lean on him and give up. His deep chest looked so comfortingly firm.

'Don't you threaten me!' she defied, her head going back so that she could glare at him.

'Oh, I haven't even started yet! I knew—right from the day we first met—that there was something you were running from. I even knew, thought I knew, what it was—it had to be a man.'

'Why,' she asked scornfully, 'had it to be a man? It could have been anything! But whatever the question, the answer is *always* "a man", isn't it? I could have been running away from anything, a job, the police, a blackmailer—why did you have to leap to the conclusion that it was a man?'

'It was, though, wasn't it?' he demanded unanswerably, and she clenched her teeth and didn't answer. Ricco steered her backwards as though they were dancing a strange new ballroom dance, pushed her down on the couch and sat next to her, an arm across her barring escape.

'I've talked to Susan,' he said conversationally.

Vicky looked at him sharply. 'I told her to . . .'

'Go to David? She did. I went to David too, and

found her there. They wouldn't tell me where you were, but they told me a great deal about Miller Osborne and that creep he comes with—I was glad I'd thrown him out on his ear after I'd listened to what Susan had to say about him.'

Vicky couldn't help a weakening towards him, remembering that he had flung Sunny down the narrow stairs at the office.

'I was glad, too. Thank you.'

'You're welcome,' he said formally. 'Why didn't you tell me what you were scared of? Why lie to me? Didn't you trust me?'

She looked up quickly, biting her lip. 'Yes, of course!' But she hadn't, had she? She had thought he was another Miller and had been very wary of him. His blue eyes watched her with comprehension and anger.

'Stop it now, Vicky. No more lies. You didn't trust me, did you?'

'I didn't trust anybody, except Susan and David,' she admitted huskily.

'There was no married boss who chased you and wanted to have an affair with you?'

She shook her head, looking down.

'Your name's Vicky Gavin, not Vicky Lloyd.'

She nodded.

'But your parents are dead and Susan is your cousin?'

'Yes, all that was true, and everything I told you about college and my job—it was Sunny who got me fired.'

'I know, Susan told me.'

She looked up, mouth wry. 'She talked a lot, for Susan! She's usually so shy with you.'

'She was worried about you.' I had to persuade

her to talk to me at all, it wasn't easy.' His hand shot out and caught her chin, forced her face round towards him, his blue eyes very dark and intent,insisting that she meet their gaze.

'Did you love him?' he asked, his voice rough.

'Did Susan tell you how I met Miller?'

He shook his head, so she explained that first meeting, the beauty of the still autumn morning, Miller on a big black horse, London still waking up beyond the gold and crimson trees.

'High romance,' Ricco said tersely.

'He's a film actor, he knows how to set up scenes, how to manipulate the emotions. It's second nature to him, just as it's second nature to make sure a camera always finds him with his best profile ready,'

'You still haven't answered my question! Did you love him in the beginning?'

'I was trying to answer it. I loved the whole story line—that was what I fell for—the girl walking in a park, the handsome stranger on a black stallion. The stuff of fairy tales, how could I resist it? We got engaged almost overnight, and then I woke up! I found that my fairy prince was a weak, conceited man with very few morals, and that the wicked wizard was his best friend and had him right under his thumb. It wasn't even a wicked spell, because Miller didn't want to break it. He thought Sunny was terrific, he relied on him. He'd have handed me over to him without a second thought.'

Ricco clenched his teeth, going pale. She saw him swallow. 'So that part of it was true, too? That animal did make a pass at you?'

'Sunny's corrupt. He always had Miller's women when Miller tired of them.'

Ricco put his arms round her and cradled her like a baby. 'I'll kill him for you,' he said hoarsely. 'What did he do to you?'

She closed her eyes and let her body yield. His warmth crept into her, encircled her, made her feel safe.

'I didn't give him the chance. As soon as I saw what was in his mind, I just ran away and came here.'

'Bastard,' muttered Ricco. He made it sound very Latin. 'I wish I'd hit him a damned sight harder.'

'Oh, forget him, forget both of them,' Vicky said. 'That's what I'm going to do. They don't matter.'

Ricco kissed her temples, his mouth slid down over her short blonde hair, pressed softly into her throat.

'My hair's dyed, you know,' Vicky said a little anxiously. He had to know it all now, the whole truth and nothing but the truth—but she was afraid he might be disappointed when he realised she wasn't a real blonde. Italians liked fair women, didn't they?

'Of course I knew,' Ricco said, his lips just under her chin now and the sound of his voice vibrating through her bone structure. 'Do you think I'm stupid? Think I can't tell a genuine blonde from a dyed one?'

'I'm really brunette.' His hands had crept about like little mice, she kept finding them in unexpected places and they made shivers run up and down her spine. She dislodged one which had made a nest between her breasts. 'Lucy may come in.'

'Not until I call her,' said Ricco with typically splendid assurance. 'Why were you climbing out of the window?'

'I thought you would be angry.'

'I am angry! You should have confided in me, trusted me. I'm more than angry—I'm hurt.'

'I'm sorry,' she said, genuinely contrite, looking up at him anxiously.

'So I should think! You have a lot to make up to me for.' He looked at her mouth, his lips parted, breathing raggedly. 'Vicky, darling,' he whispered, and she lifted her mouth with an eagerness which might shame her later but over which at that moment she had no control. She needed to have him kiss her, she needed it badly.

Their lips met, and a rush of sudden, burning passion swept through her. She stopped thinking, her arms going round his neck and clinging, her body limp and yielding in his arms. She had been trying to fight the way she felt about him from the first day they met because she was afraid that she was going to make the same mistake again, fool herself that a physical attraction was real love. The attraction between herself and Ricco had flashed at once, like summer lightning, like the sudden storm that had blown up on Saturday in the heat of the night, but she had not dared to believe in it. It had been too much of a risk, and she had been afraid of burning her fingers again.

She had known the other night, though, known deep inside herself that the way she felt about Ricco was nothing like the infatuation she had had for Miller. That had worn off almost at once, although she still hadn't got to know Miller very well—he was never there, he didn't give her a chance to discover what sort of man there really was under the beautiful mask. Vicky had a sneaking suspicion that Miller did not dare let anyone too close in case they found out just what sort of man he really was, but she had found out and she had despised him.

She knew far more about Ricco, she liked him as well as being fiercely attracted by him. She knew she could work with him, live with him, share the future with him. In the end that was what love was all about—sharing life together.

Much later, Ricco said grimly: 'If we have any more trouble from Osborne and his manager, leave them to me. I'll welcome the chance to tell them a few home truths.'

'It was Bianca who told them where to find me, wasn't it?' Vicky said, lowering her lashes and watching him through them.

'She recognised some picture of you and rang Osborne to tell him you were in Florence,' said Ricco, his eyes hard.

'She doesn't like me,' Vicky said, fighting down the jealousy she still felt. Ricco had said he loved her a moment ago, she wasn't going to doubt it, yet she couldn't help remembering that night she saw him on the loggia with Bianca. They knew each other so well.

'She hates your guts,' agreed Ricco, his mouth quizzical.

Their eyes met and he smiled at her expression. 'She's in love with you,' Vicky said tartly.

'Bianca? She's another narcissistic creature, like Osborne—they don't have normal human feelings. They're in love with their own image.' Ricco played with her hair, his eyes wry. 'Bianca is possessive, too. She didn't like it when she guessed I was in love with you.' He watched her with glinting amusement. 'It meant I wouldn't pay her so much attention in future. She's not in love with me, but she likes to have me dancing to her tune.'

'Did you? Dance to her tune?' Vicky asked jealously.

'It was business, Vicky, purely business. I have a couple of dozen such demanding stars on my books. When they're in Florence they think I belong to them.' He smiled at her passionately. 'But now I belong to you.' She closed her eyes, weak and breathing dangerously fast. She heard the deep sea swell of her racing blood in her ears and muttered shakily: 'I think I've got high blood pressure.'

'I've had it ever since I saw you at the airport that first day,' Ricco said drily. 'So very English—nose in the air, cool as a cucumber sandwich, just asking to get kissed or slapped or both.'

'Do I get a choice?'

'You get me,' he told her. 'That will have to be enough for you.'

Vicky's arms tightened round his neck. He was enough for her; she had a feeling he would always be enough.

HIDE AND SEEK

HIDE AND SEEK

BY
CHARLOTTE LAMB

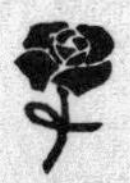

MILLS & BOON LIMITED
Eton House, 18-24 Paradise Road
Richmond, Surrey TW9 1SR

First published in Great Britain in 1987
by Mills & Boon Limited

Reprinted 1987
This edition 1993

ISBN 0 263 78208 5

Set in 10 1/2 on 11 1/2 pt.
19-9302-48198

Made and printed in Great Britain

CHAPTER ONE

DONNA first became aware that she was being followed when she turned the corner into the Boulevard Malesherbes and heard footsteps behind her immediately quicken. She'd been vaguely aware of someone behind her for several minutes without thinking too much about it. It was almost half past one in the morning; there were few other people about and almost no traffic. Suddenly realising that there was a man behind her who was running to catch up with her made the back of her neck prickle and she walked faster, too.

Marie-Louise had offered to drive her home, but she had cheerfully refused. 'No, thanks, I feel like a stroll! It's such a lovely night.'

'Don't you get nervous, walking through Paris in the middle of the night?' Marie-Louise had frowned. 'I really think I ought to drive you home, Donna.'

'After that bottle of Chablis? No, I think I'd be safer on my own two feet. At least you can't get arrested for drunken walking!'

Marie-Louise had laughed. 'Oh, I'm going to miss you! You must come and visit us whenever you can get to Lyons.'

'I will,' Donna had said before giving her a hug and walking away. She was going to miss Marie-Louise too. Paris would never be the same. People make places, and during the two years Donna had lived in Paris she had seen it through Marie-Louise's eyes and learnt to love it, to think of it as her second home—but as she quickened her footsteps now and heard the man behind her quicken his, the city seemed suddenly hostile.

For the first time she regretted the silence in the streets where she lived. She had fallen in love with the Boulevard Malesherbes the first time she saw it. It had been a hot August Sunday afternoon; little traffic on the road, no shops open and most of the apartments empty. In August, Parisians flood out of town for *les vacances* by the sea or in the country, but Donna hadn't realised that the day she first came to the Boulevard Malesherbes. She had stood under the plane trees watching their shadowed leaves flickering on to the pavement, staring at the tall shuttered houses drowsing in the heat like a row of grey cats, enchanted by the atmosphere.

She had taken the apartment she had come to see although the rent was higher than she had intended to pay, rather more than she could afford, in fact. But she had never regretted it, especially after she had begun to make friends and settle down.

Now, though, she became very aware of the deep silence broken only by the tap of her high heels and the echoing click of the heels coming closer behind her.

The Boulevard was wide and shadowy, especially under the trees. Donna looked up at the shutters and knew that most of the apartments behind them were empty now, this August, as they had been that first August. In that month Paris belongs to the tourist, before whose locust advance the French retreat in disgust.

If the man behind her caught up with her and she screamed, would anyone hear? Donna suddenly crossed the road obliquely, running. The man behind her broke into a run, too, but she was now within a few yards of the door of the apartment building. She could see the brass gleam of the doorknob, she put on speed and reached it with a gasp of relief.

Only then did she realise that the man following her had vanished. She glanced round, hearing the silence, the absence of other footsteps. The Boulevard was empty; the lamplight gleamed, the shadows of leaves flickered on the road around each lamp. There was nobody else in the street but herself.

Far from making her feel easier, that alarmed her into diving inside the building. The concierge was dozing over her table, behind her lace curtains. She started, head jerking back and Donna gave her a wave as she went past. *'C'est moi, madame. Bonne nuit.'*

It made her feel safer to know that Madame Lebrun was keeping a wary eye on anyone who went in or out. When Madame wasn't at her post, Monsieur Lebrun took over from her.

Donna's apartment was on the fourth floor. There was no lift. She had to climb the narrow stairs, which seemed to take for ever. In the first months of living here she had lost pounds. Tonight she was tensely conscious of the fact that the apartments she passed on her climb were all empty. The other tenants had left two weeks ago; they would be back when *la rentrée* started, the weekend at the beginning of September when everyone came back to the city.

This time of the year was Donna's favourite month. Her part of Paris was so still and peaceful in August; tourists didn't flock to Malesherbes, the closest they came was to the Boulevard Haussmann, to the great shops: Printemps, Galeries Lafayette, and C & A. That was a mere few minutes' walk from Malesherbes, yet it might have been another planet. Paris was a city of villages bordering each other but sharply separated.

Unlocking her front door, Donna hurriedly switched on the light in the corridor and listened. The apartment seemed silent, empty. Yet she still felt nervous. She went quickly through the rooms, switching on all the lights. Nothing had been disturbed, there was no sign of an intruder. Relaxing, she closed the front door and went into the tiny kitchen to make herself some hot chocolate to take to bed.

She was just stirring the milk into the mug when the phone began to ring.

She jumped. The shrill sound seemed very loud in the silent flat. Hurrying into the sitting-room, she grabbed up the phone, wondering who on earth could be ringing her at this hour of the night.

'Donna?' The voice was male, low, distinctly English.

'Yes?' She was instantly on her guard, her nerves prickling.

'It's me, Gavin.'

Donna's expression changed; her eyes widening in surprise. 'Gavin? Where are you? Do you know what time it is? It's two in the morning here. Is something wrong?'

'Are you alone?' Gavin asked in a whisper, and she frowned.

'Of course I'm alone. I . . .'

'Has anyone rung you from London?' he interrupted. 'Have you heard from anyone today?'

'Gavin, what on earth are you talking about? What's

happened? Why should anyone ring me from London?'

'Never mind,' said Gavin in a strangely dry voice. 'Look, I'm coming to your apartment now—will you tell that woman to let me in?'

'The concierge?' Donna's mind was working slowly, she was so tired. 'Yes, of course—do you mean you're in Paris? You're here now?'

'I'm in a telephone box just up the road. I wanted to be sure the coast was clear. I'll explain when I see you; in five minutes.'

He rang off and Donna automatically put down the phone, then picked it up to ring the concierge to warn her that Gavin would be arriving any minute. Without warning, Madame Lebrun wouldn't let him past her. She often refused to admit male visitors after ten o'clock at night, even when they were respectable middle-aged men like Donna's boss and even if they were accompanied by their wives. This was a respectable house, she always said flatly. The landlord didn't like all this coming and going at night.

'Votre frère, mademoselle?' Madame repeated suspiciously with one of her loud sniffs. Donna could imagine her expression; dourly cynical.

'Oui, vraiment! C'est mon jumeau.'

'Ah, oui,' Madame said reluctantly, remembering then that Donna had a twin brother who had visited her before. She couldn't doubt the relationship because the likeness was unmistakable. Donna and Gavin weren't identical twins, of course, merely fraternal, but they still resembled each other enough for a stranger to spot the fact that they were twins when they were together.

Madame grimly agreed to let Gavin into the house and Donna hung up and drank her hot chocolate quickly. There was no point in thinking about getting ready for bed now. She frowned anxiously as she waited for his knock. Why had he arrived without warning in the middle of the night? It was true that she had been out all evening, having dinner with Marie-Louise in her apartment, but why hadn't Gavin rung earlier that day?

He knew very well that she usually went out in the evenings—to see a play or film, go to a party, meet people for dinner. She had a wide circle of friends in Paris—half a dozen of them would be driving up to Lyons together for Marie-Louise's wedding next week. They planned to make a long weekend of it and stay at a motel on the city outskirts.

Marie-Louise was marrying a man she had known most of her life. Their families were old friends; it was almost an arranged match, except that they were very much in love. When Donna first heard how eager Marie-Louise's family were for the marriage to take place, she had been disturbed.

'Don't let them stampede you into anything!' she had warned. 'It never works, that sort of marriage. It almost happened to me once—my father wanted me to marry someone and I almost did, but I came to my senses in time. You have to stand up to that sort of pressure. After all, it's your life, not theirs!'

Marie-Louise had laughed affectionately at her. 'You think I'm crazy? I'm glad my parents are happy about it, but I'd marry him whatever they thought. There's never been anyone else for me—and Jean-Paul feels the same.'

Donna hadn't been convinced until she met Jean-Paul and saw the way he smiled at Marie-Louise. They were so radiantly in love that it made her heart ache with envy. It hadn't been that way for her.

She absent-mindedly washed up her mug and hung it back in the cupboard, listening intently for the sound of Gavin's arrival. She had a very uneasy feeling that he brought bad news.

The doorbell rang sharply and she went to answer it. 'Gavin! You choose the funniest times to drop in!'

He smiled at her, wearily leaning on the doorpost. 'Sorry. Are you as tired as I feel?'

He looked more than tired; he looked crumpled and exhausted, a thin figure in a lightweight suit, his tie undone, his collar open. He was carrying an overnight bag in one hand and she got an instant impression of someone running—from what?

'Well, come on in, you're always welcome, you know that. Any time, day or night.' She took his bag, her anxiety deepening. Had he quarrelled with their father? Had he been thrown out of the house for good this time?

He followed her into the sitting-room and threw himself into a chair, closing his eyes with a long sigh. 'God, I feel like death!'

'You don't look too well,' she said, watching his drawn face. They were both fine-boned, fair-skinned, fair-haired. On Donna that bone structure and colouring was ultra-feminine; made men's heads turn in the street, Gavin didn't have that effect on women. He was oddly colourless, his features weak, his manner unimpressive.

'Has something happened?' she asked him. She understood Gavin instinctively, they had a form of telepathy; after all, they were twins.

It was working overtime now. She hadn't had any premonition that he was in trouble, but the minute she heard his voice she had picked up tension and uneasiness. Gavin was frightened. About what?

'I've been a fool,' he said, opening his eyes to look at her warily.

Donna smiled. 'So what's new in that?'

His grin was mere pretence. 'God, I'm tired. I came over on the ferry from Dover and got lost on the road from Calais.'

'How on earth did you do that? Didn't you use the *péage*?'

'I got lost after I left the motorway. I stopped and rang you, but I'd forgotten your number and whoever answered didn't make sense. You know my French is terrible. So I pushed on to Paris, but when I got here you were out and your concierge wouldn't let me in to wait for you. I hung about waiting for a while, but a gendarme gave me a funny look so I felt I'd better go and have a snack while I waited.'

She frowned. 'Were you out in the street just now?' I heard someone running behind me but when I looked round, he'd gone.'

Gavin sat up, a tic beating beside his mouth. 'Someone was following you?'

'It wasn't you? No, I suppose if it had been you'd have caught up with me.' She looked sharply at him, alarmed by his expression. 'Gavin, what are you frightened of?'

'I'm in bad trouble, Donna,' he muttered, very pale. 'And he's found out. I had to get away before all hell broke loose.'

'He? Who are you talking about? Father?'

He shook his head, his mouth turning down at the edges. 'Brodie, but he's going to tell Father, so it comes to the same thing.'

Donna's face became paper-white. She might have known that Brodie Fox was mixed up in this somewhere. She looked searchingly at her brother. 'What have you done, Gavin?' But she was already beginning to guess; she knew him too well.

He caught her glance and bit his lip. 'I was desperate for money, Donna. I'd got into a run of bad luck, but I was sure it was going to change—it couldn't go on for ever and all I needed was a chance to win back everything I'd lost.'

'Oh, Gavin,' she groaned, flinching as if he'd hit her. 'Gambling again after you'd promised faithfully . . .'

'You don't know what my life's like,' he burst out furiously. 'You're okay, you're out of it, but I'm stuck there. Day after day the same thing—the office, the boredom of that desk, the stupid people nagging at me all the time. And Father, looking at me with that expression on his face, as if he wishes I'd never been born.'

Donna knelt down beside his chair as he buried his face in his hands, shivering violently as if he had a chill. A long lock of blond hair trailed over his fingers and she brushed it back with a sigh.

'Don't, Gavin.' If he started to cry she wouldn't be able to bear it. He was a man now, he wasn't a little boy, but he was still so helpless, he had come to her because he didn't know what else to do.

'Help me, Donna,' he whispered, as he always had.

'Of course I will,' she promised, stroking his hair. Although they were the same age exactly she had always felt she was older. Even as a child, Gavin had been in need of her protection, he had always been the weaker of the two, perhaps because he was born second, half an hour after Donna, and had almost died. He had been rushed to an incubator and watched closely for the first week. In some ways Gavin had needed to be watched ever since.

'How did Brodie find out that you'd been gambling?' she asked him.

'I'd borrowed from the private account,' he said, his face hidden behind his hands.

Her face tightened in shock. 'Gavin! From Father's account? But you said it was Brodie who found out . . .'

'Brodie runs the firm now,' Gavin said bitterly, his hands dropping to show her a face pale with angry emotion. 'Father handed over control in the spring. He hasn't been well for a long time.'

'What's the matter with him?' Donna asked urgently. She was getting shock after shock tonight. She'd had no idea that her father was ill or that he no longer ran the family firm.

'Angina,' Gavin said shortly. 'Don't look so worried—it isn't as serious as it sounds. He has to take it easy, that's all. He only gets attacks when he's upset or overtired. His doctor advised retirement at once, but Father wasn't ready to give up altogether, so he appointed Brodie Managing Director and became Chairman. He comes in for board meetings and keeps an eye on what's happening from a distance.'

'So Brodie Fox runs the firm now?' Donna's mouth took on a cynical curve. He hadn't had to marry her to get what he wanted, after all. Wasn't that nice for him?

'You sound surprised!' Gavin said bitterly.

'No, I'm not surprised at all.' Her voice was flat, careful.

'Nor was I. He's been after control ever since he joined the firm. Father's last attack was his big chance.'

'Why didn't you tell me before?' asked Donna, staring at him. 'You were over here in the spring.'

He looked away shiftily and her frown deepened. 'I didn't want to upset you.'

She didn't quite believe him; Gavin was a bad liar. Slowly she asked, 'How much did you take, Gavin?'

He moistened his lips, still not meeting her eyes. 'I meant to put it back, you know. I was sure my luck was about to change; it couldn't get worse, I thought.'

'How much, Gavin?'

'I took a thousand,' he muttered, and she made a face. Did she have that much in her savings account?

'I might be able to raise a thousand,' she thought aloud, and Gavin glanced at her and away.

'That wasn't all, you see, I . . .'

Her breath caught. 'You borrowed more than a thousand? How much more?'

'Don't get angry with me!' Gavin protested, flinching. 'You know Father keeps me short of money. He treats me like a schoolboy, doles out little sums when he feels like it. If I worked for anyone else I'd earn far more than I do—and after all, one day the firm will be mine.' He stopped, gave her a quick look. 'Ours, I meant. You know Father's will leaves it to both of us equally.' His face had become petulant, aggrieved. 'All that money lying there and one day it's going to be mine, why can't he give me more now? I wouldn't have had to take it if he hadn't been so tight-fisted.'

Donna couldn't speak for a second; his attitude

appalled her. He talked as if their father had no right to keep his money, as if he couldn't wait for Father to die.

'Gavin,' she whispered, shaking her head. 'Oh, Gavin, sometimes I . . .' She broke off as his weak mouth quivered. He hated to be reproached or blamed. The only influence she had with him was that he knew she loved him in spite of his faults, and if she began to be too critical Gavin would stop confiding in her. She had to hide her shock and distress.

'How much do you need?' she asked him patiently.

He still looked sullen. 'Sixteen thousand.'

Her head swam, as if she was about to faint. She had never dreamt it would be that much. The sum was wildly beyond her reach. They had each inherited a legacy from their dead mother on their twenty-first birthday. Donna had used her money to move to Paris, pay a deposit on this apartment and her fees at language school until she was fluent enough in French to be able to get a job as a translator. She knew Gavin had simply gambled away his money.

She took a harsh breath. 'Gavin, I haven't even got sixteen thousand pounds!'

His face broke up in tremors of pleading and agitation. 'If you talked to Brodie . . .'

'No!' she broke out, shuddering. She had promised herself that she would never set eyes on Brodie again, and even to help Gavin she couldn't face the thought of it.

'You don't understand,' Gavin said desperately. 'If he tells Father, I'm finished, he'll cut me out of the will. He told me so last time.' He broke off, looking at her, then away—first red, then white. 'Donna, I know you must despise me, but I get so depressed because I can't please Father however hard I try, and that makes me feel so low. I have to get away, and gambling is the only way I know of forgetting everything else. When you're at the tables, that's the whole world. You shut out all the problems. I've often thought that war must be like that. Suddenly all your worries seem tiny. You just have to concentrate on staying alive. That's what it feels like when I'm gambling—every spin is life or death.'

She stared at him, shaken by the sudden outburst. He had never been so frank with her before, but he had made a sort of twisted sense. Their father was partly to blame—he was too cold a man, his standards too high, his attitudes too rigid. He despised Gavin because his son wasn't made in his image, and he had never hidden that contempt. No wonder Gavin was prone to bouts of despair and tried to sink his worries at the roulette table!

She got up and ruffled his fair hair gently. 'Why don't you go to bed now? In the morning we'll see what can be done. I'll help you, don't worry.'

Some of the tension went out of his drawn face and he sighed, getting up too. 'Thanks, Donna.' He gave her a hug. 'What would I do if I didn't have you to run to?'

Would he learn to rely on himself? she wondered sadly, but knew that she couldn't risk such an experiment in case Gavin went to pieces altogether. Their mother had died when they were very small, and Donna had been all the mother he had ever known.

He gave a smothered yawn. 'You're right, I am tired. Where's my overnight bag?' He picked it up from the chair where she had placed it. 'Any chance of a cup of hot milk?'

'Of course, get into bed and I'll bring it to you.'

He grinned faintly at her, brushing that stray lock of fair hair out of his eyes. 'Could you show the brandy to it? I need a pick-me-up.'

She smiled, nodding, and watched him walk wearily down the corridor to the tiny boxroom she used as a second bedroom.

She heated the milk and added a finger of brandy, and Gavin had undressed and was in bed when she tapped at his door.

She put the milk on the bedside table, smiling down at his pallid face. 'Try to sleep. I won't be going to work tomorrow, of course, as it's a Saturday. Do you want me to wake you or let you sleep?'

'You'd better wake me by nine, if I haven't got up by then,' he said ruefully. 'Donna, I've been thinking—you said someone followed you tonight? Did you see who it was?'

'No, but I got the feeling it was a man. It can't have anything to do with you, Gavin. It was probably just a prowler who decided not to jump me.'

'I suppose so,' Gavin said slowly, frowning. 'I'm edgy, that's all. I had an interview with Brodie this morning. He told me he'd uncovered the amount I'd borrowed—he had the nerve to call me a thief, damn him! He told me he was going to speak to Father on Monday morning before the board meeting. He said he'd give me the weekend to tell Father myself, but he knew I wouldn't be able to face it. I saw his face; that look—the way Father looks at me. Brodie despises me too. I walked out of there knowing I had to run, and I think Brodie knew, too. All the way here I've felt sure he was behind me.'

Donna stared at him fixedly. His face had a peculiar greenish tinge. He looked the way he had looked as a child when he was in trouble; Gavin had usually been sick with nerves when Father was angry with him.

'Stop thinking about it,' she ordered, trying to sound calm. 'You won't sleep if you keep brooding.'

'Brooding over Brodie!' he said, laughing on the edge of hysteria. 'How can I help it?' He picked up the glass of milk in both hands, sipping it. 'I'll be okay. Sorry to keep you up, Donna. I'll see you in the morning.'

He was looking slightly better already. He had handed his problem to her. Donna gave him a wry smile and went out. She wasn't going to find it so easy to sleep. How dared Brodie call him a thief? Gavin shouldn't have taken that money, but at least he was one of the family, Brodie Fox wasn't. He had walked into the firm five years ago with the set intention of taking it over if he could. What right did he have to talk to Gavin like that?

She undressed and got into bed, her head throbbing. In the darkness her bedroom seemed unfamiliar; as if Gavin's appearance so suddenly had changed her world.

He had been here before, several times. Her father had never visited Paris since Donna moved there, but Gavin had. She hadn't been back to England since she left it; she didn't want to run any risk of seeing Brodie and knew that if she went home her father was quite capable of producing Brodie without warning.

She turned over, sighing heavily. What was she going to do about Gavin? She had promised to help him, but how? She wasn't going on her knees to Brodie Fox. She would rather die. That would feed his ego, wouldn't it?

He would love that, having her at his mercy, watching her beg.

Two years ago she had told him what she thought of him before she left for good. She hadn't minced words, or disguised her contempt, and he had watched her with icy blue eyes, not a shred of expression in his face.

She had been armoured against the threat of his presence then; if she had to go to him to plead for her brother she would be defenceless. But she couldn't think any more tonight. She must sleep. She turned over again, her body hot and aching. It was a very warm night; the sheets clung to her skin. How was she going to get any rest when her mind wouldn't stop working?

It was another half-hour before she finally unwound enough to relax, and when she woke up the room was full of sunlight and the smell of coffee. Surprised, she realised Gavin must be up already.

She stumbled out of bed, yawning. It was nearly nine. She felt as if she had barely closed her eyes, but she must have had five hours' sleep. She pulled on a cotton night-robe and tied the wide satin belt before going to the kitchen, where she found her brother making coffee and squeezing oranges.

He gave her a wry smile. 'Good morning. Did you sleep?'

'Not too well. How about you?' Her eyes searched his face. 'You look better.'

'I slept like a log,' he admitted. 'And now I'm starving—is there any bread? I can't find it.'

'I've run out. I'll have to get some from the *boulangerie* down the street.'

'I'll go,' he said. 'Tell me where it is.'

'Turn left at the next corner and you'll see it across the road. Get some croissants and rolls and a baton loaf.' As he turned to go she asked, 'Got some French money?' and Gavin nodded.

'Keep the coffee hot, I won't be a minute.'

The front door slammed behind him, and Donna drifted slowly towards the bathroom. She splashed cold water on her face, brushed her tousled hair and assessed her reflection with a grimace. Her green eyes were smudged with shadows of weariness, her blonde hair seemed lifeless, her skin was pale.

'You look terrible,' she told herself.

The doorbell rang and she sighed. Gavin had come back sooner than she had expected.

'You were quick,' she said, opening the door, then froze in shock as she saw the man outside.

Donna would have slammed the door shut again if he hadn't pushed his way into the apartment while she was still thinking about it.

'What are you doing here?' she protested, and got a smile of dry cynicism.

'Where's Gavin?' He walked into the sitting-room and looked around, his eyes curious. She had furnished it from sales and second-hand shops, picking up solid pieces of furniture from between the wars, not quite antiques yet still made by craftsmen and intended to last. The room had a late twenties feel to it; even the ornaments were in period.

'Gavin?' Donna fenced, and got another of his crooked little smiles.

'Don't play the innocent, it doesn't suit you.'

He had eyes like blue ice, deep-set and faintly hooded by heavy lids. A tall man, he was frighteningly self-contained, impossible to outthink. She felt an angry need to see him lose his temper, to watch some sort of emotion wrecking that calm certainty.

'I know he's here,' he said, walking past her. 'I discovered that he'd skipped the country yesterday afternoon and I got a Paris detective agency to check to see if he'd come here.'

'You had my apartment watched?' she snapped as he glanced into the kitchen. 'How dare you?'

He gave her a dry sideways smile. 'Don't talk like a melodrama, Miss Cowley. There was no point in my following him to Paris if he hadn't come here. I never waste time on red herrings.'

'I suppose that it was your peeping Tom who followed me home last night? He was lucky I didn't call the police!'

Brodie shrugged. 'Breakfast for two, I see,' he commented, eyeing the table Gavin had laid before he went to buy bread. 'Gavin still in bed? Or have you got a lover in your bedroom?' His smile mocked her.

'Yes,' Donna said coolly, and for once caught him by surprise. She saw his blue eyes harden. His colouring was dramatic—tanned skin, dark eyes, black hair. Raven black, she thought. What other plumage for a bird of prey?

'That's a lie,' he said tersely, lids lowered.

She smiled; a taunt in her eyes. 'I wouldn't advise you to check—he might teach you better manners.'

She saw the glacial anger in his face with satisfaction. She might not be able to draw blood, but at least she had inflicted a pinprick.

As she had known he would, he turned on his heel and strode down the corridor to the bedroom. Donna ran into the sitting-room, unfastened the high windows and stepped out on to the balcony that overlooked the street. For a second she thought she was too late to catch Gavin, but then she saw him coming, swinging casually under the plane trees with his arms piled with food. He had stopped to buy fruit, too; she saw a watermelon balanced on top of a bag full of croissants. Leaning over the ironwork railing, she was just going to call a warning, when a hand suddenly fastened over her mouth. She shot a startled look backward; Brodie's face was behind her shoulder. He pulled her, struggling, back into the room.

She tried to bite his hand and he whirled her sideways until she was arched helplessly over his arm, her eyes spitting rage at him above the hand silencing her.

'You're cleverer than your brother,' Brodie said coolly. 'You had me fooled for a minute, until I heard you scampering in here and realised you'd sent me on a wild goose chase.'

Donna mumbled furiously against his hand, tried to kick him. The doorbell rang and Brodie gave her a mocking smile.

'Too late. He's here.' She found herself being propelled toward the front door, still gagged by Brodie's hand. He only released her at the last minute, then pulled the door open after he had pushed her behind him.

'Come in, Gavin,' said Brodie, and over his shoulder Donna saw her brother's face grow white and stiff with shock.

CHAPTER TWO

THE watermelon wobbled and fell, bouncing off down the corridor. Donna chased it; that gave her time to think. She couldn't let Brodie bully Gavin, she had to separate them somehow. She heard Gavin edge into the kitchen with Brodie following him like a cat after a mouse with no hole to go to—by the time she joined them her brother had collapsed into a chair and Brodie was looming over him, talking softly. She caught the tail end of a sentence. '. . . won't get away with it. This time you're going to face the consequences of what you've done.'

Donna dropped the dark green watermelon on to the table with a thud. Brodie looked up; their eyes met as if over crossed swords.

'I want to talk to you in the sitting-room,' she said tersely.

'Later.'

'Now!' She was bristling with rage, but it didn't cause so much as a ripple in that controlled face.

'I'm talking to your brother,' he said calmly, dismissively.

The arrogance made her teeth meet. Through them, she hissed, 'Who the hell do you think you are? You work for my father. You don't employ either me or my brother, so don't talk to me like that.'

'I work for your father, not for you, Miss Cowley,' he said with a dry smile, his eyes narrowed as he deliberately emphasised her name.

Hot colour burnt in her face, her chin went up. 'What right do you have to play detective, follow my brother all the way to Paris, force your way into my apartment and use threats and physical violence on me?'

Gavin looked up. 'What did he do to you, Sis?' he asked angrily.

'Manhandled me.'

Donna was still staring at Brodie; she saw his mouth compress. 'I stopped you warning your brother that I was here—it hardly comes under the heading of grievous bodily harm.'

'Keep your filthy hands off my sister!' Gavin told him aggressively, beginning to get up.

Brodie put one hand on his shoulder. Donna watched with a sense of shock as he exerted enough pressure to force Gavin back into his chair. The little defeat made Gavin go white again; this time with humiliation.

'Don't get into a fight with me, Gavin. You'd lose.' It wouldn't have made Gavin wince so much if the older man's voice hadn't been calm; almost gentle.

'Why don't you pick on someone your own size, then?' Donna muttered.

'You, for instance?' For a second she saw a gleam of amusement in his cold blue eyes, then it was gone. 'This wasn't the way I'd planned to spend my weekend,' he said drily. 'Following your brother across the channel wasn't a game, Miss Cowley. I could have saved myself all this time and trouble by doing one of two things. I could just have told your father that his son had embezzled a large sum from the private account, or called in the police without bothering your father. If the thief had been anyone but your father's son that's what

I would have done. Your father isn't supposed to involve himself in the day-to-day running of the firm any more, especially if it might upset him.' He paused, eyeing her grimly. 'I decided to deal with the whole problem myself without involving the police, and as your brother had skipped the country I had to cancel my plans for the weekend and follow him.'

'I'm sure my father will be very grateful to you,' said Donna, thrusting her hands into the pockets of her cotton robe. 'On the other hand, if you hadn't scared my brother senseless he wouldn't have run away. You wanted *him* to go to my father, didn't you? If that had caused a fatal heart attack *you* couldn't be blamed.'

His face tightened. 'My one concern is to make sure your father *doesn't* have another attack!'

She laughed disbelievingly. 'Do you expect us to believe that? You're determined to make sure he knows about the money Gavin took. You want him to turn against Gavin and cut him out of his will. That would leave you sitting prettily waiting to move in once my father was dead.'

'If I wanted that, I could just have told him. I wouldn't have followed Gavin here.' He had himself on a tight rein again, but he was angry, she was glad to see, and she smiled again, eyes cynical.

'Oh, I think you're shrewd enough to work out that it would put you in a very good light if you galloped after Gavin and brought him home to face the music before you broke the sad news to my father!'

'You have a devious mind, Miss Cowley.'

Suddenly her temper snapped. 'Don't keep calling me that!' She wished she hadn't lost her cool a second later when she saw the glint in his eyes.

'Sorry, I had the impression I wasn't allowed to call you Donna any more.'

She looked across at her brother, too angry to be capable of answering Brodie. 'Eat your breakfast, Gavin, while I have a word with *him* in the sitting-room.' She lifted the coffee-pot and poured her brother a cup of black coffee, handed it to him, walked past and out of the door without looking to see if Brodie was going to follow her.

She heard him behind her after a brief hesitation. She watched him walk into the sitting-room and closed the door. Brodie turned to face her, his long body tensely at rest the way a panther waits in the darkness of the jungle; every muscle poised for the spring to kill and yet very still. He frightened her, although she wouldn't let him see it. She watched him, frowning, wondering how to get through to him.

'If you really care about my father, you won't tell him what Gavin has done,' she began, and saw his mouth tighten.

'Sixteen thousand pounds is missing from the accounts—how do you propose I hide that fact without incriminating myself?'

'Give me a few days and I'll see that the money is replaced,' she said huskily. She didn't know how she was going to get it, but she would move heaven and earth to do it.

Brodie folded his arms, considering her as if she were a new species he had never come across before. 'You have that much money immediately to hand?'

'I'll get it.'

'Borrow it from someone, you mean?'

'Does it matter how I'll get it, so long as I do?'

'Yes, I think it does,' he said. 'The money has to be replaced by Tuesday.'

Her lips went dry. 'Tuesday? Can't you give me more time than that?'

His brows rose. 'You don't understand—the official audit takes place on Tuesday and that money must be back by then.'

'Couldn't you explain that . . .' Her voice broke off and he bent towards her, his face ironic.

'Yes?'

'I don't know,' she muttered. 'You must think of something.'

'Lie for you, you mean?' he enquired, and her face flushed again.

'Do you have to put it like that?'

'I was merely trying to define our terms. I want to know what you're asking me to do.'

'Surely you can stall the auditors for a few days just until I get the money?'

He walked slowly to the couch and sat down, crossing his legs. Donna bitterly noted the quality of his pale grey suit. It must have cost the earth. The shirt was pale silk; a lucent blue which echoed the colour of his eyes, and the dove-grey tie was silk too. Brodie's taste had always been good; he liked the best and now he could afford it. He had climbed the mountain and he meant to stay there, whatever he had to do to make sure of it.

'Suppose I did as you asked?' he said quietly. 'You won't ever get that money back from Gavin, you know. He'll be full of gratitude for a few days, then he'll put it all out of his mind. He doesn't like to remember things that make him feel a failure.'

'That's my business!'

'In a way it's mine, too. In a few months he'll be gambling again—he's compulsive, he can't stop. It's a sickness and it ought to be treated as one, but your father prefers to believe that all Gavin has to do is make up his mind to stop—he won't admit that there's anything wrong with Gavin.'

Her green eyes held a darkness. She didn't want him to understand Gavin so well, she resented his shrewdness. It alarmed her for reasons of her own. Brodie waited, then went on, 'Sooner or later he'll need money desperately enough to steal again, but this time it won't be from the firm because I have no intention of allowing him anywhere near any large sums of money in future. And if he steals from someone else, it won't be so easy to cover up next time.'

'There won't be a next time,' Donna denied angrily. 'And you must be crazy if you plan to push Gavin out of the firm—have you forgotten that one day he'll own it?'

'I didn't say I wanted him out of the firm—only that from now on he can't be allowed access to money. He won't be able to siphon cash out of the private account again.'

She laughed furiously. 'Who do you think you are? My family run that company—you just work for them. How dare you talk as if my brother were some junior clerk caught with his fingers in the till?'

Brodie's steady gaze didn't falter. 'That's what he is—and if he weren't Gavin Cowley I'd have called the police by now. Do you think that's fair? One law for Gavin and another for any other employee?'

Donna bit her lip. 'Gavin wasn't really stealing, he was taking money which he knew was . . .'

'His father's? You think that's morally acceptable?' His lip curled and she flinched.

'Of course not.' She turned away and walked to the window, aware that he watched her, his eyes wandering. Their assessment made her self-conscious, and that made her angry again.

She swung round. 'You don't intend Gavin to be any threat to you, do you? If he's allowed to stay on he'll be given a sinecure—a peripheral job where he can be forgotten while you really run things.'

'Do you think Gavin could run the firm?' Brodie shrugged those firmly muscled shoulders. 'Within two years the company would be bankrupt and the staff would be out of work. Or don't they count? Are you happy to see them out on the streets looking for new jobs?'

She laughed shortly. 'Oh, you're clever, I grant you that. And lucky too. Gavin has played right into your hands, hasn't he? You didn't have to get rid of him, he did it for you.'

Brodie got up and she backed, gripping the windowsill. On his feet he was disturbingly tall, potentially dangerous, especially when his hard-boned features took on the look they wore at the moment—an icy impatience in the blue eyes, the mouth reined and the jaw rigid.

'Perhaps we can cut out the insults if you've got some of the poison out of your system,' he said through his teeth. 'The real question is—what are we going to do about Gavin now?'

'We?' she threw back, her eyes rejecting the plural.

Brodie took two steps and was far too near her. Her

body arched instinctively away from him, her chin defiant.

'Don't keep fighting me, Donna,' he said quietly, watching her.

Her mouth quivered. 'Oh, you'd like me to be putty in your hands, I suppose!'

The blue eyes flashed and she caught a ripple of expression in that tanned face. It alarmed her, especially when he smiled slowly.

'What an interesting picture.'

'Forget it!' She was husky with fury.

He was even closer now, his hands shot out and grasped the window-sill on each side of her. Donna found herself trapped and looked at him nervously.

'What do you think you're doing?'

His face brooded; the blue eyes very dark, the mouth level. 'What went wrong, Donna?' he asked suddenly. 'Why did you turn against me like that? What did I do?'

Her eyes shifted, her colour ebbed and flowed, her breathing became erratic and her heart beat frighteningly fast. Why did he still have this effect on her? She had thought she was cured, she had believed he was nothing to her but an enemy, a man she must be wary of and watch carefully. It was worrying to feel those physical reactions to his nearness. Her body remembered things she wanted only to forget.

'I don't want to talk about the past,' she said, not meeting his eyes.

'I do.' His body shifted, he was almost touching her, the muscular firmness of his thighs an inch away.

'I don't care what you want,' Donna muttered, staring at his grey tie. This close she could pick up the cool fragrance of his after-shave, the warm scent of his skin, muskier, more disturbing.

'Don't you?' His voice had dropped to a murmured intimacy that did crazy things to her heartbeat.

'Don't waste your time flirting with me,' she said fiercely.

'You're very tanned, It makes your hair like silvery silk.' His hand came up to touch her hair and she jerked away like a frightened horse, tossing her head to dislodge his hand.

'Don't touch me!'

'You used to like me to touch you,' he said in that soft, seductive voice, and her throat closed up. She had forgotten how convincing he could be; if she didn't know better she might almost believe that the look in his eyes was genuine attraction, not the mimicry of a shrewd operator who saw her as his insurance policy if his other plans didn't work out.

'What are you scared of, Donna?'

'Not of you, never of you,' she said feverishly, and saw his smile with dismay, wishing she had sounded more in command of herself. He picked up every tiny signal like a Geiger counter sensing radioactivity. She must learn to disguise her feelings better.

'We were talking about my brother!' she said sharply, twisting her body free. Brodie didn't try to stop her. He swivelled to watch her cross the room, her limbs not quite in control, her breathing far too fast.

'Gavin needs treatment,' he answered calmly as she sat down on a chair. 'He ought to see a psychiatrist. Gambling is a symptom of a deeper problem.'

Donna was surprised by his insight. She couldn't argue with that, it was what she had come to think herself. Brodie leaned against the window-sill, his body casual. 'I've tried several times to convince your father that Gavin is sick, but he has nineteenth-century attitudes towards any form of mental illness. He's afraid of the stigma attached to it. He simply loses his temper if I raise the matter. He seems to believe I'm telling him that Gavin isn't sane, he doesn't recognise depression and compulsive behaviour as an illness. But when he hears that Gavin has taken this money, he may begin to realise that I am right.'

Slowly Donna said, 'Especially if he has to choose between having a son with criminal tendencies, and a son who is only sick and needs medical help?'

'Exactly.' Brodie strolled towards her and sat down again on the couch, facing her. 'And it would help if you were there to add your opinion to mine.'

She stiffened. 'No!'

'If we talked to him together we might have more effect,' Brodie went on, ignoring her protest.

'You know I haven't spoken to my father for two years, and anyway, he wouldn't listen to me. He never did. Your opinion counts far more with him than mine.' There was bitterness in her voice as she finished speaking and her mouth was quivering. Her father had hurt her two years ago; she hadn't forgiven him yet. He had been duped by Brodie Fox too, and when the scales fell from her eyes she hadn't been able to persuade her father how wrong they had both been about Brodie.

'If you really care about Gavin . . .'

'Of course I do!' she interrupted fiercely.

'. . . you'll come back to London with us and help me talk to your father,' Brodie finished as coolly as if she hadn't spoken. 'He had another mild heart attack a few months back, he isn't the man he used to be. I try not to upset him or get into arguments with him. This business with Gavin is going to be a big shock to him. I want to make it as easy on him as I can—that's where you can help.' He paused and eyed her without expression. What was he thinking about? she wondered with a sharp stab of apprehension. She didn't like that look in his eyes—whenever Brodie looked as calm as a millpond you knew he was up to something. He was a born pokerplayer, but that very blankness told you a little—it warned you that behind his cool face he was thinking and whatever he was planning was likely to be potentially lethal.

'I still don't think that he'd listen to me!' But Donna knew her voice betrayed uncertainty and of course he heard it.

'I think you ought to go home soon anyway,' he told her. 'Your father may not have much longer to live.'

Her breath caught and she fixed shaken eyes on him. 'Gavin didn't tell me he was that ill.'

'Gavin probably doesn't know. Your father refuses to admit how ill he is—he's good at refusing to face things he finds unpleasant, as I said.'

'Then what makes you think . . .'

'His doctor warned me after the last attack.'

'And you kept it to yourself? Why didn't you tell Gavin?'

'I didn't think he could handle it.'

The cool answer took her breath away. She stared at him dumbly, realising that he was probably right. How would Gavin react to news like that? With shock and distress, yes, but wouldn't he run away from facing it?

'You had no right to take that decision,' she said in a husky voice. 'You should have let me know and I'd have talked to Gavin.'

His brows shot up, derision in his smile. 'We weren't exactly on confidential terms,' he drawled, and watched her flush, with apparent mockery.

'I had a right to know that my father was seriously ill. What I think of you has nothing to do with it. You should have written to me.'

'It occurred to me, but I had a feeling that if you recognised my handwriting you'd file my letter in the wastepaper basket.'

'Rung me, then,' she said, beginning to lose her temper.

'Wouldn't you have hung up when you recognised my voice?'

'Oh, don't be ridiculous!' she snapped, glaring at him. 'You know you should have let me know my father might die at any minute.'

'If I'd thought it was likely to happen I'd have sent for you,' said Brodie with the cool arrogance which made her blood boil.

'Who the hell do you think you are?' she erupted. 'You'd have sent for me? As if I were an office boy? To come when you snap your fingers?'

'Make up your mind,' Brodie said drily. 'First you're angry because I didn't send for you, and then you're angry because I say I would have done if the need arose. I get it in the neck whatever I do, it seems.'

'I don't like the way you feel free to take charge of my family's affairs without consulting any of us!' she snapped.

'I'm consulting you now,' he pointed out. 'So what are you going to do about Gavin? Are you coming back to London with us or do you want me to deal with it?'

His smile held amusement. He knew she wouldn't leave it to him, after what she had just said about resenting his interference!

'I'll come back to London,' she said reluctantly. 'But I have to make arrangements first—my boss will need a warning, I can't leave until Monday, at the earliest.'

He shrugged. 'That suits me. A weekend in Paris is always a pleasure.' He glanced at his watch and got up. 'I managed to book a room at the Ritz, I'd better go and check in—I sent my luggage on with the taxi driver.'

'You may never see it again!'

'Oh, it was only a small suitcase. I brought very little with me, and in any case, I took his number.'

He moved to the door and as they walked into the corridor Gavin's face appeared at the kitchen door.

'Have dinner with me,' Brodie said casually, sharing the invitation between them.

Gavin made a horrified face and didn't answer. Donna gave him a hesitant glance, then decided it might be wiser to accept. They were going to need Brodie's help if they were going to persuade their father to recognise Gavin's deep-seated problem.

'Thank you, what time?' she said, conscious that her brother was looking furious but not daring to say anything.

'At the Ritz at seven-thirty?'

'The Ritz?' muttered Gavin, a sneer curling his mouth. 'Nice to be able to afford it. I can't, but then I don't sign my own expenses.'

Brodie gave him a sardonic glance but didn't make the obvious rejoinder.

Donna said hurriedly, 'We'll be there,' She had never been to the Ritz for dinner, but she had once had cocktails in the bar with some friends. Brodie nodded and left.

As the door shut, Gavin burst out, 'I'm not having dinner with him—it would stick in my throat. What were you talking about in there all that time? What did he say about me? What's he going to do?'

'He was telling me that Father's really very ill.'

'I told you that.'

'Brodie seems to think his condition might be more serious than we thought,' she said carefully. 'He said I ought to come back to London.'

Gavin's face brightened. 'Are you going to? Oh, Donna, please do! You can talk to Father, you always got on better with him than I did!' He gave a half-angry, half-miserable grimace.

Gavin was insecure; he had a vulnerable personality, brittle, always under threat from pressures inside himself as much as the more obvious external pressures. Gavin had learnt to despise himself and the weakness of his personal identity made him permanently angry, put him permanently at risk.

I shouldn't have left London, thought Donna. I shouldn't have left Gavin there alone. It was selfish of me to run like that, but at the time it seemed the only thing to do.

Her own sense of self had suffered a crisis two years before. Finding out that the man you're in love with is only interested in you because he wants your family company is a shattering blow. She had had to get away to grow new scar tissue over that wound. She had forgotten Gavin, and now she blamed herself. If she had been around he might never have started gambling again.

'When will you come?' asked Gavin, as she sat down at the breakfast table with a fresh pot of coffee ten minutes later.

'On Monday. I have to talk to my boss first—I'll try to ring him at home this weekend, but he may have gone to the country. They have a cottage near Chartres and try to get there as often as possible.' She poured herself some coffee and took a croissant. Brodie's arrival had wrecked her appetite. She ate very little breakfast before going to shower and get dressed.

Gavin was just going out again when she saw him half an hour later. 'I thought I'd buy a paper and walk down to the river, have a coffee at a pavement café near Notre Dame,' he told her.

He was already more cheerful now that his problem was half solved. She smiled at him wryly. 'What about lunch? Shall I meet you somewhere?'

They arranged to meet outside Notre Dame at half past twelve and have lunch in the Latin Quarter at one of the cheap bistros. When he had gone Donna rang her boss and was lucky enough to catch him just as he was about to leave for Chartres. He was sympathetic when he heard her news and gave her a week off to visit her father. It wasn't difficult for her to arrange time off because she worked as a translator for a big international magazine and did most of her work at home, translating English articles into French. Her editor would simply transfer her workload to another translator. He had whole strings of them working for him part-time—it was an easy way for a student to earn spare cash. Donna was fully employed by the magazine and earned a considerable amount more than she had when she first arrived in Paris. If she worked long hours she could earn very well indeed, and she enjoyed the work. She knew that the magazine liked the way she translated articles; she could echo style in a way that the more pedestrian translators never did. It was a knack which had improved with practice, and she also worked part-time for other firms—several publishers gave her work and if they had nothing for her she translated letters for a multi-national company, but she rarely had to fall back on that as a source of income these days. She was too well established in the publishing world.

She spent an hour making sure that her apartment was tidy and then did some quick shopping in the neighbourhood before taking the Metro to Notre Dame. She found Gavin basking in the sun among a crowd of tourists watching a white-faced mime artist. Donna sat with her brother for a while to catch some of the act, then they dropped a few francs into the top-hat laid on the ground and strolled away to find somewhere to eat.

The Latin Quarter of Paris is well supplied with bistros of all sorts; mainly foreign—Greek, Turkish, Algerian. Gavin decided he felt like some Algerian food, so they went in to eat cous-cous followed by a sticky sweetmeat made with nuts and sesame seeds, liberally laced with honey.

'I don't know why you don't live nearer the centre of things,' Gavin commented as they wandered along the river in the afternoon sunshine. 'You're so far from anywhere in that apartment.'

Donna gave him a wry sideways look. 'That's what I like about the apartment. It's peaceful.'

He wrinkled his nose. 'Dull, you mean.'

'You and I have very different tastes!'

He was serious suddenly. 'I wish you hadn't left London, Donna. Things were better while you were there.'

She slid her hand through his arm, leaning on him. 'Don't be glum. We'll sort this out—but you must stop gambling, Gavin.'

'I will,' he said with emphasis, but he had promised that once before and broken his word.

They took a taxi back to her apartment an hour later. Gavin was sleepy after being out in the sun for some hours, and kept yawning.

'I haven't slept too well for two nights now.' He gave her a furtive look which she noticed. 'Donna, I'm not having dinner with Brodie Fox. I can't—the food would choke me. I don't know how you can be polite to the man. He's our enemy, don't you realise that?'

Her smile was grim. 'Oh, I realise it, but sometimes you have to have a truce, even with someone you don't trust an inch. You're going to need his help with Father, you'd better face that. He could do you irreparable harm if you offend him, and he wouldn't hesitate to do it, either. Having dinner with him is the least of our worries. Compared to what Father is going to say when he knows about the money, a dinner with Brodie Fox will be a picnic!'

Gavin did not appear to be any more cheerful about the prospect. As they let themselves into the apartment, he said wearily, 'Couldn't you go alone and let me try to catch up on my sleep?'

She eyed him ruefully. 'Don't be such a coward, Gavin!' But what was the use of saying that? Gavin's reluctance to face anything unpleasant was one of the problems she had to sort out.

His eyes pleaded and she sighed. 'Oh, very well. Go to bed then and I'll see Brodie on my own.'

'Dinner at the Ritz should be quite a sugar-coating for the pill,' said Gavin, immediately lighthearted again.

Donna didn't bother to answer that—just watched him saunter off to bed, her expression ironic. Gavin had no idea how hard it was going to be for her to stay cool and pretend to enjoy the food, however fantastic, while Brodie sat opposite her.

Gavin was almost entirely self-centred. He simply failed to notice what was happening to other people; their feelings passed him by, he didn't suspect what they were thinking. His private myopia had some advantages. He hadn't noticed two years ago that she was wildly in love with Brodie Fox. He knew, of course, that their father had wanted her to marry Brodie—like Gavin, their father was blithely ruthless about getting what he wanted. He had made his views crystal clear and expected her to fall into line. Gavin had sympathised and urged her to defy James Cowley, but the complexities of the situation had escaped him. He had no idea how hard it was for her to refuse and go away rather than put up with their father's bullying, and she hadn't bothered to enlighten him.

She changed into an austere black cocktail dress, knowing full well that she was going to find the Ritz crammed with elegant Frenchwomen. Her dress wasn't expensive, but it had the chic of utter simplicity and had been made by a friend of Marie-Louise who was studying *haute couture* in Paris. Most of Donna's friends were also Marie-Louise's; Donna had met them through Marie-Louise, who had been a nurse in a private clinic in Paris. Through her job, she had met a good many famous and influential people, a few of whom had become her friends, and through her had become Donna's friends too.

She had met Marie-Louise in a dentist's waiting-room shortly after she came to Paris. They had had to wait for ages while the dentist attended to an abscess on someone's tooth, and had begun to talk because it took their minds off their own nerves. They might never have met again if fate hadn't taken a hand. The very next day they walked into each other outside Galeries Lafayette and at once stopped, smiling. They had coffee together and from then on they were friends. Perhaps if she hadn't met the other girl, Donna might never have settled down so happily in Paris. Marie-Louise had a wide circle of friends and a busy social life into which Donna fitted easily. Having come to Paris to train as a nurse to be near her fiancé who had been working in a Paris hospital, Marie-Louise had stayed on after he got a job back in Lyons because she could earn so much more in the clinic and they needed as much as possible to start their married life. Every so often she would fly home to Lyons and occasionally Jean-Paul flew to Paris to meet her. They were both very disciplined, which had misled Donna into thinking Marie-Louise wasn't really in love, but she had realised she was wrong in time.

There was no sound from Gavin's room as she let herself out of the apartment. He must have gone to sleep immediately. Her face wry, she thought that it was just as well. He would make an uncomfortable third that evening. Brodie didn't hide his impatience with him and Gavin resented Brodie's strength.

She took a taxi to the Place Vendôme where Napoleon's column brooded over the pale canopies of the Hotel Ritz, a favourite spot for Parisian society to dine on summer evenings in a garden haunted with pale pink sphinxes. The desk clerk told her that she would find Brodie in the bar on the left; he had walked that way a moment ago.

Turning into the bar, Donna found it full of people. A pianist was playing Cole Porter by the window, which stood open, a warm breeze bringing the fragrance of geraniums into the slightly stuffy room. Donna hovered, looking around, but couldn't see Brodie at any of the tables.

Someone saw her, however, and stood up, waving. 'Donna! *Ça va, chérie?*'

'Alain! *Comment allez-vous?*' She went over to his table, smiling in surprise. Alain Roche was a small, dark, rather ugly little man with faintly bulging eyes which had given him the nickname *la Grenouille*. He was a journalist on a satirical newspaper run by the Left in Paris and had enormous charm which made him apparently quite irresistible to women, who fell for him in such vast numbers that his friends called them *les mouches*. Alain's flies buzzed everywhere he went. His friends said he gobbled them up, but in fact they rarely lost touch with him, even after an affair was over. Alain's lady friends became just friends once passion had burnt out. Donna had never been one of them, but she was fond of Alain who was very witty and sophisticated, a charming companion, and he, in his turn, seemed to like her, perhaps because he found his sexual reputation trying, to live up to, and was grateful that with one woman, at least, he did not have to play the conqueror.

He asked what she was doing at the Ritz, made a mock grimace at hearing that she was there to have dinner with another man, and invited her to have a drink, but, aware of the far-from-cordial gaze of the woman sitting next to him, she smilingly excused herself and left the bar again, in search of Brodie.

Alain followed her a moment later and caught up with her. *'Au secours, chérie! C'est une peste! J'aimerais mieux être avec toi!'*

She laughed. 'Poor woman, what's wrong with her?' she asked in French.

He told her in his hoarse, rapid French that the other woman was a shrew; jealous, demanding, exhausting. *'Je vais devenir un ennemi des femmes!'* he announced to her amusement.

'Bravo!' she said gravely, kissing him on both cheeks. The idea of Alain as a woman-hater was so absurd it was hard to keep a straight face.

Alain returned the formal salute, assumed a suffering expression and went back into the bar. It was only then that Donna realised that they had an audience. Brodie was standing a few feet away, radiating brooding displeasure.

'Where did you find that weird-looking character?' he asked curtly, moving towards her. 'Is he a sample of the sort of men you've been dating while you've been here? I can't say I admire your taste. No amount of kisses would turn him into a fairy prince.'

CHAPTER THREE

THEY had dinner in the famous garden behind high walls, the sound of music floating out from the bar at one end and the chatter of French voices from the dining-room to one side of their table. Among the flowerbeds lurked the pink sphinxes carved with the Pompadour's face. Moths were just beginning to flit around the candles lighted on each table. The sky had an almost purple bloom pricked with sharp white stars. It should have been a magical, romantic occasion. It was more like a duel to the death.

'Alain is a friend,' Donna had told him an hour earlier in the foyer outside the bar, and Brodie had been asking ever since about her life in Paris over the last two years. Donna told him as little as she could; she resented his questions, and felt that every scrap of information she gave him might some time, somehow, be used against her.

'So there's nobody special in your life?' he asked, watching her with eyes that gleamed like blue fire in the candlelight.

'I didn't say that.'

'You don't say much at all, do you?'

She gave him a tight little smile. 'Why should I? You keep asking me about my private life—you don't tell me anything about yours.'

'You haven't asked.' He gave her a curling, inviting smile which she met stonily.

'I'm not interested.'

He didn't like that. The hooded lids lowered and his smile smoothed out, the pared planes of his face taut again. Donna put out a hand to her glass; relieved to see that her fingers were steady. Brodie's repressed anger had made her nervous, but luckily it didn't show.

They had both had cheese soufflé, light as air; melting on their tongues. The wine had a smoky tang which matched it perfectly. It had irritated her that Brodie hadn't asked what she wanted to drink. During her two years in Paris she had learnt a great deal about French wine and enjoyed choosing what to drink with food. She had to admit, though, that he had picked the right wine for the soufflé. She didn't tell him so; she was giving nothing away tonight.

'Gavin couldn't face dinner, I gather?' he enquired.

'He couldn't face your company, would be more accurate,' she said frankly.

His eyes were ironic. 'He resents me,' he agreed. 'Not very logical of him, but then I suppose one can't expect logic from someone as screwed up as Gavin.'

'Why should it be illogical for him to resent you?' she asked sweetly. 'Doesn't everybody?'

The waiter removed their plates. When he had gone Brodie leaned forward and said, 'You and Gavin aren't everybody.'

The wine waiter appeared and poured red wine into their second glass with the sort of reverent expression that made Donna want to giggle. Wine buffs were okay so long as they didn't take themselves or their wines too seriously, she had learnt. Wine was to be enjoyed, not treated as a holy sacrament.

When they were alone again, she smiled coldly at

Brodie. 'My father thinks you're the cat's whiskers, I'm aware of that.'

'And that's why Gavin resents me? If I hadn't joined the firm, does he think his father would think any more highly of him? I'm not in competition with Gavin, even if he imagines he's in competition with me. I do my job as well as I know how . . .'

'And you're ambitious,' Donna said curtly.

'What's wrong with that? You think ambition is some sort of unmentionable disease?'

'It depends how you pursue it.'

'Now what are you implying? That I'm not honest?'

She laughed angrily. 'Oh, I'm sure you're far too clever to make the mistake of being dishonest. You're not human enough to make mistakes.'

'Not human enough?' he repeated, his jawline taut. 'What the hell does that mean? You admire Gavin's brand of humanity more, I suppose? If I had a few more weaknesses you'd like me better. What do you want me to do—embezzle money, drink, start taking cocaine?'

'Don't be absurd, that wasn't what I meant, and you know it!'

'Then what did you mean? You prefer your men to be weak so that you can get them on their knees?'

The waiter reappeared looking professionally blank, but Donna saw his quick, curious glance at her and knew that he had not only overheard Brodie's last remark but had understood it. She felt herself flush and clenched her teeth with rage. At least she didn't have to reply to that while they were being served with their next course, but she brooded over it while she sipped the red wine and toyed with her food. It was a pity that the meal had been eaten in a tense atmosphere, because the cuisine here was superb. She had always wanted to eat at the Ritz; all her friends said it was fabulous. She couldn't wait to tell them they were absolutely right. There were no prices on the menu, and she shuddered to think how much all this was costing. Of course she wasn't paying, but she couldn't help wondering if her father approved of Brodie living like a king on company expenses.

Through lowered lashes she assessed his elegant dark suit; his clothes were obviously very expensive. He sneered at Gavin for embezzling money from the firm—but how on earth did he get her father to approve of the way *he* spent money? He had said that he didn't bother her father with the day-to-day running of the company, hadn't he? Did that mean that her father no longer checked up on him? Was Brodie quite as incorruptible as she had imagined? Was he quite as faultless?

While they were being served with their coffee Alain and his companion came through the french windows to have dinner in the garden. The woman noticed Donna, gave her a frosty stare, but swept past. Alain lingered, asking in French how Donna had enjoyed her meal.

'Marvellous,' she said, smiling, in the same language. 'Try the *foie gras frais*, it's out of this world.' She wondered how good Brodie's French was—did he understand what they were saying? She had noticed that he understood the menu without needing help, but he had spoken English to the waiters. Perhaps he was sensitive about his accent? After two years, hers was no longer so obviously foreign, but she had been through a phase of feeling self-conscious about it.

Alain gave Brodie several brief glances, so Donna politely introduced them. Brodie smiled coldly, inclined his head. Alain looked amused. He was used to getting hostility from other men. His reputation made them wary, especially if they had wives.

Ignoring the smouldering looks he was getting from his own table Alain asked quickly, 'Will you be coming to the party tomorrow?'

'Olga's party! Oh, I'd forgotten—no, I'm afraid I can't make it, I'm leaving for London on Monday.'

Alain pulled a droll face. *'C'est affreux! Est-ce tu pars longtemps?'*

She shook her head, aware of Brodie watching her closely. 'No, I doubt if I'll be there long—and I'll be coming to Lyons as arranged, so I'll see you then.'

Alain gazed into her eyes, smiling wickedly. He was as conscious of Brodie's icy attention as she was and deliberately played to the gallery, taking her hand and kissing it lingeringly.

'I look forward to our weekend together more than I can say,' he murmured. *'Au revoir, chérie—jusqu'alors.'*

He sauntered away, and she glanced at Brodie with hidden apprehension, trying not to smile.

Brodie called for the bill with a peremptory wave of his hand. It wasn't until they were outside the hotel and the doorman was getting Donna a taxi that Brodie asked crisply, 'You're going away for the weekend with that Frenchman?'

Donna turned innocent eyes on him, nodding. 'Next weekend, to be precise.'

'You'd better cancel it. You won't be going,' said Brodie, biting out the words like someone snapping cotton with their teeth.

'Oh, yes, I will,' Donna said firmly. The taxi drew up and the doorman opened the door for her. She began to get in and Brodie leaned forward, his face dark.

'You'll still be in London next weekend.'

'Thank you for the wonderful meal,' she said, her tones melting. 'Goodnight.'

He stood back, the door was closed and the taxi moved away. Donna leaned back, closing her eyes. She hoped he wasn't going back into the restaurant to have a vicious confrontation with poor Alain, although if he did, Alain would have brought it on himself because he hadn't been able to resist showing off. He'd deliberately given Brodie the wrong impression because it amused him. He must have been very curious when he saw her dining alone at the Ritz with Brodie. Donna usually went around with a crowd of friends. She didn't have a boy-friend. She had had plenty of offers and had gone out with a few people briefly, but none of them had been what she was looking for, they didn't measure up to her memories of Brodie. She couldn't take any of them seriously, and there was safety in numbers.

Many times during the past two years she had been angry with herself because after Brodie all other men seemed shadowy. He hadn't been what she thought he was; it had all been an illusion, a clever conjuring trick performed by an ambitious man who knew precisely what he was doing. She hated him but she couldn't forget him and she couldn't fall in love with anyone else, however hard she tried.

The next day she and Gavin had lunch in a small family restaurant on the Quai Voltaire across the river from the Louvre. It was a café-tabac, simple and unpretentious, with tables out on the pavement. They ate Risotto de Homard and drank Sancerre, watching the people flocking along by the river, crossing the Pont du Carrousel. The food was good and inexpensive for what it was.

'Voltaire died in one of the rooms up there,' Donna told her brother, pointing upwards.

'I think I'd like to live in Paris,' said Gavin, showing no interest in the great French writer whatever. 'I like the pace of life here.'

'Oh, but it's August,' Donna said. 'Paris is a different place in August—come back in November and see how you like it then!'

'You obviously like it,' her brother pointed out.

'I love it,' she agreed, laughing. 'But I work here, my life's here. When you're on holiday, there's no hassle. Try getting the Metro late at night or try catching a taxi during the rush-hour, in the rain. When you live somewhere all the time you see it differently.'

They walked back to her apartment slowly, stopping several times to have a glass of mineral water or a coffee at pavement cafés en route, so that it took them a long time. Gavin loved to sit in a café watching the flow of people, the rustling leaves of the chestnut trees, the rush of traffic. The drawn look had been smoothed out of his face and his smile was brighter. He would have been much happier if he hadn't had to please their father all his life. Gavin couldn't take any sort of pressure; he was too weak.

'Have you got a girl at the moment?' she asked him lightly.

He gave her a wry grin. 'Dozens.'

'I meant one you were serious about!'

'I know you did. No, not really. What about you?'

Her face sobered. She shook her head.

'Do you think we're too hard to please?' he murmured with a rueful expression. 'Do you want to get married, Donna? I don't, I couldn't take the responsibility—just thinking about it makes me shudder. Mortgages, insurance policies, being tied down to one woman and having kids—no, not me!'

'It's a pity you don't like working in the firm, though,' she said, sighing. 'Is it the work itself you hate, or . . .'

'I stifle shut up in an office all day,' Gavin said sulkily. 'I sit at my desk and dictate letters to this boring woman who's supposed to be my secretary and sometimes I can hardly keep my eyes open. Brodie Fox picked her out for me. You should see her! I think she takes steroids; she has muscles like an all-in wrestler, and a little moustache. I keep waiting for her to grow a beard. She marches into my office with her pad and barks at me like a drill sergeant, and I'm too scared of her to tell her to go away and leave me alone.'

She laughed. 'Poor woman—I don't envy her.' She glanced at him uncertainly. 'Maybe if you took more interest in the glass production you'd enjoy work more.'

Gavin laughed shortly. 'You mean start working at the factory? That's probably where I'm going to end up—when Brodie Fox is in charge he'll put me on a stool beside the conveyor belt watching for flaws.' A flicker of laughter went through his face. 'When I was a kid I remember I used to want to be the guy who took a hammer to the rejects and fed them back into the process to be re-cycled. There's something rather satisfying about smashing glass, don't you think?'

Their company was one of the biggest manufacturers

of industrial glass in Britain. They had several factories; one in the Midlands and another in the North and a third near London in one of the new towns built since the Second World War. The company head-quarters in London co-ordinated the running of all three. They had offices in a large building a stone's throw from St Paul's Cathedral, in a new modern office complex. Until six years ago the firm had been entirely family owned, but then their father had decided to go public in order to raise more capital with which to finance an expansion programme. That was when they had taken over the factory site in the new town. Fifty one per cent of the shares had been retained in James Cowley's hands so that he hadn't lost control of the firm, and his gamble had paid off—the stock was more valuable today than it had been when it was first launched and they were paying a good dividend.

Donna looked thoughtfully at her brother. 'I wonder if you shouldn't have started at the factory long ago? You liked making things, didn't you? All those model kits, remember?'

Gavin grimaced. 'Not the same thing. That was fun. Making moulded glass is work and even today the factory's hardly a comfortable work place. The sort of glass I might have liked to make is . . .' He broke off, shrugging. 'Oh well, what does it matter?'

'Of course it matters! What were you going to say?' she asked as they went into the apartment building.

Madame Lebrun and her husband were behind their lace curtains, eating a late lunch. Donna recognised the smell of *soupe de poissons*—rich, aromatic, heavily spiced. Madame often made it; throwing all sorts of cheap fish into a pot with herbs and spices and tomatoes, letting it cook for hours so that the smell permeated the whole house.

They didn't stop eating, but they watched Donna and her brother walk past, their eyes unblinkingly curious. 'What on earth are they eating?' muttered Gavin. 'Extraordinary smell.'

'Fish stew.'

'Fish? It smells like curry.'

'That's the spices. I think Madame uses lots of spice to hide the fact that she buys the cheapest fish.'

Gavin paused, panting. 'My God, how do you put up with all these stairs every time you go in and out? Why do you live right at the top of the house?'

'It's cheaper than the lower floors and the view is better. It's quieter at night, too,' Donna told him.

'You're so damned practical,' he muttered.

When they were in the kitchen of her apartment drinking some tea, she asked him, 'What were you going to say as we got here? Something about the sort of glass you would have liked to make?'

'Oh, it was just a stupid idea I used to have when I was a kid—I always thought I'd rather like to blow glass. Not work on the factory line, I hate the automated production process we use in the factories. I used to daydream about actually making glass the way they used to in the days before automation. There's something so magical about blowing glass by hand; shaping it, making it do what you want. It's a bit like blowing bubbles; watching them grow, all shimmery, like rainbows, then float away. Sheer magic!'

'Did you ever tell Father that you wanted to blow glass by hand?'

Gavin gave her an angry smile. 'Oh, I was crazy

enough to mention it when I was about fourteen, I remember.'

'What did he say?'

'That I was joking. When I said I was serious he told me to grow up, he said there was nothing in making glass by hand, it was a game for amateurs. He said I had to learn to run the company and wasn't to waste my time daydreaming. So I gave up the idea.'

Donna looked at him grimly. 'Just like that?'

'What was I supposed to do? Argue with him? You know what he's like. He doesn't really listen. He just waits for you to see it his way and if you don't he gets very nasty.' Gavin pushed his cup away, his mouth sulky. 'And, anyway, I doubt if I'd have been very good at glass-blowing. I would only have wasted a few years trying to pick up the techniques and then had to crawl back to Father with my tail between my legs.'

'Oh Gavin, don't be so defeatist!'

'I'm not defeatist, I'm just realistic.'

The phone began to ring and Donna sighed, getting up. 'Sometimes I think you need a good shake.'

'I get one every day of my life.' Gavin said, and laughed. Donna didn't think it was so funny.

It was Brodie on the phone, sounding oddly far away. 'We'll be flying tomorrow at ten,' he said. 'Where have you been all day?'

'Showing Gavin around Paris.'

'Show it to me tonight. We could walk along the river—there's a glorious moon.'

His husky voice made her see stars. She swallowed. 'If we're leaving early tomorrow I'd better get an early night.'

'Coward,' he said softly, but he didn't try to talk her

into going. As she put down the phone a few minutes later she crossly admitted to herself that she had half hoped he would. He might at least have tried. It was a gorgeous night and she could see the moon above the Paris skyline, mysterious and glimmering; it must look terrific on the Seine. They might have taken a trip on the Bateau Mouche, floating on the silvery waters, under the bridges, silently, romantically. Donna shrugged, laughing at her own imagery. It sounded fabulous, but she had taken those trips, she knew that there would be children running about yelling and wanting to go to the toilet, a nasal Tannoy telling you about the famous buildings on each bank, people eating and drinking all around you.

That didn't mean it would have been wise or safe to go. Brodie was a lethal combination with anything, however unromantic. He would have been there, those blue eyes inviting, mocking. She would have had difficulty staying cool. No, much better to turn him down and stay in tonight. Tomorrow was going to be a trying day. Tomorrow she was going to see her father for the first time in two years.

Brodie picked them up from the apartment next morning in a taxi and they all drove to the airport together in the usual heavy traffic. It was the rush-hour both ways—people driving into Paris to work, people driving out of Paris to get to Charles de Gaulle airport. Their taxi driver made frustrated, Gallic noises as he tried to make his way through other traffic. Gavin chewed his fingernails and ignored Brodie. Brodie stayed calm as a cucumber and Donna wished she wasn't so aware of being sandwiched between him and

Gavin; Brodie's knee touching hers, his arm laid along the back of the seat, ostensibly to make room for her. She kept feeling his fingers. They didn't quite touch her, but they were there, almost against the nape of her neck, softly drumming on the back of the seat. They drove her crazy.

She was glad when they finally got to the airport and were sucked into the usual formula of checking in, going through passport control, hanging around waiting to board. She hurried into the duty-free shops to buy some perfume, bought herself some magazines to read on the plane and had a cup of coffee. Brodie and Gavin sat in the café in silence. Brodie read his morning paper. Gavin stared at nothing. This morning he was very sullen. He was going home under escort, like a naughty boy who had run away from school. He wasn't looking forward to his reception, even though Donna would be there to act as a buffer against the worst of their father's anger.

As they arrived in London it was raining. 'Home, sweet home,' Donna said bitterly, following her brother down the steps of the plane. 'Wouldn't you know it?'

'Laid on just for us,' Gavin said glumly. His gloom infected her. She felt deeply depressed at the thought of being back in London, returning to her father and the home she had thought she had left for ever. Throughout her childhood nothing had ever seemed to change in James Cowley's house, any more than it had in him. From all that Gavin had told her, that still applied—and yet from Brodie she had picked up a very different picture. He seemed to think her father was a changed man; a very ill man who was slowly winding down.

Of course, Brodie and Gavin saw it from sharply

separated angles. Brodie merely worked for James Cowley. Gavin was subject to his father in many other ways—not least the emotional slavery of being a highly unsatisfactory son.

A loved and happy child has an emotional security which means the freedom to come or go, knowing that either way it is still loved. Gavin was neither free nor secure because he felt he wasn't loved.

Her father didn't feel much for either of them. He had been silent ever since she went away. At times she had wondered if he had really noticed that she wasn't there.

Well, he was going to notice her return, because she was going to tell him what he had done to Gavin, what he was still doing to him.

Brodie's car was parked in the car park at Heathrow, and within a few minutes of landing they were driving north-east, making for James Cowley's home near Saffron Walden. He had a flat in town, too, so that he didn't have to make the long trip out into Essex late at night on the occasions when he had a dinner to attend, but since he had retired no doubt he had given up the flat, Donna thought.

Brodie drove and she sat beside him in the front seat, watching as London suburbs gave way to familiar countryside. Two years away hadn't altered much.

As they got deeper into the countryside it stopped raining and a rainbow broke; watery, shimmering, a blue sky behind it. The fields were full of ripe, golden wheat and barley just being harvested; they passed several machines trundling back and forth behind the berried hedges. Black wings flapped above the tumbling barley; crows following the harvester and watching for disturbed mice and perhaps a baby rabbit. Donna frowned, looking away. She didn't like crows. Ominous birds.

She glanced over her shoulder at her brother who was also staring out of the window. Gavin was wrapped in thought; not very happy thought, from his drawn face.

'How does it feel to be back?' asked Brodie, abruptly.

She started, looking at him. 'Odd. Like going to the dentist.'

'You'll feel better once it's over,' he deduced, a wry smile curving his mouth.

'Does my father know we're coming?'

'No, I decided not to tell him anything in case I didn't get Gavin back here.'

'You thought he might bolt again before we arrived?'

'It occurred to me.'

It had occurred to her, too, and she was relieved that her brother hadn't slipped off before they got into the car.

'That's really why you insisted that I came, wasn't it?' she said, watching his profile. It had a carved authority in the afternoon light. He wasn't smiling; he could have been a statue.

'One reason,' he admitted drily. 'I thought it might make sure Gavin actually went home.'

'What were the other reasons?'

His eyes slid sideways, a glint in them. 'I'll tell you when we're alone.'

Her nerves jumped. What did he mean by that? 'I can't stay long.' she said hurriedly. 'I have to be in Lyons next weekend, remember.'

Brodie's face changed, the smile going, a harsh frown taking its place. 'You can't be serious!' His voice was curt. 'I don't believe you're having an affair with that little creep.'

'I didn't say I was—yet,' said Donna, finding it ridiculously hard to lie to him.

He shot her a hard look. 'And you're not going to!'

The peremptory tone made her bristle. 'That's my decision, not yours.'

'We'll see about that,' he muttered, turning into the drive of her father's house. She hadn't even noticed that they were almost there, she had been too absorbed in arguing with Brodie.

'You'll mind your own business,' she told him through her teeth, staring at the house ahead of them. It was a simple late Georgian house with a classic façade: flat windows, a columned portico, the local pargeting on the stucco covering the bricks, in a pattern of curved lines.

'I'm not letting you go,' Brodie said, and hot colour stung her face.

'*You're* not letting me go? I don't remember asking for your permission—it's nothing to do with you who I sleep with.'

He pulled up outside the house with a screech of tyres on gravel and swung round towards her, rage in his face. She had never seen him that angry before; she had never seen the usual calm of his face broken by such violence. It made her flinch, as if she thought he was going to hit her.

Then he turned away and got out of the car, slamming the door with a thud that made the glass in the windows rattle.

Gavin whistled. 'Hey, what's up with him?'

She looked round and her brother was very pale;

trying to smile, to hide his nerves.

'Come on, Gavin, let's go in together,' she said, smiling at him. 'Father doesn't know anything yet, Brodie says—so let me tell him later. Don't you say anything to him.'

Gavin groaned. 'I couldn't if I tried. I've been sitting here all the way from Heathrow, wondering what to say.'

'Just leave it to me,' soothed Donna. She was afraid that even at this late stage, Gavin might bolt for it.

Brodie was under the portico, ringing the front doorbell. By the time Gavin and Donna joined him, the door was opening. Their father's housekeeper, Mrs Eyre, looked incredulously at Donna.

'Good heavens!' she exclaimed.

'Hallo, Mrs Eyre. How are you?'

'Well, I never,' the woman babbled, laughing. 'Oh, I'm fine, your father didn't tell me you were coming, Donna—he must be getting absent-minded. Don't you look brown? No need to ask how you are. I can see. I'd say your hair's fairer than it used to be too; bleached by the sun, I suppose. I've never been to France. Is it very hot there? Good heavens, this is . . . well, I'm speechless. It's been such a long time. You've changed, yes, you have. But it's lovely to see you again. Come in, come in, we mustn't stand here all day, your father will be wanting to see you.'

Donna wasn't so sure about that. Brodie had just brought the cases from the car; his ironic eyes met hers as she glanced away from the housekeeper's excited face.

Attracted by the commotion in the hall, James Cowley suddenly came out of his study at the far end, pulling his glasses off, his eyes irritated.

'Really, Mrs Eyre! What is all the noise? You know I can't work with ...' His voice broke off as he recognised his daughter. 'Donna?' he whispered, as if unable to believe his eyes.

She hadn't expected to be so overthrown by seeing him. He looked older than she had remembered, older than she had feared. His hair had gone quite white, his face was thin and lined, and he looked ill. She could see the etching of pain on his face and winced. The neck rising out of his collar was hollowed, wrinkled, grey; his eyes had sunk deep into his head. If she had seen him from a distance she might not have known him.

'Hallo, Father,' she said huskily, going towards him to kiss him.

'You've come home?' he asked in a shaky voice as her lips brushed his face. His eyes were glistening; Donna had never known him to show emotion before, not to her. Brodie hadn't been lying to her—her father wasn't the same man. The change was deep-seated; his personality had been wrenched into other paths by the approach of death. Brodie was right—her father hadn't long to live. She couldn't speak, biting her lip and blinking back tears she was ashamed to shed, feeling an emotion she had not been taught to express. All her life her father had been a cold distant figure in the background. She didn't know how to respond to this stranger; involuntarily her eyes moved to Brodie, asking him to help her.

'I brought her back from Paris,' he said, reading the plea in her face as he put down the cases on the carpet.

James Cowley looked at him, his eyes widening. '*You* brought her back?' There was an odd, excited note in his voice, he began to smile and threw an arm around his daughter, hugging her awkwardly. It was the first time in many years that he had spontaneously shown her affection and he was self-conscious, very aware of it.

'My dear girl, this is wonderful news! Brodie, you've been very secretive, but never mind—I can't tell you how glad I am to see you two together again!'

Donna stiffened as she realised he was jumping to conclusions from what Brodie had said. She looked angrily at Brodie; eyes commanding him to tell her father he was wrong, to say or do something, not just stand there looking amused.

'When will . . .' James Cowley began, and suddenly broke off, gasping for breath, his hands clutching at his chest. Donna saw him sag at the knees and caught hold of him instinctively, going white.

'Father? What is it?'

Brodie got there before the older man fell to the floor. It was Brodie who caught his waist and lifted him over his shoulder, carrying him easily into the sitting-room, where he laid him down on the couch. 'Get the ambulance,' he threw over his shoulder at Mrs Eyre, who ran to the phone. 'Donna, top drawer in your father's desk, in the study—pills, run, get them. Gavin, get a glass of water, quickly, quickly, don't gape at me!'

Donna was already out of the room and into the study. She pulled open the top drawer in the desk and at once found the bottle of capsules. As she straightened she saw the photo on the desk: a studio portrait of herself, framed in silver. It had been taken when she was eleven; she had freckles across her nose and a gap between her teeth. She had totally forgotten the photograph until she saw it again.

She turned away biting her lip, and ran back to Brodie with the pills. Had that picture been on her father's desk for more then twelve years?

Brodie grabbed the pill bottle and shook out two capsules into his hand, looking round. 'Hurry up, Gavin!' he said impatiently as Gavin slowly came through the door.

James Cowley's eyes were shut; he breathed stertorously, his face grey. Donna found herself twisting her fingers behind her back like a child making a wish. Please God don't let him die, she thought with an intensity that amazed her. He mustn't, he mustn't! She stared fixedly at Brodie as he gently, deftly, lifted her father's head and helped him take the capsules with a swallow of water. Brodie knew what to do. He hadn't lost his head. She hated him, but in this crisis she had instinctively relied on him. He was that sort of man.

CHAPTER FOUR

DONNA fell asleep in the hospital waiting-room. When Brodie shook her gently she woke up, bewildered, staring at him with wide startled eyes. She had forgotten what had happened, where she was, for a few seconds. Then she remembered, and the flush of sleep ran out of her face.

'Is he . . .?'

'Sleeping,' Brodie told her quickly. 'He's stabilised, and the doctor's quite pleased with him.'

A sigh of relief made her shudder. She had been sitting there for hours waiting to hear how the fight for her father's life was going. She felt totally disorientated.

'There's no point in waiting, they won't let you see him,' Brodie told her. 'I'll drive you home now.'

'Home?' The word had a lost sound. He looked at her sharply.

'Come on, Donna. What you need is some breakfast and then you're going to bed. You know it's morning, or hadn't you noticed yet?'

The stark waiting-room was full of grey daylight, she realised with surprise. She hadn't noticed dawn; she must have slept through it.

'Where's Gavin?' she asked, frowning, looking around the room. Her brother had sat with her all night, but he had vanished now.

'He went for a walk to get some air half an hour ago. He said he'd get a taxi home.'

'And you let him go?' she asked angrily, immediately anxious.

'I'm not his keeper.'

'What if he runs away again?'

'With his father this ill? You don't think he'll do that, do you, Donna? I don't.' Brodie's voice was calmly assured. She wished she felt quite as sure about it. Gavin was unpredictable, especially when he was emotionally disturbed.

'He might do anything,' she muttered, following Brodie out of the waiting-room. The hospital was waking up; clangs and rattles came from all the wards, nurses walked quickly, their shoes squeaking, patients groaned to see another morning come so soon. There was a smell of hot fat from the vast kitchens on the ground floor as they made their way to the exit, and Donna's stomach protested. She was hungry and yet queasy. She didn't feel like food, although she hadn't eaten for many hours.

It was as they were driving away that she really looked at Brodie, noticing that his jaw carried a faint stubble. He hadn't shaved since yesterday morning and it was beginning to show.

'You look quite sinister,' she told him with faint malice.

He threw her a puzzled look. 'What?'

'You need a shave.'

He glanced into his driving-mirror, grimaced ruefully at what he saw and ran a hand around his chin. 'Distinctly dishevelled,' he agreed, then smiled teasingly at her. 'Have you seen yourself?'

She blinked. 'I'd rather not.'

Brodie laughed. 'Very wise. We both show signs of

wear and tear. It's been quite a night.'

She sighed and he put out a hand to her knee, patting it lightly. Donna flinched and he took his hand away, frowning.

They finished the drive back to the house in silence. Mrs Eyre opened the door to them, her face pale, eyelids red as if she had been up all night too, or had been crying.

'How is he?' she burst out.

'Comfortable,' said Brodie, smiling at her. 'Holding his own is how they put it, I think. It wasn't a major attack, thank God.'

Mrs Eyre looked at Donna. 'I'm so glad. You look very tired, you ought to go up to bed and catch up on your sleep.'

'I think we ought to have breakfast first,' said Brodie.

'No, I'm not hungry,' Donna said flatly.

'Some coffee and toast, Mrs Eyre—and a boiled egg?' Brodie ignored her protest. 'Orange juice? Fruit?'

Mrs Eyre vanished and Donna turned on him. 'I don't want any breakfast—do you really think I can eat after last night? I feel sick.'

'I think you ought to try. It will make everything feel more normal. Even if you just drink some milk and eat a slice or two of orange it would give your stomach something to do and stop you feeling as though your insides had turned to water.'

How had he known the way she felt? Donna eyed him moodily. She didn't like the way he seemed to guess what went on inside her; it made her feel exposed.

'You'll see, you'll be able to sleep after a light meal.'

Brodie pushed her into the downstairs bathroom. 'Go and wash your face and hands and come into the morning-room.'

She gave him a sulky look. 'Sure you don't want to check that I wash behind my ears?'

She didn't wait for an answer, she banged the bathroom door and ran the taps noisily. Splashing lukewarm water on her face made her wake up a little. She didn't bother to put on fresh make-up. She joined Brodie in the morning-room, her face clean and faintly flushed, her blonde hair combed and tidy.

The room was small and with early sunlight dancing across the pale green walls looked cool and yet bright. Brodie stood at the window, staring into the gardens.

Donna picked up the morning paper on the table and glanced without much interest at the headlines. Nothing much seemed to matter this morning. She felt a million miles from the rest of the world. Fear and emotional exhaustion did that to you; pushed you out of the herd, isolated you.

'I thought he was going to die,' she said suddenly, voice husky.

Brodie turned and smiled at her. 'I know. But he's a fighter—he wants to live now, that's a big help. You have to be motivated; to have a reason to live, Donna. And your father's got one now.'

She wasn't really listening. She was noticing that he had had a quick shave while she was in the bathroom. His skin looked smooth and cool; sunlight showed her the graining of his pores, the angle of cheekbone and jaw. Her senses reacted so sharply that she suddenly got angry.

'What are you talking about?' she demanded, scowling at him.

'He wants to be here to see his first grandson,' Brodie told her with teasing amusement.

'What?' She felt herself flushing. She had forgotten all about what had happened just before her father collapsed. Fear had wiped her memory clean. Now it came flooding back and her hands clenched at her sides.

'Where did he get that crazy idea? Did you tell him you were bringing me home? That we were going to get married after all?'

'I haven't been in touch since I left to catch up with Gavin! It was just wishful thinking on your father's part.' He still looked amused, though, and Donna resented that.

'Why didn't you tell him it wasn't true?'

'Why didn't you?' he countered drily.

'I was speechless!'

'So was I,' he said with a blandly grave expression, and her head almost exploded with fury.

'You liar! You thought it was a big joke, I can't think why!'

'If you'd seen your face you'd know why,' Brodie assured her.

She looked at him with intense dislike and said through her teeth, 'Well, because of your stupid sense of humour my father's got the wrong impression and how on earth are we going to tell him it isn't true?'

'We aren't,' he said coolly.

Mrs Eyre came into the room while Donna was digesting that remark. She deftly laid the table, apparently oblivious of the fact that they were staring at each other in a blank silence.

'Your eggs will be another two minutes,' she said, going out.

'Thank you, Mrs Eyre,' said Brodie.

The door shut behind her. Donna said in a hoarse voice, 'What do you mean, we aren't? Of course we must! Sooner or later he's got to realise it isn't true.'

'Not while he's in danger of having another heart attack,' said Brodie, sitting down at the table as casually as though they were merely discussing the weather. He poured himself some orange juice from the iced jug, then filled her glass, ice clinking as he poured.

'We've got to tell him,' whispered Donna, appalled.

'Do you want to run the risk of causing a relapse?' Brodie buttered a slice of toast, took a sip of juice.

She must have been slow-witted after all the worry of the last twenty-four hours, because it was only beginning to dawn on her now that she was caught in a trap.

She leaned on the back of her chair, biting her lip. 'But sooner or later he's got to know . . .'

'It will have to be later.' He began to eat his toast as though that disposed of the subject, and Donna stared at him, maddened by his air of cool assurance, by the blithe disregard of how she felt. Mounting anger seemed to press against the top of her skull; she saw him through a red mist of pure temper.

'If you think for one minute that I'm going to pretend I even like you, you're crazy!' she seethed, turning to leave the room.

Mrs Eyre reappeared with a tray and looked at Donna in surprise. 'Your eggs,' she said with a faintly pitying kindness, as if Donna was out of her mind but it was only to be expected under such strain.

Donna sulkily sat down, managing to mutter, 'Thank you,' as the housekeeper placed her eggs in front of her.

There was a barbed silence until Mrs Eyre had left the room. Donna didn't look up; she cut off the top of her egg and ate without really tasting a spoonful.

Only when she had finished the first egg did she ask, 'What are you going to do about the money Gavin took? You said it had to be back in the account before the auditors started work.'

'It is back.'

'How? When.' She stared at him incredulously.

Brodie poured himself some more coffee and refilled her cup. 'I put it back before I took off for Paris,' he answered as calmly as if he were giving her the latest weather forecast.

She made a strangled noise, her eyes enormous and her face dark red with fury.

'Something go down the wrong way?' he enquired in concern.

'You put it back *before* you came to Paris?'

'Eat your egg before it gets cold.'

'You lied to us!'

'Mrs Eyre won't be very happy if you don't.'

'Why didn't you tell Gavin? Why did you pretend you hadn't put it back?'

'This toast is cold,' he murmured, buttering another slice.

Donna slammed her chair back and got up. 'Will you answer me? Stop playing games!'

Brodie put down his toast and wiped his fingers on his napkin. 'You'd better go to bed and get some sleep. You're worn out.'

Her voice had a raw quality by then. 'Answer me!'

He leaned back in his chair, considering her with wry eyes. 'I replaced the money from my own account as soon as I realised Gavin had bolted. If I'd told him do you really think he would have learnt anything? I wanted to scare him into starting to think. Gavin has to learn to face up to himself, to the consequences of what he does. Why should he just lift sixteen thousand pounds and get away scot free?'

'Then why did you put it back?' she asked.

'Because I didn't want your father embarrassed by a public scandal.'

'You have no right to take over our lives like this!' she said hoarsely. 'Fixing this, fixing that, giving Gavin orders—pushing me around. Who the hell do you think you are?'

'You're tired, go to bed.' Brodie got up; a tall, lean man with a coolly impervious face set in lines of authority.

She resented him visibly, her eyes flashing with temper. 'Stop telling me what to do!'

'Don't be obstinate, Donna.'

'I'll be what I like, do what I like,' she muttered in confused irritation. 'I won't dance to your tune.'

'Won't you?' He was coming towards her and she found that far too disturbing. Sometimes Brodie reminded her so much of her father; that cool insistence on his own way, that ruthless self-assertion. She looked at him with hectic eyes.

'I want to have this out now. You're not manoeuvring me into pretending we're back together again!'

'What do you suggest we do? Walk into your father's room at the hospital and tell him he made a mistake, we aren't reconciled?' The dry voice made her nerve ends flicker with angry fire, but what he said had the deadly ring of fact. She couldn't do it, of course. She couldn't risk upsetting her father. She looked at him with homicidal yearning.

'I'd like to kill you!'

Brodie's eyes flashed; dark, burning blue, infinitely alarming. He took hold of her waist with one arm and lifted her bodily as if she were a featherweight, an arm under her back.

'Put me down!' she gasped, taken aback.

He took no notice, carrying her out of the room too fast for her to have time to grab anything to hit him with.

Mrs Eyre was coming across the hall. She stared in amazed consternation at Donna's wriggling, kicking body.

'I'm carrying her up to bed, she's feeling rather faint,' Brodie explained smoothly, smiling.

Donna made a noise like a kettle coming to the boil, but went limp and stopped struggling, under the housekeeper's curious gaze.

'Would she like a hot-water bottle? Some warm milk? If there's anything I can do . . .'

'Thank you, Mrs Eyre,' said Brodie, going up the stairs, one eye on Donna's brooding, ominous expression.

When they were out of earshot of the housekeeper she said tersely, 'One day . . .'

His mouth twisted. 'Yes, one day,' he murmured, and she had a sudden stab of apprehension as she heard the way he said that. What did he mean? Not what she had meant, she was sure of that.

He carried her into her own room and put her down on the bed, but he didn't move away, he knelt above her, holding her shoulders down on the pillows, his face inches from her own.

'Get out of my room,' muttered Donna avoiding his gaze. Her throat beat with a frantic pulse; she hoped he couldn't see it.

'Don't you want me to help you get undressed?' he taunted.

'Lay one finger on me and . . .' Her ragged voice died away in sheer confusion under his curling smile. He thought he was so funny!

'What's the matter, Donna? Why are you so worried about having me in your bedroom?' His eyes were fixed on her neck; she tried desperately to still the rapid beating of that telltale pulse. Her helpless reaction to him wouldn't matter so much if it weren't visible, but her body betrayed her all the time.

'Mrs Eyre will be shocked,' she muttered.

'I doubt it. We're both adults, and she thinks the same as your father, remember.'

'I'll tell her the truth!'

'Not until we've told your father,' he contradicted flatly. 'She might say the wrong thing to him, even if we warned her that it was all a mistake. We'll explain to her once your father knows, but not before.'

'No, that's going too far,' she said furiously, trying to sit up, but he held her down on the bed by the weight of that powerful body. 'Let go of me, will you? I won't be manhandled by you!'

He was too close; she didn't want to see his hard-boned face inches away from her. She didn't want to be forced to notice the pared strength of cheekbone and jaw, the sensual potential of that firm, male mouth. One brief glance was enough to send her stupid pulses wild again.

'She may talk about it, tell people—the next thing I know, I'll be reading the announcement in *The Times*.'

'You're overreacting,' Brodie assured her, but there was a glint in his eye that made her very nervous.

'Will you let go of me?' she mumbled, trying to unlock the grip of those strong hands. 'You're going to leave bruises on my shoulders.'

'Where? Let me see,' he said, his hands moving down to unbutton her shirt, putting on a contrite expression.

Donna knocked them away, seething. 'Get out of here!'

He sat up, one hand raking back his ruffled black hair. 'I'll tell Mrs Eyre to let you sleep, not to wake you. Don't worry about your father. I'll keep in touch with the hospital, and if there's any news I'll wake you up to hear it.'

'Aren't you going to sleep?' He had been awake all night too. He showed far less sign of that than she felt.

'I may catch an hour or two, but I have to go to the office. Today is the start of the annual audit.'

Her face lost colour. 'Oh, yes, I'd forgotten. You're sure the books are okay now?'

'Quite sure. They won't query the movement of a large sum in and out of the account—that's what the private account is for: a temporary transfer of funds without needing to go through the long rigmarole of using the company accounts. As long as the books balance and the money is accounted for, there will be no problem.'

'You might have told me that in Paris, instead of letting me worry myself sick about Gavin!' she snapped crossly.

'Would you have come back if I had?'

Donna lay there, her fair hair tumbled across the pillows, looking at him angrily.

'No!'

He shrugged. 'That's what I thought.'

'You're despicable,' she told him in a low, shaky voice.

'I had good reasons for wanting you to come back.' He unknotted his tie and Donna stiffened, watching him warily.

'So that I could persuade my father to make Gavin see a psychiatrist, you said—what was the real reason?'

And why was he undoing his shirt collar? she wondered, but didn't ask because if he laid one finger on her again she'd scream until not merely Mrs Eyre but the whole village came running to find out what was going on.

'That was one very good reason,' he said casually, unbuttoning the rest of his shirt.

'What do you think you're doing?' she burst out, ready to jump off the bed if he came any closer.

'I'm just going to have a bath,' he said, getting up. He paused, eyeing her taken-aback expression. 'What did you think I was going to do?'

'Oh, get out!' yelled Donna, throwing a pillow at him. Brodie went, grinning, and it didn't make her feel any happier to follow him to the door and bolt it once he was outside.

She slid out of her clothes, tense with rage. She might have known that Brodie was up to something. He had been lying to her and Gavin—playing some complex game of his own and using Gavin's folly to trap them both. She had been a fool to take his bait and let him lure her back here. She had been on her guard from the minute she set eyes on him, but it hadn't done her much good. She had still fallen for his plausible lies, exactly as she had before.

But what was behind it this time? Naked, she paused, her face stiffening, 'Oh, no,' she whispered. 'He couldn't . . .'

He couldn't still hope to talk her into marrying him? Could he?

Hadn't she made her views on him very clear two years ago? He must have armour-plating to be able to forget what she had said to him, the insults she had hurled at him. How could he think he would ever get her to marry him, after that?

She went over to find a nightdress in the tall Georgian chest of drawers. Mrs Eyre had unpacked her clothes and put them neatly away. She pulled a short white cotton nightshirt out and was about to drop it over her head when she caught sight of her reflection in the long mirror in the corner of the room.

That was when she saw that her breasts had hardened; the nipples darkly pigmented against the pale gold of her flesh. She closed her eyes angrily, bitter stabs of desire penetrating her. Brodie wasn't stupid. He must have known what was happening to her while he held her down on the bed, watching her with those hooded blue eyes. She hated and despised him, but he was in her bloodstream. She had told herself for two years that she was free of the disease; cured for ever. She had lied, deceived herself. At the first opportunity it got the addiction had resurfaced; the yearning had begun again. From the minute she saw him in her apartment in Paris, she had been torn apart by the old craving. A few minutes ago she had felt it so painfully that she had had a hard job of hiding it, but Brodie was far too clever not to have picked up her hidden feelings.

If he did realise that in spite of her anger and her open dislike, she still felt a deep attraction towards him, it would explain why he hadn't given up on the idea of marrying her. He had made it clear that Gavin was never going to run the firm, but Gavin and herself would inherit the family shares, controlling the company. Brodie would want those shares badly. Without them his hold on control was weak. Once their father was out of the way they could always get rid of Brodie.

She pulled the nightshirt over her head and ran both hands over her weary, disturbed face. She felt almost as distraught as she had two years ago, when she first found out the sort of man Brodie Fox really was. She had been on the point of getting engaged to him when she met a girl as a party given by old friends of Brodie's. Donna had gone alone, but Brodie had promised to meet her there—he had been held up by a strike threat at one of the factories.

Brodie's friends were a married couple—Tom Reed, a wealthy stockbroker, and his wife Jinny. They lived in a spectacular house in Virginia Water and made a big fuss of Donna, insisting on showing her around, making sure that she had a glass of champagne and a plate of delicious hors d'oeuvres, introducing her to other guests. While she was circulating, chatting to people, she kept seeing another girl who didn't come over to her but who watched her oddly from a distance. What struck Donna was the other girl's beauty—it was the opposite of her own and far more obvious. Tall, sexily dressed in a scarlet silk dress, she had rich silky black hair and liquid black eyes—her figure was attracting quite a bit of attention, but she seemed indifferent to the men who kept trying to chat her up.

Donna perched on a window-seat when she was tired of wandering around the room and a moment later the other girl came over.

'You're Donna Cowley, aren't you?'

Donna gave her an uncertain smile. 'Yes, how did you know?'

'I've seen a picture of you. I'm Christabel Clair, by the way.'

Donna did a double-take, realising then why the other girl had been so familiar—Christabel Clair was a well-known photographic model.

'I should have recognised you,' she had said, offering her hand. 'I knew I'd seen that face somewhere. Where did you see a picture of me? I'm not famous.'

Christabel had hesitated before offering her own hand and her fingers had been icy cold.

'Brodie showed me a picture of you.' Something in the quiet bitterness of the voice made Donna freeze. As if she had a premonition she felt like getting down off the window-seat and running away, but she was too sensible to give in to such crazy impulses, so she went on smiling politely.

'Brodie? You're another friend of his?'

Christabel gave a hard laugh. 'A friend? No, I wouldn't call myself that, exactly.' She suddenly lifted her right hand and Donna stared blankly. Christabel was wearing a ring on it; one big diamond surrounded by a number of smaller ones. It glittered as she moved her hand: cold, icy, beautiful.

'He gave me that.'

Donna's mouth had gone dry with fear. She had looked from the ring to the girl's lovely face, and that was when she saw the hostility behind Christabel's tight smile.

'I thought of sending it back after he broke off our engagement but I was too angry.'

Donna swallowed, shaken. 'You were engaged to Brodie? When?'

Christabel kept her eyes on Donna's pale face; her smile was acid now. 'For six months before he met you—we were going to be married last week. I'd even bought my wedding-dress. But then he was introduced to you and decided I wasn't good enough for him.' She snapped open the little silver evening-bag she was carrying in one hand and produced a folded piece of paper. 'He sent me that the day after he first met you.'

Donna hadn't wanted to take the paper, drawing back from it, but Christabel had impatiently pushed it into her hand. 'Read it! Go on, read it! You ought to know what Brodie's really like. I've no doubt he's fooled you the way he fooled me!'

Pale, her fingers trembling, Donna had unfolded the creased piece of paper. It had been written on the firm's stationery, and she recognised Brodie's handwriting. There was no doubt about it, he had written it. It was a brutally brief note. First a scrawled date—she hadn't needed to check her diary to realise that Christabel had spoken the truth; Brodie had written this the day after he first met Donna. That had been a landmark in her life, she couldn't have been mistaken about that date, the day she first met Brodie. Below the date a few callous words.

We won't be getting married, Christabel. It's over. I don't want to see you again, and don't make a fuss, it wouldn't do any good. I'm going to marry someone else.

She had stood there, staring at his name; hurried black scrawl right across the paper. Brodie.

Christabel had taken the note back abruptly, and Donna had looked up, blank-faced with shock.

'You had what I couldn't give him,' Christabel had said bitterly. 'Money, status, a future—I didn't have any of them. I hadn't made it in modelling then; I was just getting a few jobs. Brodie's ambitious, he couldn't wait to see how my career worked out. He's always been in a hurry to get to the top and you looked like an easier ladder, but if I'd been the one with money he'd have stayed with me, I'm certain of it. We were terrific in bed—it really worked with us. You'll never turn him on the way I did, for all your money.' She looked Donna up and down, her lips curling, 'I'm sorry for you, Miss Cowley. If you love him, you're going to have a tough life with him. I'd think again if I were you. You may buy Brodie, but you'll never own him.'

She had laughed, then turned on her heel and walked away, and Donna had sat there white-faced for a while until she felt able to walk away herself. She had somehow managed to smile politely at her hostess and explain that she had a headache and couldn't wait for Brodie any more. She was going home, Jinny had looked worried and asked if there was anything she could do—Donna had wondered if Jinny had noticed Christabel talking to her and been shaken. No doubt all his friends knew Brodie had been engaged before; no doubt they had all been whispering about it behind her back, wondering how long it would be before she found out.

She had forced a smile and said it had been a lovely party, she'd had a wonderful time, but she had to go now, her headache was so bad. Jinny had followed her to the front door, still concerned, and Donna had been deeply relieved to get away from her, from the bright lights and laughter, the music and cheerful voices. She had driven home and gone to bed, and next morning she had gone away for a couple of days to give herself time to think.

She knew she couldn't marry Brodie after discovering that he had so callously broken an engagement to another girl as soon as he had met someone richer. That wasn't what she had to decide.

The question was: *how* should she tell him she wouldn't marry him? She could simply tell him she knew about Christabel, had read that note, knew the whole story—but that would be so humiliating, it would tell him she was hurt and jealous and angry. It would make him think that all he had to do was soothe her down, reassure her, wind her round his little finger.

If she didn't tell him why she no longer wanted to marry him what *was* she to say? And how was she going to explain to her father that she wasn't going through with the marriage?

After two days of sleepless thinking and crying and coming up with no answer she had gone home and Brodie had been with her father.

Oddly, it had been very easy. Brodie had wanted to know where she had been—and with whom. He had been dark with rage.

Her father had been glowering at his side; in one of his more icily bullying moods.

Donna had refused to tell them where she had been or why or with whom; she had refused to tell them anything. Her father had stamped out, saying, 'You talk to her, Brodie. Get some sense out of her.'

Brodie had demanded an answer, but Donna had refused to give one. Instead she had taken off his ring and thrown it at him, then she had told him at length what she thought of him. She hadn't known that she could be so fluent. She hadn't realised until then the painful depth of her hurt and her anger.

Brodie had stiffened as he listened; first white, then an angry dark red, staring at her as if he couldn't believe his ears. She hadn't given him a chance to interrupt, to ask any questions, to protest. When she finally ran out of insults she turned on her heel and walked out, slamming the door behind her.

Of course, that hadn't been the end of it. Neither Brodie nor her father could believe she meant it. They saw her outburst as a fit of female rage. They tried to soothe her, to coax and wheedle her, to find out what had happened, why she had turned against Brodie so suddenly.

Donna had become silent; obstinate, dogged. She had made her arrangements without telling them what she meant to do and then one day left for Paris. Her French had always been good; she decided to become fluent and get a job in France, where she had always felt at home. She had known she couldn't stay in London, where she ran the risk of seeing Brodie all the time. She had to put space between them if she was to learn to forget him. Over the past two years she had been stupid enough to think she had managed it; that Brodie was just a dark shadow in her past, locked away and forgotten.

Now she knew how wrong she had been—Brodie wasn't locked away. He had sprung out, like a jack-in-the-box, and Donna wasn't safe any more. If Brodie had guessed that, she was in more danger than she had ever been before, because this time if he turned on the heat she might wake up to find herself married to a man she did not trust or like but who had a dangerous power over her senses.

CHAPTER FIVE

DONNA didn't wake up until the middle of the afternoon. After a cool shower she dressed in a pair of white cotton trousers and a blue tabard, put on some make-up and went downstairs. She found Gavin in the garden wandering around with his hands in his pockets and a worried look on his face.

'Oh, hi!' he said, turning to face her. 'Had a good sleep?'

'Yes—where did you get to this morning?'

He shrugged. 'Went for a walk. I needed to think, and I don't find that easy around Brodie Fox.'

'No,' she accepted, her mouth taut. 'I was worried about you.'

Gavin grimaced at her. 'Sorry, Sis.'

'Have you seen Brodie since you got back?'

He nodded. 'We had a talk.'

'Did he tell you about the money?'

'Yes. He says there's no need for Father to hear about it now, so long as I stay put and don't run off again.' Gavin stared at her, his eyes fixed and strained. 'I can't go back to that office, Donna, I couldn't bear it. What am I going to do?'

'Did you tell Brodie how you felt about the job?' She didn't need to see him shake his head; she had known Gavin wouldn't be able to talk to Brodie, any more than he could bring himself to talk frankly to their father.

'What's the point, anyway? I'm not trained for

anything else. I should have done what you did—got out and got myself some training.' Gavin put a casual arm around her, making a face. 'I respect you for that, you know, Donna. Leaving, taking time to study and then doing a difficult job—I admire you for it. I wish I'd had the guts to do it, but I've never been able to stand up to Father.'

'Father isn't here,' Donna pointed out.

Gavin looked sharply at her, puzzled. 'Well, I know, but he's going to be coming back home quite soon. I mean, it wasn't a serious attack, was it? Brodie said he'd be home within ten days or so, although he'd have to take it easy.'

'Ten days is a long time,' Donna pointed out. 'There's a lot you can do in ten days—you could start seeing a specialist who'd help you fight that addiction to gambling.' She felt Gavin stiffen, pull away. She wound her hand through his arm and held on to him, going on lightly, 'You could investigate glass-blowing, find out where you could get some training.'

He laughed impatiently. 'You're kidding—I'm too old to start an apprenticeship.'

'How do you know? Have you checked up on it? You could go to a technical college and train—aren't there colleges who take older students? Gavin, sitting around daydreaming won't get you anywhere. You've got to get out there, make your dream a reality. Okay, if you find it's too hard or you just can't bring yourself to make the effort, at least you'll know yourself a little better. But whatever you do, you must get help with the gambling. It will ruin your whole life if you don't. It's a sickness, like alcoholism—it isn't your fault you've got it, but it will be your fault if you don't do something to get help.'

His mouth was turned down at the edges in sullen resistance. 'What are you saying? That I'm crazy? I'm not crazy, I just like to get away from here, grab a little excitement.'

'You know it isn't just that.'

Her grave voice made him angry. 'Oh, why don't you mind your own business! You know nothing about it.'

He pulled free and walked back towards the house, his fair hair gilded by the late afternoon sunlight. It gave him a halo. Donna stared after him, sighing. She hadn't done that very well. It wasn't going to be easy to talk Gavin into having treatment, and she hadn't been as tactful as she should have been.

She began to follow him, but found herself suddenly facing Brodie. 'Mrs Eyre thought she'd seen you out here,' he said, standing between her and the garden door through which Gavin had just gone. 'I just came from the hospital—your father's condition is quite stable now. They're pleased with the progress he's making.'

'I know,' she said shortly. 'I rang the hospital as soon as I got up.'

He was wearing a pale grey suit with a formal grey and white striped city shirt and a stiff white collar. The clothes were as immaculate and as expensive as all his others, and again she wondered how he could afford to spend like that. She knew so little about him, she realised. What had he done before he joined their firm? She had a vague idea that he had worked for another similar firm in the north, but Brodie had never been very forthcoming. He didn't talk about himself or his past—with good reason, no doubt.

'They thought he shouldn't have visitors until

tomorrow,' said Brodie.

'I know, they told me.'

His eyes raked her cold face. 'What's wrong now?'

Her eyes rejected his curiosity. 'I don't have anything to say to you, that's all.' She moved to walk past and he side-stepped, blocking her way again.

'There's one thing you might tell me,' His voice was dry.

'What's that?'

'Why you changed your mind about me two years ago.' He sounded calm; his curiosity was purely academic. She hadn't hurt him, because he had never felt anything for her. Marrying her had been good business strategy; it had gone wrong, and Brodie would like to know why so that he wouldn't make the same mistake twice. He was a clever man; he learnt from his mistakes, unlike Gavin—and herself. They were both idiots, it seemed; they couldn't shed their follies so easily, or live the way their minds dictated. They were stupid enough to follow their hearts; that made you weak and vulnerable, especially to people like Brodie Fox.

'I realised what a mistake I was making,' Donna said curtly. 'I thought I'd made that clear at the time.' She didn't want to see too much of him while she was back here; she was afraid of what she might have betrayed in her room a few hours ago. Brodie didn't need to have a diagram drawn—she was afraid he might have picked up enough clues already.

'Oh, you were very clear,' said Brodie, his mouth tense.

She shrugged 'Well then!' She tried to walk past again, but he wasn't letting her get away that easily. He caught her arm between finger and thumb and she looked down at it distastefully as if it were an insect landing on her.

'Get that off!' She flicked her fingers at it, trying to look cool. She did not want him to pick up any more echoes of her emotional reactions to him. Her face must not give anything away. He had once acted well enough to convince her that he loved her; surely she could act an icy indifference to him?

'I was too numb to think straight at the time,' said Brodie, without releasing her. 'It was only later that it dawned on me that I didn't really know why you turned against me, what I'd done to make you look at me as if you hated me.'

'You were just yourself, I suppose,' Donna said with acid sweetness, baring her teeth at him. 'And I'd realised a little late what sort of man you really are.'

'No,' he said tersely, shaking his head. 'Something must have happened. Something triggered it. What?' His finger and thumb held her like pincers; she winced, pulling her arm away.

She was free now, but made the mistake of going in the wrong direction. Instead of making for the house she backed further into the garden and Brodie advanced, making her agitation deepen.

'I thought about it for weeks,' he said in that cool, deep voice. 'I went over everything that had happened before you told me it was off—looking for the significant break in the pattern. There's always one; a moment when something breaks and after that things are different, whether you're talking about a stock-market graph or a love affair. Everything was fine between us that spring, but then it dawned on me that just before you went off on your own you went to a party at Tom Reed's place.'

Donna stiffened, paling. She should have realised that he would try to work it out; he was brilliant with tiny detail. Her father had often said so, Brodie was a man with a careful, complex mind. He hadn't just let it go; he had worried at the problem. Had he come up with the right solution?

'I never made it to the party, did I? I got called in to settle a strike at one of the factories—I remembered then that I'd rung you at Tom's and he said you'd just left. He made a joke about it—said I'd lose you if I didn't pay you more attention. He was kidding, but when I thought back to that night, after you'd gone to Paris, I wondered if he hadn't hit on the explanation.'

Her eyes flickered away to hide the relief in them. Brodie hadn't found out that she had met Christabel Clair that night, after all. Obviously Tom Reed hadn't noticed them talking. Or had he deliberately left out that telltale detail? Why had Christabel been at the party, anyway? The Reeds must have known about her engagement to Brodie. If they were friends of his, why had they invited Christabel along when they knew that Brodie and his new fiancée were going to be there too?

'Was that it, Donna?' asked Brodie, an odd roughness in his voice. 'Didn't I take you seriously enough? Did you think I cared more about the firm than you?'

She took another step backwards, disturbed by the note in his voice, as well as by her own thoughts. Had the Reeds been involved in what happened that night? Had they deliberately set up a meeting between herself and Christabel? Why would they do that?

'I didn't think—I knew,' she said coldly. 'You wanted to marry me because it would make you father's son-in-law, but that wasn't why I walked out. I went for my own reasons—because I suddenly knew I couldn't bear being your wife.'

His eyes glittered in a taut, hard face. 'Just like that?'

'I'd thought I wouldn't mind marrying you to please my father,' she lied hurriedly, shaken by that expression, 'but I woke up and realised I didn't have to let him run my life for ever. I knew you just wanted to marry me for business reasons, you're ambitious and cold-blooded enough to go through with something like that—but I'm not, and once I'd realised what a crazy mistake it would be I knew I had to get out of it.'

He was breathing harshly, his brows black and drawn above those ominous eyes. 'Cold-blooded?' he repeated through his teeth. 'You think I'm cold-blooded, do you? Maybe it's time you discovered how wrong you are!' His hands shot out and grabbed her shoulders, pulling her toward him in spite of her struggle to get free.

'Don't,' she muttered hoarsely, terrified of what would happen if he kissed her. She would lose her head, he would know she had lied about how she felt. He must not kiss her. She kicked him and he gave a grunt of pain, his hold on her slackening enough to allow her to break away, and this time she remembered to run towards the house instead of away from it.

Brodie came after her, but as she shot through the French windows into the sitting-room she ran straight into Gavin, who looked at her in surprise.

'Where's the fire?'

A second later Brodie burst into the room, and Gavin

stared at him with hard eyes, comprehension coming into his face.

Brodie stood still, staring back at him. 'I want to talk to your sister alone, Gavin.'

'No way,' said Gavin with sudden angry malice. 'Leave her alone, she wants nothing to do with you. How many times do you have to be told? Do you want it in writing?'

Brodie's hard-boned face radiated pure rage. 'Don't take that tone with me, Gavin! This has nothing to do with you.'

'While I'm around, you won't push my sister into doing anything she doesn't want to do,' snapped Gavin, bristling at the dismissive contempt in Brodie's voice. 'You dont scare either of us. You may have a lot of pull with our father, but as far as we're concerned you can drop dead!'

Donna slid her hand into her brother's and Gavin held it tightly, looking at her sideways. 'Okay, kid, no panic. I'll deal with him.' There was complacency in his voice, he grinned at her, cocksure and pleased with himself for having defied Brodie. He had never dared to defy their father. She couldn't remember him tackling Brodie head on before, either. This must be a first for Gavin, and he was enjoying it.

Brodie watched them both, his mouth crooked. After a pause he walked past them out of the room, and Gavin swung her hand to and fro, laughing.

'Hey! He backed down. What do you know?'

'Thank you,' she said, smiling indulgently at him.

'If you have any more trouble from him, let me know,' Gavin boasted, squaring his narrow shoulders. There was a flush in his face; a flush of triumph. 'That will teach him to push women around—he'll have me to deal with in future if he tries again!'

'I'll keep out of his way,' she thought aloud.

Gavin sobered. 'That won't be easy. He's moved into the house while Father's in hospital.'

'What?' Her voice rose sharply and Gavin shrugged, looking at her helplessly.

'He did that last time Father had an attack—Brodie said it was so that he would be close to the hospital and able to get there fast if anything happened. It takes so long to drive from London.'

'Did he just move in without your permission?' asked Donna, frowning.

'Can you see him asking my permission for anything? No, he just moved in and I knew Father would approve, so there was no point in arguing. Anyway, Brodie often stays here at weekends. He and Father shut themselves in the study and talk business for hours. He uses this house like a second home.'

'Or a hotel,' Donna said tersely. The thought of having Brodie under the same roof made her blood run cold. 'What about the office? Will he be commuting from here every day?'

'Why would he tell me? Last time he didn't go into the office for a couple of days, until Father was out of danger, I remember. He was on the phone most of the time, doing business from here.'

'And Father just lets him do as he pleases,' she mused, frowning blackly.

'You know Brodie's the sort of son he really wanted,' Gavin muttered, and she looked at him with anxious compassion.

'He loves you, Gavin, I'm sure he does—in some

ways the two of you are very alike.'

Gavin laughed shortly. 'Are you being funny? I'm nothing like Father.'

'You don't recognise it because you can't see yourself, but you both have similar personalities, and that may be why you don't hit it off some of the time. Father resents the very qualities in you that he has himself; that's why he keeps nagging at you to change.'

'You're crazy,' Gavin said, but he looked shaken. Perhaps subconsciously he had always known that he was rather like his father; he might not want to admit it, but wouldn't he secretly be aware of it?

He gave her a quick, almost furtive look, smiling shyly. 'I thought over what you said about finding out about courses in glass-blowing. You may have something there. I might check it out.' His voice was casual, throw-away, deliberately off-hand.

Donna didn't want to be too eager. She smiled back. 'Great!' Having put the idea into his head she would let him work it out without further interference. What Gavin really needed was to start running his own life without dictation from their father or Brodie. It might actually help him to realise that their father wasn't as perfect as Gavin had always believed.

'But I'm not seeing any doctors,' Gavin said flatly.

She didn't argue. She had to feel her way towards trying to persuade him into thinking about it. Gavin had the obstinacy of the weak—she suddenly wondered if he had the weakness of the strong, too. Was that why he had always let their father order him around? Gavin obviously wanted another sort of life than the one he had always had. His admission that he had always had a secret ambition to be a craftsman, blow glass of a very different sort, showed that. Did he gamble to fill an emptiness in his life? Their father had a drive towards success which he had channelled into his business. If Gavin had the same drive but was drawn to other fields he must have been angry and frustrated ever since he began to grow up, but however much he resented his father's tyranny he hadn't actually walked out as she had. He had stayed there, pleasing neither their father nor himself. Why?

She looked at him thoughtfully. Could it be that Gavin loved their father too much to break with him openly as she had done?

'I'm hungry,' she said. 'Have you eaten? Did you sleep, by the way?'

'For a couple of hours,' he admitted. 'I don't find it easy to get to sleep in daylight. I had a sandwich and some coffee when I got up, but I wouldn't say no to another snack if you're having one.'

'Let's go into the kitchen and see what we can find,' she said, 'Mrs Eyre won't mind if I borrow her domain for a little while. She used to let me learn to cook with her, do you remember?'

'I remember eating some rock-hard fairy cakes you made,' Gavin teased.

'What a lie! They were delicious!'

Gavin laughed at her. 'Well, I survived the experiment, but to be on the safe side why don't we have something simple, like beans on toast, today?'

The kitchen was empty. Donna hunted through the rows of tins in the pantry until she found some baked beans, then she handed the tin to Gavin to open while she cut some bread and popped it into the toaster. Gavin put the saucepan of beans on the hob and they found themselves some plates and knives and forks. It was a long time since they had relaxed together like this. As children they had been very close. Growing up had meant growing away, too, keeping secrets from each other, no longer sharing everything.

They ate in the kitchen and had just finished their snack when Mrs Eyre came bustling into the kitchen with a basket of freshly picked soft fruit from the orchard at the bottom of the garden. She stopped in surprise, seeing them.

'We just had some beans on toast,' Donna told her, feeling she had to apologise for being in the housekeeper's kitchen.

'If I'd known you were hungry, I'd have got you something,' said Mrs Eyre. 'You only had to ask, I'd have been happy to do it.'

'It was fun doing it ourselves,' Gavin murmured, and the housekeeper softened, giving him a fond look. She had always had a weak spot for Gavin.

'Well, is there anything else I can get you?' She took their plates and put them in the sink. Donna and Gavin shook their heads, getting up, feeling they were being politely but firmly turned out of the room.

'I'm going to make a summer pudding for your dinner,' Mrs Eyre told her, seeing Donna glance at the basket of fruit.

'Would you like some help with preparing the currants?'

'No, thank you, Donna, I can manage. That's my job.' Mrs Eyre had never liked having her in the kitchen. Donna had got under her feet too much. Occasionally, Mrs Eyre would let her spend an hour there, learning to cook something, but more often she would say she was too busy and push her out of the room. Donna had had to learn all her housewifery when she began living in an apartment in Paris. That was the first time she had ever been given the chance to find out what domestic skills she could acquire.

In the hall, Gavin looked at his watch. 'What time does the library shut? I thought I might drive over there and see if they have any books on glass-blowing.' He was self-conscious, a little sheepish, his ears pink.

'What a good idea! You might try the bookshop if the library haven't got any books. Oh, I just thought—why don't you ask the library if they've got a list of the classes the technical school are giving: I remember when Mrs Eyre did pottery at evening class one year she asked me to get her a leaflet from the library—they usually have the syllabus handouts on the counter at this time of year, because the classes start in the middle of September.'

Gavin went off, nodding, and Donna heard his car start up a few moments later. She wandered idly around the house, looking at familiar objects with a strange sense of *déjà vu*—nothing had been moved let alone changed. While she was in Paris her father's life had gone on just the same, although she wasn't there. The thought made her sombre. Paris seemed so far away; her two years there had flown. Yet she had come back here to find exactly what she had left behind.

Mrs Eyre knocked on the sitting-room door a few minutes later. 'I'm just going shopping, is there anything I can get you?'

Donna shook her head, smiling politely. 'No, thanks.'

'I'll only be half an hour or so,' Mrs Eyre told her. 'Mr

Brodie should be around, if you need him. I saw him going upstairs.'

She vanished before Donna had realised what she had said. Brodie was still here? She had thought he must have gone out. With a shock it dawned on her that they were alone in the house. She simply couldn't face him again—the last time had been traumatic enough. She tiptoed into the hall, listening intently for any sound. She would go down into the orchard where she would be safely out of view of the house and stay there until either Gavin or Mrs Eyre got back. Brodie was bound to assume that she had gone off with one of them.

As she was creeping across the hall the telephone began to shrill and she froze, mid-step, shooting an apprehensive glance towards the stairs. What if Brodie came down to answer that? As if in reply, he called from somewhere upstairs. 'Mrs Eyre! Answer that for me, would you? It's probably my call to the office—tell them I'll be down in two minutes, ask them to hang on until I get there. I'm just getting a file from my room.'

Donna bit her lip. If she didn't pick up the phone he would probably come down to find out why it was still ringing. She ran back across the hall to the nearest phone and lifted it.

'Can I speak to Mr Fox please?' a woman's voice said langourously.

Donna's brows lifted. Was that his secretary? She sounded more like a *femme fatale*. Perhaps a telephone manner which was seductive had been one of the qualities he had insisted on for his secretary? Perhaps it wasn't merely on the telephone that she had to be seductive, Donna thought viciously.

'He isn't here at the moment,' she said in a voice tipped with ice. 'Can you ring again later?'

There was a pause. 'Could you ask him to ring Christabel as soon as possible, please?'

Donna took a sharp breath, her body stiffening. 'Christabel?' she repeated huskily, as if not sure she'd heard correctly.

'Yes, he knows my number,' the purring voice said.

There was a click. She had hung up. Donna slowly replaced her own phone, staring down at it as if it were a snake. Brodie was seeing that woman again—which meant that the affair wasn't over after all. He had gone back to Christabel the minute Donna was out of the picture.

Her mind raced like an overheated engine; coming up with one conclusion after another. He had gone back to Christabel and she had been ready to forget and forgive, had she? No doubt she had been waiting with open arms, damn her. Was that what she had been banking on when she came up at that party? Had she been hoping that by dropping a little poison in Donna's ear, she would get Brodie back?

And it looked as if she had been right! Oh, she had been clever, Miss Christabel Clair! What woman could have listened to what she said without feeling the sting of jealousy?

Donna had never forgotten a syllable of that conversation at Tom Reed's party. The words had been burnt into her brain. She had woken up at night, long afterwards, remembering them, maddened by them.

'We were terrific in bed, it really worked for us. You'll never turn him on the way I did.'

Donna groaned, closing her eyes, her teeth grating.

She hadn't wanted to believe it, even in the first shock of hearing it—but Christabel's smile had carried such conviction. Her black eyes had glittered—she had eyes that knew everything, and a body that advertised her knowledge. A full, luscious red mouth; rich black curls; a body charged with sexuality—Donna had looked at her and felt positively naïve. Christabel's stare had dismissed her scornfully, given Donna back the reflection of herself that she had taken to Paris with her and brooded over jealously for months. Compared with Christabel she had felt small and pale and washed out; an insignificant little mouse.

A thud of feet on the stairs made her jerk back to the present. She began to hurry towards the kitchen, to escape, but Brodie appeared on the stairs and looked down at her.

'Did you answer the phone?'

She nodded, unable to say a word.

'Was it for me?'

Her lips parted and snapped off the one word. 'Yes.'

'Are they hanging on?' He glanced along the hall.

'No.'

'Who was it?' he asked, looking curiously at her, puzzled by her grim expression.

'Christabel,' she said, the name hurled at him. She saw him start, caught the flicker of alarm in his deceitful blue eyes. He pulled himself together quickly. Of course he would; he had had plenty of practice at lying. The more you did something, the better you got at it, and Brodie must be a past master at deceit by now.

'Did she say what she wanted?' he asked casually.

Donna held on to her self-control. She wasn't going to scream jealously at him; she had more self-respect.

She wouldn't laugh bitterly, either, much as she felt like it, or tell him scathingly that he knew damned well what Christabel wanted—and what he no doubt gave her in private from time to time when he wasn't too busy. How could Christabel accept her situation? If their engagement was on again, Brodie had managed to keep it very private, and he couldn't have married Christabel without it getting to James Cowley's ears. Their affair was hole-and-corner, furtive, hidden from all Brodie's friends.

If Donna hadn't disliked her so intensely, she might have felt sorry for the other girl, but she wasn't saintly enough for that.

'She wants you to ring her back,' she said icily. 'She said you knew her number.'

Brodie shrugged. 'I don't suppose it's urgent.' He came down the stairs, apparently unaware of the fact that she was looking at him with loathing. 'Where's Mrs Eyre?'

'Out.'

'And Gavin?'

It was only then that she caught the glimmer in his eyes, the watchful little smile that meant he knew Gavin had gone out. Had he seen him go in his car?

'He's out too,' she said defiantly. If he thought for one second that being alone in the house with her was going to give him a chance to get at her, he could think again! Five minutes ago she had been agitated and on edge at the prospect, but that had been before Christabel rang. Now, Donna would have no problem keeping him at bay if they were marooned on a desert island for weeks.

'So we're alone,' Brodie said softly, coming closer

and looking at her through his thick black lashes, a coaxing smile curving his mouth. She eyed him coldly. Did he really think she would fall for that obvious stuff?

'What am I supposed to do now? Swoon?' she asked sarcastically.

If she had hoped to surprise him or deflate him she was disappointed. Brodie merely laughed as if he thought she was playing hard to get, running so that he could follow.

'I promised to prove something to you, didn't I?' he murmured, close enough to touch her now and looking down at her, a mocking threat lurking in the depths of his eyes.

Donna didn't get the point at first; they were thinking at cross-purposes. She had Christabel on her mind. Brodie had something very different, as she realised too late.

'Prove . . . what?' she stammered, thinking for one stupid instant that he was about to tell her about Christabel, deny it all, give her some plausible explanation which, of course, she wouldn't believe, but which she half hoped he might make at least half convincing.

'That I'm not cold-blooded,' he whispered an inch from her mouth.

She saw too late where he had been leading and tried to get away, but his arms had gone round her waist and as she twisted in his grip his mouth burrowed into her throat, just below her ear, the brush of his lips warm and tormenting. Her whole body seemed to shiver; every cell melting, her pulses wild with fever and her breathing totally haywire.

'Let go,' she mumbled almost inaudibly as his kiss travelled upwards, searching for her mouth. She was terrified by the waves of excitement pounding through her. She didn't want to feel like this. Was she so weak-minded that she could just forget what sort of man he was the minute he took her in his arms?

Still holding her with one arm, Brodie took her chin in his other hand and firmly drew her head round. Donna's eyes opened, she hadn't known they were shut until then. She looked dazedly at him, saw his hard face poised above her for a second. Those narrowed eyes watching her seemed to read her emotions at a glance, then his mouth descended and she was lost.

She had almost forgotten the sensual power of his kiss; it was a revelation to her, behind her closed lids flashed a lightning which lit up her own feelings and Brodie's power over her. His mouth moved hotly, possessive and demanding, and Donna was helpless to halt her own hungry response to him. Her body swayed yieldingly, her arms going round his neck, and she kissed him back with a sensuality which matched his.

Brodie lifted his head a moment later and Donna heard the ragged drag of his breathing above the hoarseness of her own—they sounded like people saved from drowning, their bodies weakly leaning on each other.

Her eyes drowsily opened and saw dimly. Dusk had invaded the house; she stared up Brodie, still clinging to him, her mind completely off balance, as if she were waking from a dream.

His eyes smiled. 'Did I prove my point?'

She didn't know what he meant—everything that had happened before he kissed her seemed a million light-years back in the past.

'I'm not cold-blooded,' he reminded her huskily, and bent his head to kiss her neck, a sharp desire in the way his lips burnt on her skin. 'I want you, Donna,' he muttered, his hands moving, touching her passionately.

She still had her eyes open and now her mind was working, too. She remembered Christabel's phone call with a stab of pain. How could she have been so weak-willed, so stupid? She had been complacently telling herself that she was armoured against him, he wouldn't get to her again—but one kiss and he was under her skin, back in her bloodstream. Hadn't he hurt her enough two years ago? She must be a masochist to come back for more, clinging to him like this, begging him to hurt her again.

Cold-blooded? Wasn't he? How else did you describe a man who kisses you like that when he's having an affair with another woman?

'Well, I don't want you!' she spat out furiously, pushing his head away and breaking free at the same moment.

She caught Brodie off guard. He looked at her blankly as if she'd slapped his face.

'I just wanted to see if I still fancied you, but I don't,' she said with vicious iciness. 'I wouldn't touch you with a bargepole. Stay away from me!' He had taken a step back towards her, his jaw taut, the blue eyes flashing rage. 'If you lay one finger on me again you'll have to leave this house. I won't have you under the same roof with me if I have to be on my guard all the time. You're a guest here. This is my home. Just remember that.'

He seemed speechless, which satisfied her. She turned on her heel and ran up the stairs. She should have kept going, but her temper betrayed her. She looked back down at him, from the top step, her eyes molten with fury.

'Now you'd better ring your girl-friend before she gets impatient. You needn't keep her a secret any more—I'll make sure my father knows all about her!'

CHAPTER SIX

BRODIE'S face seemed to freeze; the cheekbones angular under the tanned skin, the mouth hard and straight, the blue eyes piercing as they stared up at her.

'What?' He dropped the word like ice into a glass, and Donna had a rush of fear to the head.

She turned and ran, knowing that he was coming after her, his long legs carrying him up the stairs faster than she was moving. She had a head-start, though; she got into her room and slammed the door and bolted it, leaning on it breathlessly, wishing to God she had held her tongue.

He crashed a hand against the panels and the door shook. 'Donna! Open this door!'

She backed, her eyes stretched wide until they hurt. She was furious with herself for having let him see that she knew all about his secret love affair. He might start thinking backwards, guessing too much about the past—she didn't want him to realise why she had broken with him and gone to France. Brodie was quite capable of using that information against her. Knowledge was power, hadn't someone said? It was far safer to keep him in the dark about her motives, then he coudn't think of ways of persuading her to change her mind.

'What did you mean by that? Open this door! You can't just chuck that sort of accusation at me and run away. Tell me what you meant. Donna, open this door—I can't talk to you through it!' His voice was hard and angry and she wasn't tempted to do as he asked.

She sat down on the bed and stared around the room, trying not to listen to him. Nothing here had been changed, either—there were her books on the built-in shelves in alcoves on either side of the bed; her dressing-table still held bottles of perfume she had never used, a set of silver brushes and combs which her godmother had given her on her twenty-first birthday but which she hadn't taken to Paris in case she lost them; on the wall hung the same two pictures that had always been there, prints of Pre-Raphaelite paintings, one of girls with flushed, healthy faces lighting a bonfire of autumn leaves and the other Millais' 'Blind Girl' in a cornfield speckled with scarlet poppies. Donna had gone to sleep and woken for twenty years with those pictures above her head. When she was a child they had been mysterious and intriguing; now they held a poignant familiarity. Both of them had an elegaic echo which haunted. Why had her father chosen them?

'Donna, sooner or later you're going to have to tell me,' Brodie threatened. 'If not now, next time you come out of there. You don't really think I'll let it pass without explanation?' His voice rose sharply. 'What the hell did you mean?'

She turned her head suddenly, hearing the roar of an engine on the drive. Gavin was home. The car braked, the engine died, Gavin got out and slammed his car door.

'Okay.' Brodie said curtly, 'I'll talk to you later. Don't think I'll forget about it.'

She heard the thud of his feet on the stairs with deep relief, but it was only a respite she had gained—he meant what he said, he wouldn't forget or give up, not now that he had had a glimpse of what was going on inside her head. Why had she been so stupid? All this time she had held her tongue, not betraying what she knew, and then in an incautious moment of sheer rage she had given herself away.

She went to the window to get some air, but the evening was so warm. Laden with the fragrance of honeysuckle and rose, the air hardly moved. How many summer evenings had she lain in this room, breathing that heady sweetness, listening to the stillness of the night? Saffron Walden was out of sight across the green fields, but a few lights sprang up as she watched, in houses in the village down the road. She looked at her watch; it was still early and still light outside.

Was her father awake in his hospital bed? Was he frightened? She bit her lip—she had never got to know him very well, had she? She had resented his impatience with her brother. She always felt what Gavin felt; they were twins, after all, how could she help it? Their father hadn't been fair to Gavin; he had wanted him to be someone else, and that was never fair to a child. Gavin was himself; with all his faults he wasn't difficult to love—she had managed it easily enough. Why couldn't their father? If he had loved Gavin more end expected less of him, things would have been so different.

She heard the bang of the front door, and startled, she glanced down in time to see Brodie walking to his own car. He didn't look up at her window, so she could watch his tall, lean body without hiding what she felt.

He moved with power and grace, his body as streamlined as his car, as capable of speed and dynamism too. Her mouth went dry with desire and she was instantly furious with herself. When would she learn?

He got behind the wheel, the engine flared, the car shot away at a terrific speed, churning up gravel. Where was he going in such a hurry?

Donna's mouth twisted cynically. To see Christabel, of course—where else? To placate her, no doubt, tell her she needn't be jealous, Donna didn't mean a thing to him. Or perhaps Christabel didn't know she was back! Had Brodie been going to spend the weekend with her—and cancelled their plans to go to Paris? Was he hoping to keep Donna's return from Christabel as long as possible?

Donna knew the other girl was still one of the top models, her face appeared in women's magazines from time to time and Donna always flipped over the pages averting her eyes. She hadn't wanted any reminders of Christabel.

Her eyes watched his car disappear, then flicked over the beautifully kept gardens; the billiard-table smooth lawns, the cypresses on each side of the gate, the roses and the white marble fountain playing among the shrubs. All this was a symbol of her father's wealth and status—this was what Brodie wanted so much that he was ready to sacrifice his self-respect, even his deepest feelings, for it.

She didn't understand how he could want anything so worthless so much. There was more beauty in a violet growing in a hedge. There was more happiness in a tiny flat shared with someone you love, more pleasure in eating a hot-dog walking in the rain in a city street. A thousand things meant more to her than money or power. Why did Brodie want them so badly?

He must love Christabel, or he wouldn't have gone back to her. Donna hated admitting it, but it was dogged insistence on facing up to things as they really are that had sent her off to Paris two years ago. There was no point in living in a fool's paradise, and it was obvious that even though Brodie had sent Christabel that brutal note of dismissal he must be deeply involved with her or he would never have gone back to her.

Yet he wasn't prepared to marry Christabel, was he? They must have been together for some years now—how long had they known each other before he met Donna? Yet whatever his feelings, Brodie had pushed her aside with that callous shrug. What sort of love was it that could act like that?

And Christabel had to be crazy about him or she wouldn't have gone back when he snapped his fingers, knowing what she did about him. How could she do it?

She turned away from the window, her fingers curled inwards, her nails digging into her palms. She had no right to mock Christabel for being ready to forgive Brodie anything! Only a short time ago hadn't she herself been in his arms, kissing him back with hunger, clinging to him?

There was a tap on the door and she started. 'Donna?' Gavin's voice said uncertainly. 'Are you asleep?'

She ran her hands over her face to erase the emotions she had been feeling, and went over to open the door.

Gavin grinned excitedly at her, several books under his arm. 'I got three books—two from the library and one from the bookshop in Saffron Walden. They're a bit heavy going, but one of them has some useful illustrations, and I did get a brochure from the library—they had a pile on the counter, you were right. The technical college opens again in early September, but if I'm going to take a course I've got to enrol fast or there may not be a place.'

She laughed at his breathless rush of words. 'Come downstairs and we'll go through the syllabus while we wait for dinner. Is Mrs Eyre back yet?'

'Yes, she's in the kitchen and there's a gorgeous smell of steak and onions floating about.' Gavin gave her a shy look. 'I called at the hospital. Father was asleep, but they let me peep through the window in the door. He looks better than I'd thought he would. They said we could visit him tomorrow afternoon at three.'

Gavin had a very human need to love and be loved which their father had never understood. Donna linked her arm with her brother's and smiled affectionately at him.

'Is he allowed to have flowers?' she asked.

'I think so. Should I have taken him some?' At once Gavin looked guilty; he had failed in something again.

'Idiot—I meant we'll take him some tomorrow.'

He grinned. 'Oh, I get you. Right, we'll do that. Come on, let's go through this brochure and find out if I have to have any qualifications to take the course.'

'Are you going to discuss it with Brodie?' she asked later as they were eating their dinner alone. Mrs Eyre had come up with a delicious sirloin steak with black peppercorns and fried onions followed by meltingly light summer pudding which fell apart as you touched it, spilling raspberries and redcurrants across the plate.

'He'd tell Father,' Gavin said sullenly. 'And they'd find a way of stopping me.'

'Let me talk to him,' said Donna, her eyes hard. It had just dawned on her that she had a weapon to use against Brodie—he wouldn't want James Cowley to know about his long affair with Christabel. If he wasn't afraid his boss would disapprove, surely he wouldn't have been so secretive about her for so long?

Gavin stared at her. 'What makes you think Brodie will listen to you?'

'Oh, I think he will,' she said with a cold smile. 'And anyway, he won't be sorry to see you out of his way, Gavin. If you take up a craft and stop bothering about the company that will be quite a relief for Brodie Fox.'

'That's true,' Gavin agreed, much struck by this thought. 'You're cleverer than me, Donna. I should have realised that a long time ago.'

'Everyone has a personal motive somewhere,' Donna said with a cynicism that made her brother frown.

'You've toughened up a lot since you went to Paris,' he said reproachfully.

'Grown up, maybe,' she shrugged, quickly smiling at him. 'Being away from home changes you. A little independence wouldn't do you any harm.'

'It hasn't been as easy for me to walk out on Father,' Gavin said, his face sober. 'I don't know why. I just couldn't do it. And now there's the sixteen thousand I owe Brodie—he put the money back himself, how on earth can I ever pay him back? I'll have to tell Father so that I can repay the money and, once Father knows, I'm back with my head in a noose, caught in the same old trap—not wanting to stay, not wanting to go. I've made a mess of my life, Donna.'

'For the moment, don't say a word to Father,' she said hurriedly, her eyes anxious. Gavin's confession could precipitate another heart attack.

'I'm not that much of a fool!' protested Gavin, offended. He yawned, looking at the clock. 'I'm going to bed now. It's been a hectic day and I haven't really slept properly for ages.'

Donna went to bed, too, but couldn't sleep. She lay awake listening for the sound of Brodie's car returning. He had been gone for hours now, she thought, sitting up to look angrily at the clock beside her bed. It was nearly one in the morning. Wasn't he coming back at all tonight?

Was he in bed with Christabel? The thought made her throw herself down again, on to her face, her hands screwed up into fists. She wouldn't be jealous, she scolded herself. Why should she lie here on edge with nerves when Brodie was with another woman, making love to her, perhaps talking about Donna, laughing behind her back?

She hated him, hated both of them, hated herself for going through this—next time she saw him things were going to be very different, from now on Brodie was dancing to her tune instead of the other way around.

If he wanted to keep his affair with Christabel from James Cowley, he was going to have to pay her price. Brodie knew that her father was old-fashioned—he might laugh at gossip about other men having affairs, but he would be furious if he found out that Brodie had pulled the wool over his eyes by having an affair while he was pretending to be in love with James Cowley's daughter. Her father would see that as a personal insult to himself.

Brodie would have to agree to help Gavin if he wanted her to hold her tongue about what she knew.

Donna must have drifted off to sleep shortly after that, because the next thing she knew was that she was opening her eyes to daylight and the smell of coffee right under her nose.

She blinked dreamily, then came awake with a rush as she realised it was Brodie holding the cup of coffee.

'What are you doing in my room? Get out before I scream the place down!' She sat up, clutching the sheet to her chin.

Brodie put the cup down on the bedside table and settled himself comfortably on the bed. 'Scream away. There's nobody in the house but us.' He linked his hands behind his head and surveyed her flushed face with quizzical enjoyment.

'Gavin!' she yelled. 'Gavin, come here!'

There was no answer. Brodie's smile mocked. 'He went for a drive ten minutes ago. Mrs Eyre's in the orchard picking gooseberries by the bucket to make into jam. You'd have to use a megaphone to get her to hear you.'

Donna held on to the sheet with fingers that trembled. 'Don't push your luck, Mr Fox!' she hissed. 'I'm getting very tired of your idea of a joke. Get out of my bedroom! If Mrs Eyre comes back and finds you in here she'll think . . .'

'Yes?' he asked softly when she paused in confusion, realising that it might be foolish to finish the sentence.

She felt her face stinging with hot colour and couldn't meet his eyes. The way Brodie was smiling didn't make her feel any less uneasy, either.

Donna pulled herself together with an effort. He thought he had her pinned in a corner, did he? Well, he was going to find out his mistake.

'I wanted to talk to you,' she began, and he unlinked his hands and leaned back on them, across her legs, tethering her to the bed.

'Good, I wanted to talk to you, too!' She didn't like the sound of that or the glint in his blue eyes. He had shaved recently; she looked angrily away from the smooth brown skin, the strong jaw and warm, masculine mouth. She didn't want any reminders of his sexual potency; she knew all about that. That was what got her into this tangle in the first place. From now on she wasn't going to let the sexual issue cloud her mind.

'About Gavin,' she said firmly. 'He wants to learn how to blow glass by hand, he doesn't want to work in the office any more, he isn't interested in industrial glass of the kind the company makes, but he is keen on learning the history of glass-making, the techniques of doing it today. My father isn't going to be too happy about it, but if you're on Gavin's side he may accept the plan, so I'll make a bargain with you . . .'

'Done,' he said quickly, too quickly. She stared at him in stupefaction.

'I hadn't finished,' she said warily—what did he think she had been about to propose? Had he realised that his affair with Christabel put him at risk with her father? Had he been about to suggest some sort of bargain about that?

'You don't need to—I like the idea. Believe me, Gavin's no addition to the work force—half the time he isn't there, and the other half he gets under people's feet and drives me scatty.'

Donna looked grimly at him. 'In other words, you're only too glad to get him out of your hair?'

He nodded. 'And when he's learnt all he can—or wants to—about glass, he could always come back as a consultant. I think it's an excellent idea, but of course I'll want something in exchange for my support. If I persuade your father to agree about this, I'll expect Gavin to see a psychiatrist. I still believe he needs straightening out, and I don't think he's going to stop gambling until he understands what makes him do it.'

She gave a little sigh. 'He may not agree to that.'

'Then you'll have to talk him into it. You have more influence with Gavin than anyone else does.' He glanced at the cup on her bedside table. 'Hadn't you better drink that before it gets cold?'

She picked up the cup with one hand, holding the sheet up with the other. Brodie observed her balancing act with dry interest.

'I saw Christabel last night,' he said conversationally.

The cup shook in her hand; a few drops of coffee splashed over the edge.

'Lucky that isn't hot any more,' Brodie remarked, his blue eyes ruthless as they watched her flushed face.

'I don't think my father would be too happy about your rather furtive private life,' Donna ground out between her teeth, glaring at him.

He sat up with a sudden movement that had violence in it, and she tensed, her eyes flickering. Brodie was alarming when he looked like that. Male rage was always unpredictable and hard to handle, especially when you were at such a disadvantage as to be half naked and in bed.

'All right!' he said tersely. 'What's this all about?'

'Ask your girl-friend!' she threw at him with bitterness.

His eyes were dangerously dark blue; the pupils dilated with fury. 'What do you know about Christabel and myself? Who told you?'

'She did.'

'Last night on the phone?' He looked baffled; furious but incredulous. 'Why on earth should she start talking about that on the phone? You've never met her, have you?' He must have caught something in the expression on her face, because he focused on her intently. '*Have* you?' he repeated, and she could see him thinking, the little wheels going round behind those blue eyes. Brodie was nothing if not clever, and she had given him a clue at last. 'You've met Christabel?' he thought aloud. 'Where? When?'

'Does that matter? I know what's been going on between you and I don't think my father would like it if I told him, do you?'

Brodie considered her, a harsh frown on his face. 'Are you trying to blackmail me, by any chance?' he asked slowly, as though the idea amazed him. No doubt it did. He was good at blackmailing people himself, but he didn't expect the tables to be turned, certainly not by her.

'You wouldn't like him to know the whole sordid story, would you?' Donna asked bitingly. 'His opinion of you wouldn't be so high after hearing that.'

'You don't think so?' he murmured, almost blankly, staring.

She laughed; the sound more rage than amusement. Did he still think he could talk her round?

'My God, you're cool, I'll say that for you,' she said

with contempt. 'In your place most men would be embarrassed, not to say ashamed—but you think on your feet, don't you? Well, if you're trying to work out how to wriggle out of this you can save yourself the trouble. You won't hoodwink me a second time!'

'When did I hoodwink you the first time?' he asked, and she saw that he was still trying to find out how much she knew and how she had heard about it.

'Never mind that,' she said impatiently, because the last thing she wanted was for him to realise why she had left him two years ago.

'I do mind it,' said Brodie with a snarl. 'I mind very much.' He leaned towards her and she shrank instinctively; the rake of his blue eyes made her skin grow cold. 'I want to know precisely what you think you're talking about and how you came to get this story.'

'Don't try to bully me! Unless you want me to go straight to my father with what I know!'

His smile held menace. 'You *are* blackmailing me . . .' He laughed shortly. 'I was beginning to get the distinct impression that you were.'

'I wouldn't call it blackmail!'

'No? Then what would you call it?'

'What do you call the way you got me to come back here from Paris?'

His mouth twisted. 'An appeal to family loyalty?'

Donna's smile was scathing. 'And what do you call the way you let my father believe we'd been reconciled?'

'Silent amusement,' he said blandly. 'I told you—I was afraid I'd laugh if I tried to explain he was wrong.'

She fizzed helplessly, longing to hit him. 'You expect

me to believe that? My father played right into your scheming hands—you're always looking for weapons to use against people. That's how you operate. Well, I've got a weapon to use against you now—and in future you'd better remember that!'

He shifted on the bed and she shrank against the bedhead, the sheet held higher. She felt very vulnerable in her flimsy nightie and the sheet was all the protection she had.

'You're scaring the hell out of me!' he mocked. She could see he didn't mean a word of it; his eyes held a secret enjoyment. 'But you still haven't told me what exactly you're blackmailing me with!'

'You know very well,' she said shortly. 'You and Christabel!'

He still gazed at her, his brows lifting in enquiry, and her temper flared again.

'I know you were engaged to her just before you met me!' she spat furiously. His face lost the smile and darkened.

'Who told you that? Christabel?'

'What difference does it make how I found out? You didn't tell me, did you? You never breathed a word about her, about having been engaged before.'

'It wasn't something I wanted to talk about,' he said curtly.

She laughed. 'I bet it wasn't!'

'Did she tell you why I broke off our engagement?' he asked harshly.

'Oh, yes, she told me that,' said Donna, swallowing on humiliation she didn't want him to see.

'Then you must see why I wouldn't want to discuss her when we first met—I was still too angry. I just wanted to forget her.'

Donna looked at him uncertainly; his tone wasn't quite what she had expected. He didn't seem to be on the defensive—on the contrary, he was looking angry.

Slowly she asked, 'What's your side of the story, then? I've only heard hers.' She didn't intend to believe everything Brodie said, but suddenly she wondered if there was an alternative explanation to the one Christabel had given her. Something didn't quite add up—Brodie's reactions to discovering that she knew about Christabel weren't what she had been expecting.

His mouth was hard, his eyes cold. 'I discovered she'd been away for the weekend with a married friend of mine. Is that what she told you?'

Donna's nerves jerked in surprise. She had been expecting some sort of plausible excuse, but somehow Brodie's words had a ring of truth—perhaps because she could hear the anger in them. Had Christabel been unfaithful to him, had he been jealous enough to decide to break with her and marry for ambition instead of love? She bit her lip, looking down.

'No, she didn't tell me that—but she did show me the note you sent her, and I did notice the date. You wrote that the day after we first met, didn't you? And you said you planned to marry someone else. Did you mean me? Did you decide to marry me there and then?'

There was a short silence. She looked through her lashes at his face; it was tense and angular.

'No,' he said flatly. 'The day we first met, Donna, I was too bloody angry to notice you much at all. I'd only just discovered what Christabel had been up to—it was the only thing on my mind. You hardly impinged at all.'

Hoarsely she whispered, 'But you decided to marry

me all the same because it would give you more power with my father?' His words had stung, she felt her eyes grow hot with unshed tears. How stupid to be hurt by his admission—she had known for two years that he had never loved her, why should she feel as if he had slapped her round the face by telling her the truth?

'I didn't decide anything of the sort,' he said sharply.

'In your note to Christabel you said . . .'

'I was saving my face,' he snapped. 'How do you think I felt? Finding out that she'd gone away with someone else, that she was cheating on me with one of my oldest friends, what do you think that did to me? I felt a fool, to say the least. I wanted to hit back. I did have a blazing row with the guy involved—we had a fight and I lost my temper and broke his nose. He had to go to hospital for a week, we narrowly escaped a police enquiry. He lied, as much to save his own skin as mine. His wife didn't know—still doesn't. I never told her and I'm damn sure he didn't. But however furious I was with Christabel I don't hit women, so I took out my temper with a few terse words. I said I was marrying someone else because I didn't want her to think she'd broken my heart.'

'Had she?' Donna asked huskily, watching him jealously. It was partly a rhetorical question—Christabel had obviously hurt him badly. Why, otherwise, would he have beaten up his oldest friend? Who? she thought suddenly. Who had Christabel gone away with? But then no doubt the friendship had ended there and then. Brodie wasn't likely to forgive the man involved, so she had probably never met the man.

Brodie shrugged drily. 'I thought so for a few weeks, but it was my pride that was wounded, not my heart.

Christabel's stunning—the most beautiful girl I've ever known, I think.'

Donna's lips tensed, her teeth gritted. She knew it was true; that didn't make it any easier to listen to.

'But she's like one of those tropical plants that have ravishing flowers; the first time you see them you're bowled over by them, but then you realise how gaudy and unreal they are, what shallow roots they have and how quickly they fade. There's a lot to be said for the English rose, its beauty lingers longer.' His blue eyes were on her face, caressingly moving from her eyes to her mouth in a leisurely scrutiny that made her flush. She pretended not to notice the insinuating compliment—he wasn't wheedling her into forgetting the obvious!

'But you went back to her after all that,' she said icily. 'And don't give me that innocent stare, as if you didn't know what I was talking about! She rang you last night and you rushed over to see her and stayed out half the night.'

'How do you know how long I stayed out?' he asked smoothly.

Donna's flushed face tightened. 'I do, that's all, and I'm not so naïve that I can't guess what the two of you were doing all that time! So don't give me any fairy story about having got over her, because it's obvious you're still just as involved.'

'Your imagination *has* been working overtime!' he drawled, moving even closer on the bed.

'And let go of that sheet!' Donna snarled. 'Get out of my bedroom before I hit you with something!'

'I'm shaking in my shoes!' murmured Brodie, laughing, and far from letting go of the sheet his hand slid down over her, moulding the sheet smoothly over her body, like a sculptor making a plaster cast with infinite care. The slow movement of that hand made her shudder with abrupt awareness, a pulse throbbing crazily in her neck.

'Stop that,' she muttered breathlessly.

Brodie watched the way the fine linen clung to her shoulders; her breasts, her waist, and her face burned at the way he watched.

'How long have you known about Christabel?' he asked in a soft voice, and Donna stiffened, but she didn't have to answer after all, because at that moment she heard Gavin running up the stairs. He must have come back without either of them hearing his car, which wasn't surprising considering their intense concentration on each other for the last half-hour.

Brodie turned his head, grimacing, and got up in a lazy movement.

He heard Donna's sigh of relief and looked wryly at her. 'Saved by the bell? Don't be too complacent. I'll talk to you later,' he promised, but at least he left the room a moment later, almost colliding with Gavin.

Her brother stood in the doorway, frowning, staring at her. 'What's been going on? Why was he in here?'

'We were talking about you,' Donna said evasively. 'He's going to help us persuade Father to let you take that course—but only if you agree to meet some tame psychiatrist of his.'

Gavin scowled. 'No way. I'm not going to any head-shrinker. There's nothing wrong with my mind.'

'Gambling's an addiction, Gavin,' she said gently. 'Like taking drugs or drinking too much. And it can be cured, but you need expert help.'

'I can stop whenever I like,' he said flatly.

'What harm would it do to see someone about it? It would be purely voluntary, you could stop going to see the doctor as soon as you liked, but if you agree to go at least once, Brodie will be on your side with Father.'

Gavin made an irritated face but shrugged after a minute. 'Oh, very well, but only once, mind. I'm not spending hours lying on a couch talking about my childhood or my dreams to some quack. If it means Brodie will talk Father into letting me leave the firm to start classes in glass-blowing I'll go through the motions anyway.'

Donna smiled at him, relaxing. It was some sort of progress.

CHAPTER SEVEN

JAMES COWLEY'S face seemed colourless against his pillows. His lips were sunken and pallid, his cheeks lined, his eyes half hidden under drooping lids. The Sister had already warned them that he was heavily sedated, they mustn't stay long or talk too much, but the weariness was still a shock to Donna.

She sat close to the bed and held her father's hand. 'Anything we can get you, Father?' she asked gently.

He whispered his reply, not moving. She got the impression he was afraid to move. 'No, thank you. I'm fine.'

Gavin stood behind her, looking miserable. He hated the atmosphere in the hospital and he was upset to see his father so ill.

'Brodie?' James Cowley asked with that care not to use up too much energy which betrayed his own fear.

'He's coming later.' They had been asked not to go in together. Two visitors were all he was allowed, Donna told him, smiling. 'Brodie is waiting outside. Gavin and I wanted to come in together.'

Her father's fingers pressed hers a little more tightly. 'You and Brodie—wonderful news. Always wanted it. Like a son to me.'

Donna managed a smile. 'I know.'

Gavin shifted resentfully, his eyes hurt. 'I'll let Brodie come in now,' he said.

His father looked up at him. 'Hardly seen you yet,' he said.

Gavin bent and kissed him awkwardly. 'You're looking great today, Father. Better than yesterday.'

James Cowley frowned. 'Did you come yesterday? I don't remember that.'

'You were asleep. I just had a peep at you.' Gavin sounded sheepish. Their father gave him a faint smile.

'Oh, I see. Thanks for coming, Gavin.' His eyes watched his son back out of the room; Donna heard his sigh.

Tentatively she said, 'You know, Gavin's studying the history of glass-making, Father? He's become really interested in it. I'd no idea how far back the process went. Gavin says Roman glass is a beautiful bluey colour, cloudy, because the process was so erratic. Too many imperfections, he says.'

James Cowley stared at her in surprise. 'He always did have a romantic streak; impractical, I'm afraid.' He sighed again.

Brodie joined them and she watched her father's eyes brighten a little. 'Good of you to come, Brodie. How's the order book?'

'No business,' Donna ordered flatly.

Her father frowned as petulantly as a sick child. 'I just want to know what . . .'

'No business,' Brodie agreed, smiling teasingly. 'You heard her. You don't want to get me in trouble with her, do you? She may not scare you, but she scares me!'

Donna bristled at the mockery but hid that from her father, who was chuckling delightedly.

'Start as you mean to go on, lad,' he said in his tired voice. 'Don't let a woman rule the roost.'

Donna pretended to laugh, but her hackles rose, especially when Brodie gave her another sidelong glance, his blue eyes gleaming with amusement, not at what her father had said, but at what he knew full well must be her reaction to it.

'Oh, I'll keep her under control,' said Brodie, winking.

This little masculine fun had one good effect—it put a trace of colour back into her father's face and he was really smiling now. Donna swallowed back the irritation she was tempted to express.

It wasn't until she and Brodie had left the room and began walking down the corridor that she turned on him, flushed and indignant.

'Don't do that again!' she snapped.

'What?' He opened blue eyes at her, innocent as a baby's.

'Don't give me that sweet stare—you know very well what I mean! All that stuff about keeping me in my place. I didn't say anything because I didn't want to upset my father and you knew I'd have to grin and bear it, that's why you did it.' She was angry enough to get confused, her words tripping over each other.

A student nurse came towards them, very young and pretty in her rustling uniform. She stared at Brodie, listening to them, as she passed, and he gave her a wink, as he had James Cowley.

'No need to get so grim about it. Your father thinks a woman's place is in the home. I was humouring him.'

'You don't think a woman's place is in the home?' she threw at him disbelievingly, suddenly realising that the nurse was listening and irritated about that too.

'Me? No, I think a woman's place is in a man's bed,'

said Brodie, grinning. The nurse gave a little giggle and pattered away.

'Typical!' muttered Donna, even more furious now. He was playing to the gallery again and she was sick of being his straight man. If he wanted someone to bounce jokes off he could find himself another victim.

They came out of the main doors and turned towards the hospital car park where Brodie had left his car. Gavin was sitting in it; he had fled the hospital ambience as soon as he left his father's room, obviously. He was sitting in the back of the car, his head back against the cushions, his eyes closed. Donna looked at him anxiously—had he been very hurt by his father's obvious preference for Brodie's company? Gavin opened his eyes and looked at her blankly.

'I think I'll go up to town and see a film tonight,' he said in a casual, offhand way. 'I feel like some bright lights.'

Donna got into the car, her face concerned. 'I'll come with you,' she offered.

'We'd better not both go in case there's an emergency call from the hospital,' said Gavin.

Brodie drove back to the house without commenting, but as he parked outside on the drive he looked over his shoulder at Gavin. 'Skip it for tonight, Gavin—go tomorrow. You're still tired and out of sorts. You'll feel better in the morning.'

That was a red rag to a bull. Gavin wasn't taking any advice from Brodie tonight.

'Damn you, mind your own business!' he snarled, and banged out of the car.

Donna hurriedly got out too, but he was already opening the door of his little sports car. By the time she could get over to him his engine was racing and he was moving away at a speed which made her jump out of his way with a startled cry.

'Oh, damn,' she muttered, on the point of tears, staring after him. Brodie loomed up beside her, frowning, and she looked at him angrily, her face pale and stiff.

'He's going to one of those clubs—he'll gamble again. Why didn't you try to stop him?'

'We'll try,' Brodie said in cool tones. 'Come on—run in and change into something pretty and we'll do a tour of his usual haunts. We'll find him at one of them, but they won't be open until around nine. Gavin will probably catch a film first, have a meal, then start gambling. We'll have plenty of time to get on his trail, so stop looking so desperate. It might not be a bad thing for you to see what exactly he's hooked on.'

She stared at him, biting her lip. 'How do you know where he may be?'

'I've had to pay some of his debts,' Brodie said drily, and she flinched. 'When Gavin doesn't pay they get in touch with his father—I take the calls and keep it from the old man's ears.'

'You knew he'd been gambling and you didn't put a stop to it?' she broke out, and Brodie gave her a long, hard stare.

'What do you suggest I should have done? Tied him up? Smacked him? Or told your father and got him to stop Gavin's money supply? I did what I could—I talked to Gavin, he promised he wouldn't do it again and for a while he'd keep his word, but sooner or later he'd break out again. The least pressure and he snaps. Do you think I don't know why he's gone off tonight?

Seeing his father upset him, didn't it? It's always the same trigger. You could almost say Gavin's allergic to his father. He loves him, but it's a destructive love. It's no good for Gavin, anyway.'

Donna listened soberly and had to admit that Brodie was shrewd in his assessment of her brother's problem. She nodded and said huskily, 'I'm sorry, I wasn't fair to you. I'd no right to say that. It isn't your fault, and I'm grateful for everything you've done for Gavin.'

She went into the house and upstairs to her bedroom to change into a dress more suitable for hitting the nightspots in London. She picked out an apricot satin, very low cut, leaving her shoulders bare and hiding very little of her breasts. The lustrous material gave a deep gold to her skin and heightened the colour of her blonde hair; she felt a little more cheerful when she saw herself in the mirror. Colour altered her mood; it always had. As a child she could remember sitting staring at a rainbow with rapt delight.

Her eyes were misty, faintly sad, even after she had smoothed a glittery green eyeshadow over her lids. She glossed her lips with a warm orangy pink, brushed blusher over her cheekbones—and tilted her head to consider the result. Well, she had given her face a little more colour, even if it was merely artificial. She looked as if she were going to a party now, but she found it hard to smile. She didn't want to go to London with Brodie, to scour the nightspots and gambling clubs for her brother. But even less did she want Gavin to stay out all night losing money he didn't have.

He was deeply in debt to Brodie already—how would he pay him back unless the money came from their father? Why did Brodie go to the trouble of paying

Gavin's gambling debts?

Anxiety and suspicion darkened her eyes, as she got up and walked to the bedroom door. What was Brodie up to? Where did he get all his money? That car of his, his expensive clothes, the sort of hotels and restaurants he frequented—all added up to money, and a great deal of it. Where did it come from? How could anyone afford to pay Gavin's debts to the tune of sixteen thousand and more when it was obvious that repayment might be a long time coming?

As she came to the head of the stairs she saw him waiting for her in the hall. There was only one lamp on; the dusk was still falling gently in the warm summer evening. By that soft light she saw Brodie look up at her, his black head gleaming, his eyes a vivid blue between their swept-back lashes. Her heart turned over and she could hardly breathe.

He had changed, too. He was wearing a black evening jacket now with a crisp white shirt and black tie. Formal clothes suited him; he looked even more striking in them. He came to the foot of the stairs, watching Donna walk down carefully, her long skirts lifted so that she shouldn't trip over them. She was intensely self-conscious under his gaze. She wished at times she really knew what he thought of her. Now and then she almost believed he did find her attractive—at others she suspected it was all pretence. His face was unreadable; set in that sculptured mask, the dark blue eyes fixed on her.

Nervously she stumbled into speech. 'We ought to tell Mrs Eyre we're going out before she starts cooking dinner.'

'I did. Told her to have an evening off for once.'

She gave him a sharp look. He gave orders here as if he were already master of the house!

Brodie caught the look; his smile wry. 'She saw me in my dinner jacket and obviously wondered what was going on—so I explained that I was taking you dancing.' His eyes mocked. 'She thought it was a very good idea, give us some time together. Mrs Eyre has a very romantic streak.'

Donna said crossly, 'You shouldn't let her get ideas like that! When she realises it was just an act, she's going to feel a fool—I know I would. I'll go and explain to her now.'

His hand looped round her arm, pulling her in the other direction, towards the front door. 'If we're to catch up with Gavin, we'd better get a move on.'

She let herself be led out to the car, but gave him an obstinate look. 'I'll tell her tomorrow, then.'

Brodie pushed her into the passenger seat of the car without comment and she settled down, arranging her full, shimmering skirts carefully. Satin creased too easily, that was the problem with it.

Brodie got behind the wheel and started the engine. 'Your dress is ravishing,' he said softly without looking at her. 'It reminds me of a peach, that colour—rich and luscious, and very tempting.'

She felt her face flow with colour. 'Thank you.'

He drove away, a smile curling his mouth, as though her reaction to the compliment amused him.

'Aren't you going to ask me what's so tempting?' he murmured.

Donna stared out of the window at the leafy hedgerows rushing past; pink campion and white rambling roses among the nettles and traveller's joy and the small pale stars of the nightshade.

He shot a quick look at her stubborn profile, then answered his own question. 'Most men will find the idea of peeling that dress off very tempting.'

She threw him a cold stare. 'Can we have some music? I don't feel like talking, especially if you're going to make remarks like that all the way to London.'

'Pick out a tape,' he shrugged. 'They're in the glove compartment.'

She flipped through the neat row of tapes she found and picked out some Gershwin piano music. Leaning back in her seat as the music began, she watched the sky turning a warm, purplish shade. Brodie drove in silence at great speed, his car moving smoothly along the motorway to London, eating the miles while Gershwin's melodies occupied the forefront of her mind. Under cover of that, she was able to worry about Gavin, about Brodie's taste for luxury and how he paid for it, about her father and the future for all of them. In Paris she had got away from this tangle; now she was caught up in it again, like a fly caught in a sticky web. With every day that passed she wondered how she was ever going to break free again.

When they reached London Brodie parked the car in the private car park of the first club they visited. They took the lift from the subterranean vault up to the top floor of the hotel that owned the club.

'Good evening, sir,' the manager greeted them, giving Brodie an assessing glance. 'A table? I'm not sure if we have one free—if you'd care to wait?'

Brodie took a step forward and glanced round the room; dimly lit and noisy with the clamour of a cabaret singer currently occupying the small stage. She wasn't beautiful, but she was throbbing with vitality and the audience obviously loved her, a ripple of applause and laughter kept breaking out. Donna was so busy staring at her that she didn't notice whatever Brodie said or did, but suddenly they were being shown to a table. How had he persuaded the manager to let them jump the queue? she wondered cynically. A discreet bribe? Probably.

Brodie ordered champagne and caviar casually, and Donna stared at him, all her suspicions surfacing again. How could he afford this? Did he come to places like this often?

'You don't really think we'll find Gavin here?' she said, and Brodie leaned over and said very softly in her ear, 'If you look in the corner you'll see some of his friends—the noisy crowd in evening dress, see them?'

Donna stared through the blue, smoky air. She didn't recognise the people at the table, but they were a type she identified easily enough. Two young men and a couple of girls; all very well dressed, flushed faces, a little drunk, rather silly, obviously wealthy.

'Gavin goes around with people like them?' Her mouth was stiff with distaste, as one of the men called a waiter over and ordered champagne in a cut-glass English accent that rang with arrogance.

'Lately he has, so I gather. They gamble, too—and make a nuisance of themselves in places like this. Having fun, they call it. Expensive fun for Gavin.' Brodie's mouth was hard with contempt.

'He'll never be able to pay you back unless he gets the money from my father,' Donna said suddenly. 'Can you afford to wait?'

He shrugged without answering, sipping his champagne.

She picked up her own glass and drank a little. 'I expect these people charge the earth for champagne and caviar,' she added pointedly. 'Does this go on the firm's expenses?'

'No, I wouldn't call you a legitimate business expense,' he said ironically, staring into her suspicious eyes. 'Now what's eating you? I know that look. What am I being accused of now?'

'I'm not accusing you of anything, I'm just curious—you seem to live very extravagantly. That car can't have been cheap and your clothes are very good. I suppose you feel you have to project a successful image, but it can't leave you much of your income at the end of a year.'

Brodie's mouth twisted. 'I see,' he said slowly. 'You wonder if I'm cooking the books? Embezzling your father's money, the way Gavin did?'

'I didn't say that!'

'The implication was obvious enough.' His face hardened.

'I merely wondered . . .'

'The answer is no, Donna,' he said curtly, his brows drawn above his fixed blue eyes. The frown made her nervous. She shouldn't have said anything—the only evidence she had was guesswork based on her own observation of the way he lived. There might be a simple explanation—perhaps he had money of his own? He had never told her much about his background. He was oddly secretive about the past, about his family, his earlier life. She hadn't noticed that until she met Christabel at that party and realised how little she really knew about Brodie. Until then she had been too wildly in love to think of anything but him—where he came from, what he was, didn't seem to matter.

'Do your family have money?' she asked, her eyes lowered and her face flushed.

'Have some caviar,' he invited coolly, pushing the silver dish towards her.

She wasn't hungry, but she took a spoon of the black pearls, a slice of lemon and a little chopped boiled egg. The toast was wrapped in a damask napkin and still warm.

If he thought she was going to stop questioning him, he was wrong, though. 'Are your parents alive?' she asked him, pushing the dish back to him. The salty taste of the caviar was perfect with the wine.

He helped himself, his eyes on her. 'No. Both dead.'

'Oh. I'm sorry. When?' She softened, her eyes sympathetic as she watched his face.

'I never knew them.'

Her head came up and her eyes widened. 'I didn't realise . . . you mean they died when you were very young?'

'Yes.' The admission was terse, the face rigid. Brodie didn't like talking about this and he changed the subject firmly. 'If Gavin doesn't show up here within half an hour we'll go on to the Rambouillet—he gambles there more regularly than anywhere else.'

She nodded, aware that he was putting up a no entry sign. Looking back, she realised how often he had done that in the past. Whenever she did come close to asking him questions about himself Brodie managed to steer her away from the subject.

This time though she wasn't going to let him shut her

up. 'How old were you when your parents died?' she insisted.

She saw the reluctance in his face—why was he so unwilling to talk about himself? What was he hiding?

'I was just a baby,' he said shortly, refilling her glass. 'More caviar?'

'No, thank you.' She absorbed what he had told her, feeling very shaken. What would such a childhood do to someone? Her own early years had been happy until her mother's death and the sudden icing up of her father's feelings towards his children. Looking back, she realised how much those first years had meant to her later—creating a golden image to which she looked back nostalgically whenever she was unhappy. Her early childhood had been radiant; the sun had always seemed to be shining. Perhaps it did for everyone when they were very young. But what had it been like for Brodie?

'Who did you live with, then?' she asked hesitantly. Had he been brought up in an orphanage?

'An uncle. My father's brother.'

'Did you like him?'

Brodie gave her a barbed smile. 'Not much, no. He didn't like me much, either. We existed in the same house and tolerated each other.'

Donna bit her inner lip, eyeing him uneasily. 'Was he married?'

'No. I suppose you could call him a convinced misogynist. There were no women in his house at all. Not that he liked anyone much—he was a surly, bad-tempered man, full of grievances, and very suspicious. I didn't have to put up with him once I was old enough to go away to school. As soon as I was eight, he packed me off to boarding-school and forgot all about me.'

'It must have been very lonely,' she said. 'Did you like school?'

'It was Okay. At least I had friends and wasn't always on my own.'

'Is your uncle . . .'

'He died when I was fifteen,' he interrupted, looking at his watch. 'We might as well move on now—if Gavin was going to come he'd be here by now.'

He turned and signalled to the waiter just as the cabaret began again with a pop group playing vibrant, noisy music of their own. Donna watched Brodie settle the bill and got up from her chair.

As they made their way out a new party arrived in the foyer next to the lifts. Their table wouldn't be empty long, Donna thought drily. The place was packed—she couldn't imagine why, because the champagne had been faintly flat and the music far too loud. Even the caviar seemed tired, but then some people liked this sort of place. It wasn't her own taste. Was it Brodie's?

It wasn't until she and Brodie were at the entrance that she realised that one of the group just arriving was Christabel Clair.

Donna felt her body stiffen in shock, her face tightened and the smile she hurriedly put on seemed totally phoney, but she wasn't going to let her real feelings show in front of either Christabel or Brodie.

A second after she had noticed Christabel, the other woman saw Brodie. Donna bitterly watched the glance they exchanged; even if she hadn't known about their private relationship she would have guessed there was something between them if she had seen that look. They hadn't been expecting to see each other. Their faces were unguarded for a second; Christabel flushed, Brodie became tense.

Christabel pulled herself together quickly. She was a wonderful actress, Donna had to give her that. She smiled radiantly and held out her hands. 'Brodie! Lovely to see you. It must be ages since last time.'

Brodie almost didn't take her hands, Donna noticed. Christabel leaned forward and kissed his cheek, or rather, brushed her cheek against his, making a kissing sound. Brodie's face was grim.

'Darling, don't you look gorgeous? Having a night out?' It was only then that Christabel looked from him to the girl with him and her eyes widened, startled, before they hardened and glittered like jet.

'Good heavens—it's Donna Cowley, isn't it?'

'Hallo,' said Donna with ice in her voice.

The other people with Christabel were a few feet behind her, watching smilingly. She saw a man nodding to Brodie and Brodie said something coolly polite in reply.

There were diamonds in Christabel's ears. She tossed her head back stagily and the jewels flashed; her laughter was just as unreal.

'I thought you lived abroad these days.'

'I do.' Donna couldn't bring herself to pretend like her; her hatred was too intense. Brodie had to be passionately in love with Christabel or he would never have forgiven her for being unfaithful to him, he wouldn't be seeing her again. Christabel had just said lightly that it was ages since she had seen him—yet Donna knew they had been together for hours last night. She knew Christabel was a fluent liar, but it still shocked her to hear such a smooth lie coming out of that beautiful, selfish, greedy mouth.

'I'm thinking of going abroad myself,' Christabel said, her eyes flickering to Brodie's stern profile and away again. 'I fancy the States, New York. That's where the action is, isn't it?' She laughed over her shoulder at one of the men in her party and he smiled back eagerly. Donna saw the surreptitious glance Christabel gave to Brodie as she turned back. She might be pretending to talk to Donna, but what she was saying was really for Brodie's ears. Was she threatening to leave him if he didn't marry her? wondered Donna bitterly. How would he react to that?

'Are you still modelling' asked Donna. 'It's a very short career at the top, isn't it?' The malice in her own voice made her feel ashamed as she felt Brodie give her a sideways look.

Christabel showed her teeth in a dazzling, hostile smile. 'Darling, modelling's only a stepping-stone to better things.'

Like sleeping with rich men? Donna thought viciously, her face flushed. She wanted to slap Christabel across her lovely, assured face, but she hung on to her self-control.

Christabel looked her up and down dismissively. 'What a colourful dress! Terribly sweet, isn't it, Brodie darling?'

Donna's teeth met. Her lustrous apricot satin seemed as gaudy as a marigold next to the sophisticated black silk which clung lovingly to every curve of Christabel's sexy body. Donna knew enough about style to guess the name of the designer; that dress had cost the earth. It was intended less to clothe a woman than to emphasise her sex appeal, and on Christabel it certainly did that.

Brodie put a hand under Donna's elbow, moving closer. 'We must rush, I'm afraid. Nice to see you.' He didn't look at Christabel, though, he smiled politely at the people behind her, her friends, who had been curious and silent throughout the little interlude. Did *they* guess at the secret relationship?

Angrily flushed, Donna let herself be steered past into the waiting lift. She felt that Christabel had won that round. She should never have let herself challenge the other woman; losing your temper was always a mistake with people like that.

The doors shut; they sank downwards smoothly, silently. Donna stared at nothing, her mind in turmoil. What had been going on between Brodie and Christabel back there? Was their affair really over this time? Or had they been playing some complicated poker game behind their smiles, a mixture of bluff and threat? Who had been the winner?

As the lift stopped and the doors slid back Brodie asked her, 'What are you brooding over?'

'I'm not brooding,' she denied with vehemence, walking out into the darkened, empty car park.

'No?' He sounded unconvinced, quizzical. She ignored that and walked towards his car, her footsteps echoing in the concrete vault above and from the solid concrete walls. Brodie kept pace without hurrying. She saw their black shadows leaping up the dimly lit walls in a strange, manic dance.

'Why did she lie about having seen you lately?' she broke out suddenly. 'It was such a silly, pointless lie!'

'Ah,' he said with mockery in his tone, 'it's Christabel you aren't brooding over—I suspected it might be.'

'What was all that about, anyway? Have you quarrelled again?' She tried not to sound hopeful. What did she care? Let him have an affair with anyone he liked. It didn't matter to her. She despised him.

He unlocked his car and held the door open for her without answering her questions, but as he drove up out into the lamplit street he murmured, 'It's too complicated to explain tonight—first we have to find Gavin.'

Donna gave a rough sigh. 'If he came to London.'

'I have a hunch we'll find him at the Rambouillet.'

'If we don't?' Her voice shook a little.

'Then we'll scour London until we do find him.' Brodie sounded so confident and calm. She resented it, for some reason.

'We should have followed him when he first drove away!' she said angrily. 'Your car is faster than his—you could have hung on his tail until he stopped.'

'Or crashed,' Brodie said coolly.

She looked at him, startled. He turned his dark head and his eyes smouldered between their jet lashes.

'Hadn't that occurred to you? If I *had* driven after him, what do you think he would have done? Put his foot down and driven like a madman and heaven help anyone who got in his way. Gavin can be a little crazy once he gets into the sort of mood he was in tonight. I wonder how well you know your brother.'

He parked again a few doors down from the St James's Club to which they had headed. 'Why don't you wait in the car while I take a look to see if he's there?'

'I'd rather come with you,' she said belligerently. 'I doubt if Gavin would leave if you asked him, but he might for me.'

'He will if I ask, too,' said Brodie with a menace that made her stiffen. 'Stay in the car, Donna. It would be wiser. I may need to use force and you'd just get in my way.'

He got out and walked away and she hesitated, wondering whether to disobey him and follow. On the whole she decided he was probably right. If Gavin was drunk there might be a scene, whether she was there or not. Whatever methods Brodie used to get her brother out of that club it would be best is she didn't have to witness them.

Nervously, she watched in the driving-mirror as Brodie turned into the club entrance. It was stupid to feel guilty, as though in letting Brodie go there alone she was betraying Gavin. If she thought for an instant that her brother would come home if she asked him, she would have gone in there alone, but she couldn't get Gavin's bitter face out of her mind. Her brother was hurt and angry and off balance. He wouldn't listen to her, whatever she said.

She didn't have to wait very long. She heard the scuffle as Brodie pulled Gavin out of the door, heard her brother's voice raised in drunken fury. Gavin was swearing, using words that made her wince.

Brodie ignored what he was being called. He had Gavin's arm twisted up behind his back and he was propelling him along the road as fast as he could in the face of Gavin's violent struggles.

Donna got out shakily and opened the rear door of the car. Brodie thrust Gavin inside a moment later, and Donna got a look from her brother that made her face go white.

Brodie got behind the wheel and she sank back into

her seat. Gavin was wrenching at the door handle, but Brodie had already locked it electronically from the dashboard. Gavin was a prisoner. Realising that, he slumped back, fuming, and said nothing at all as Brodie drove back to the Cowley house along the motorway at a speed that made Donna clutch at the seat and swallow in sheer terror.

They pulled up on the drive and Brodie switched off the automatic door lock. Gavin stumbled out and into the house without a glance at either of them.

CHAPTER EIGHT

WHEN Donna visited her father next day, she was astonished to find that he was out of bed. She stopped and stared, her arms full of books and flowers, and James Cowley chuckled.

'Your eyes don't deceive you!'

'Do the staff know you're out of bed?' she asked, coming slowly towards him.

'Of course.' He was seated in an armchair, his thin body draped in a thick dressing-gown, maroon terry towelling, a newspaper clutched in one hand.

She bent and kissed his cheek. 'You look so much better! At this rate you'll be coming home soon.'

'In a week or so, they tell me. They think I'm making good progress. These days, they believe in getting you out of bed as soon as possible. Lying in bed for weeks just gives you bedsores and makes your recovery slower than it has to be.'

She laid the bunch of roses on his bed-table and showed him the detective stories she had brought him. 'Nice light reading for you—that will keep your mind active without making you agitated.'

He grimaced. 'I had a heart attack, not a brainstorm! My mind's fine.'

Donna looked around for another chair and saw one in the corner. She pulled it over next to him and sat down. 'How long have you been out of bed?' she asked.

'About five minutes before you arrived!' he said,

smiling at her. 'And I'll be put back as soon as you've gone. The general idea is to feed me back into ordinary life as fast as they can. They want my bed and don't scruple to tell me so.'

She laughed. 'It *is* a busy hospital!'

'As you say,' he agreed, nodding. 'Are those roses from the garden?'

'Yes, I thought you'd like to have your own roses instead of hothouse flowers.'

'Can I smell them?' he asked, and she got up and brought them over to him.

He bent his head and inhaled, closing his eyes, 'Ah, yes. Shop-bought flowers never seem to have a real scent. They're lovely, thank you, Donna. Did you pick them yourself?'

'Every one!' she said lightly. 'And got a thorn in my finger to prove it.' She held out her finger, smiling, and her father stared at the tiny dark red mark, then bent forward and kissed it.

Donna was utterly shaken. They both were, flushing and unable to look at each other. It was the first time her father had really shown affection since she was a very small girl. He pushed the roses into her hands in silence and she got up and replaced them on his bed-table.

'Where's Brodie today?' her father asked huskily.

'He went to work.' Donna sat down again, her eyes restlessly skating around the spotless, antiseptic room. 'He hadn't been since . . .' she broke off, not liking to say that Brodie hadn't been into the office since her father had his heart attack.

'Well, work must go on,' James Cowley said approvingly, nodding. 'Brodie's got a lot on his plate at the moment. I expect he's told you.'

He hadn't asked about Gavin, and she resented that on her brother's behalf and reminded her father edgily, 'Gavin would have come, but he isn't very well and we thought he'd better not visit you in case he was coming down with a cold.' It wasn't true, of course. Gavin hadn't emerged from his room by the time Donna was ready to leave for the hospital. No doubt he was sleeping off the excesses of last night. He had obviously been very drunk by the time Brodie caught up with him in the gambling club. It had been one in the morning by the time they got back to the house and Donna hadn't got to sleep until well past two. It hadn't been easy for her to get up that morning, and *she* hadn't been drunk, the night before. Gavin would probably have a head like a furred kettle this morning. She wasn't eager to see him again. He was going to be in one hell of a mood.

Her father frowned. 'I don't know what to do about Gavin, and that's the truth. I'd hoped he would get his act together sooner or later. He's not a fool. There's no reason why he shouldn't do well in the firm—but he just doesn't give his mind to it.'

Donna considered him wryly. How could you get it through to him that he was trying to force a square peg into a round hole?

'Did you ever dream about being a painter, Father?' she asked.

James Cowley looked amazed. 'A painter? An artist, you mean? Good God, no. Can't draw to save my life.'

'Gavin's a talented artist, did you know that?'

Her father gazed, brows heavy. 'Are you trying to tell me he wants to be a painter?'

'No,' she said, and he looked relieved.

'Well, thank heavens for that! You had me worried for a minute. I don't know anything about artists and I don't much care to know, either, A ramshackle lot—live in a hand-to-mouth way, morals don't mean a thing to them. I've always had a question mark against Gavin, he was a funny child, and he isn't much better now, either.'

'He wants to do something more with his life than work in an office,' Donna said gently. 'I think he may have real talent.'

'For what? Gambling? Drinking?' Her father was very flushed and his voice had an agitated note. She wished she had never started this discussion and drew back at once, smiling soothingly.

'I just meant that I think there's more to Gavin than you realise. He'll grow out of his wildness, I'm sure he will.'

Her father relaxed a little. 'I wish he was more like you,' he grunted. 'I'm proud of the way you've grown up. Going to France, getting a job, learning the language the way you did—I was angry at first, but as Brodie said, you needed to be independent for a while, find out what the world's like before you settled down. That might have been the right thing for Gavin to do. Maybe I was wrong, making him come into the firm. I'm human, I make mistakes, like anybody else. But for goodness' sake, Donna, he's nearly twenty-four! When is he going to stop acting like a fool?'

She had prickled at hearing Brodie quoted as an authority on what she did. So that was what Brodie had told her father, was it? It sounded remarkably like 'give her a little rope, then we'll pull her back to us'. A shiver ran down her back. Had Brodie always intended to come after her sooner or later? How had they kept an eye on what she did? Through Gavin? Her brother had visited her several times and she had written to him, but she hadn't communicated with either Brodie of her father and they hadn't been in touch with her. Had Brodie used the detective agency who had been watching her flat the night Gavin appeared in such a startling way? She wouldn't put it past him. It made her feel hunted to imagine him keeping a long-distance eye on her for the two years she had been in Paris.

'Talking about Paris,' she said flatly. 'I've got to go back there this weekend—a good friend of mine is getting married and I promised to be at her wedding. So I won't see you until I get back, Father. Next Tuesday, probably.'

'Is Brodie going with you?' he asked, frowning.

'No. He'll visit you. And so will Gavin. If I'm needed, they can get in touch with me quickly, don't worry, and I will be back, I promise.'

She wouldn't have gone if her father hadn't been so much better. Only that morning she had remembered that she must ring Alain Roche and explain that she couldn't come back that weekend, and then ring Marie-Louise to explain to her too, and wish her all the happiness in the world. But having seen how well James Cowley looked she decided she should go to Lyons. She could fly back from there on the Sunday, in fact, which would mean that she would only be away for two days.

She heard the bell signal the end of the visiting-period and got up to kiss her father. 'I'll try to be here on Monday, how's that?'

He smiled, nodding, but even when he looked

cheerful it made her wince to see how thin and frail he had become in the last two years. He had more colour today, it was true. His mouth no longer had that blue tinge nor was his face a deadly grey. But his neck resembled the neck of a tortoise, wrinkled and scaly, and his eyes were so sunken and tired, watering a little all the time.

When she got back to the house it was half past five because she had stopped in Saffron Walden to do some shopping and have tea in a little café close to the market square. Mrs Eyre was in the hall, polishing the table vigorously. She looked round, smiling.

'How's your father today?'

'Much better—out of bed and reading his newspaper!'

The housekeeper straightened her back. 'Well, that's marvellous news! Those doctors are wonderful the way they get him back on his feet. It was the same last time he had an attack. I really thought he'd never pull through that one, and Gavin was so upset—well, he would be, wouldn't he? It was all his fault, but then he and his father have always quarrelled like dog and cat.' She gave Donna a rueful smile.

Thoughtfully, Donna asked, 'How did Gavin cause my father's attack?'

'I shouldn't have spoken out of turn, it's not my business,' said Mrs Eyre, looking agitated. 'It was just another of their arguments. Your father collapsed and was whisked off to hospital and Gavin didn't eat a thing for days. He's one of those who brood over everything, isn't he? A funny boy, he always was.'

Donna went up to her room, frowning. Was that why Gavin hadn't told her about their father's weak heart?

Guilt? A reluctance to talk about something he secretly felt he had caused?

She looked into his room, but it was empty, the door wide open and no sign of her brother. When had he got up? She turned back to ask Mrs Eyre where he was, but at that moment Brodie came out of his own room.

'Oh, you're back early,' she said stupidly, feeling her heart flip over. He had been gone by the time she got up that morning, and she had been expecting him back much later. She knew that office hours ended at five-thirty, and even if he left on time—which, being Brodie, he rarely did—she had worked out that it would take him several hours, at least, to get back here from the city during the rush hour.

'I left after lunch with a client,' he said. 'I'd managed to get through the backlog on my desk by midday, went off to lunch, then drove back to have a word with Gavin.'

'Where is he?'

'Oh, he's gone,' Brodie said coolly, walking back into his own room.

Donna followed, startled. 'Gone? What do you mean—gone?'

Brodie began unbuttoning his shirt. 'I'm just going to have a shower,' he said. 'It was damned hot driving back from London.'

'Where's Gavin?' Donna insisted, too agitated to notice at first what Brodie was doing.

'He's gone to the Midlands—he'll be away for a couple of days.' Brodie shrugged out of his shirt, and her nervous eyes flickered over his smooth, muscled shoulders, the deep tanned chest, the rough curls of black hair growing up the centre of it, and the flat midriff. Brodie might work in an office at a desk five days a week, but he had the powerful body of an athlete. In the confined space of the bedroom Donna became intensely conscious of that fact and backed towards the door and safety.

She swallowed an odd little lump in her throat. Her voice sounded rusty when it finally came out. 'Why?'

Brodie put a hand to the zip of his trousers. 'Can we talk later? I'm dying for that shower.'

Hot-cheeked, she spun on her heel and stood with her back to him, saying crossly, 'Just tell me why Gavin has gone to the Midlands. I thought we'd agreed that he wasn't to be left alone again until he saw this psychiatrist friend of yours?'

She heard the zip slide and hurriedly moved even further away, until she was actually in the doorway.

'Donna, you can't treat Gavin as if he were a child. If he's determined to gamble, nothing you can do will stop him. But he isn't alone, as it happens. One of our sales reps was going up to the Midlands this afternoon and Gavin went with him. George is level-headed, he knows Gavin's problem and he'll keep a fatherly eye on him. He has a son not much younger than Gavin. He can deal with it.'

She heard him stepping out of his trousers, and was about to leave when Brodie said, 'I've made an appointment for Gavin with a small private glass-works—if they like him, they might give him an apprenticeship. It's mainly stained glass they make, but it isn't a factory, it's an honest-to-God workshop, and he could learn far more there than he ever would at a technical school.'

Donna began to turn, then remembered that he was

probably naked, and stopped, her face very flushed.

'That's very good of you, was Gavin thrilled?' she stammered.

She heard Brodie move and tensed as his voice came from right behind her. 'He seemed excited, and he jumped at the chance to leave with George. His appointment is tomorrow morning and we'll know whether he's got the apprenticeship by tomorrow night.'

'Oh, good,' she said, shakily, anxious to get away from him, but as she began to walk off his hands caught her arms and held her back, pulling her against him.

'What are you doing?' she burst out thickly, a tremor running through her.

His mouth moved against her nape, his breathing stirred her hair. 'Is that all the thanks I get for going to so much trouble for your brother?'

'I thought you wanted a shower,' she muttered, fiercely aware of his thighs leaning against the back of her legs.

'It can wait,' he said, his hands sliding down her arms and closing on her waist, yet still holding her a prisoner.

'I've got a lot to do,' she protested, trying to break free.

His hands had wandered upwards, she felt his fingertips lightly brush her breasts and that galvanised her into a real struggle. Brodie let her go and laughed as she tore across the landing and slammed into her room.

She leaned on the door, breathless, angry, hot. How dared he maul her about like that when he was still having an affair with Christabel Clair? Whatever they had quarrelled about and whatever threat of leaving for

America she had made, Donna couldn't believe their affair was over. It had survived Christabel's infidelity—there must be a very serious bond between them. Perhaps Christabel had been unfaithful to him because Brodie had strayed first? That had never occurred to her until that moment—but now she thought back over the way he had acted ever since she saw him again in Paris and angrily bit her lip.

He had been flirting with her for days and he was good at it. She wouldn't find it hard to believe he meant it when he smiled at her like that. Yet she knew he still saw Christabel—which meant that Brodie wasn't to be trusted. He was deceptive; how many other woman had there been in his life? She had no idea, had she?

Was that why Christabel had been unfaithful to him? Donna didn't know her very well, but she could imagine that Christabel Clair was a jealous woman, capable of ruthless retaliation for a slight. Christabel wouldn't stand for any sort of treachery from him. She was tougher than Donna could ever be.

Brodie was a match for her, though. He was good at omitting facts, practising sleight of hand with the truth. After all, he had never told Donna about his relationship with Christabel. Not a syllable had passed his lips. Her father hadn't known he was engaged to anyone before he met Donna, had he?

She thought back bitterly to the first weeks after they met. She could have sworn that Brodie had nothing on his mind but work and herself. Who would have guessed that such a short time before they met he had been engaged to marry another woman and, presumably, in love?

They had met at a dinner-party in this house. Donna

had just finished college and was uncertain what to do next, but while she made up her mind she had taken a job with her father's newest factory in the personnel department. She had made it clear to her father that it was a temporary job. He had never taken much interest in her career stategy—she knew that that was because he didn't think girls needed careers. Her father had an old-fashioned view of women's rights. He simply thought that girls got married and stayed at home, unless their husband needed a little extra money for a year or two, in which case they worked until they could afford to have a baby.

Donna had always intended to have a career, in spite of that. Then she had met Brodie and her plans had dissolved. She knew, of course, almost at once, that her father was eager to pair them off. James Cowley made no secret of it. He pushed her at Brodie. She might have been furious if she hadn't been so attracted to Brodie anyway, right from that first meeting over dinner.

It was several months before Brodie first began to hint that they should get married, and by the time he did mention the idea Donna was head over heels in love. She couldn't remember a formal proposal. Brodie just talked casually about the future and seemed to take it for granted that it would be a future they shared. The moment when it crystallised for her was when he asked her where she wanted to live.

'Do you prefer the country? London would be more convenient,' he said lightly. She had breathlessly said either was fine.

A few days later as they walked past a Bond Street jeweller's Brodie had stopped and looked at rings in the window. 'Any stone you particularly fancy?'

She hadn't expected him to go down on his knees. That wasn't the modern way. Men today approached marriage practically; she was happy with Brodie's casual attitude.

She had been all too ready to fall in with whatever he suggested. Now she despised herself—she had been so easy to get! Brodie had lazily stretched out his hand and she had dropped into it like a ripe fruit.

Just at the moment when he was bitterly angry with Christabel he had met a girl who could offer him what Christabel couldn't—a solid gold future. He had begun chasing her with his eyes wide open while she had gone around in a besotted dream.

She bolted her door and sat on the bed, burning in self-contempt. What a fool she had been! And still was—even now that she knew just what sort of man he was, she couldn't get him out of her heart. Did he know she still cared?

If he didn't, it wasn't because she was so good at hiding her feelings. Angrily she faced the fact that she kept giving herself away. Every time he came near her she went weak at the knees. She was so jealous of Christabel that she couldn't stop herself from making a cheap, vicious remark, something she would never do in normal circumstances!

She got up reluctantly and went to her warbdrobe to find something to wear. If Gavin was away, she was going to be alone with Brodie, apart from Mrs Eyre, and the housekeeper stayed in her own flat once her work was done. Donna couldn't ask Mrs Eyre to join them. She could imagine the expression on the other woman's face if she did! Mrs Eyre thought they were lovers again, thanks to Brodie's insistence that they shouldn't tell her the truth.

He had an ulterior motive, of course. Donna wasn't fooled. She knew Brodie was plotting against her—but it wouldn't do him any good, because this time she wasn't going to be taken in by any of his smooth talk.

As she took a quick shower herself and changed she thought uneasily about the future. She couldn't leave her father alone. If Gavin did get a job in the Midlands she was going to have to give up her apartment in Paris and settle back at home again. That meant that Brodie would be around all the time. And that, in turn, meant trouble; she didn't need help in working that out.

Angry though she was with Brodie, she had to be grateful to him for helping Gavin to get this chance of an apprenticeship. No doubt Gavin had been over the moon about it. She was glad he was happy, but it left her such a problem! Could she bear to return to this battlefield on which she had been defeated so painfully once, knowing in her secret heart that her weapons were no more powerful this time, that Brodie had one overriding advantage—that she was still passionately in love with him?

When she had dressed in a simple green linen sheath with a stiff white collar and cuffs she sat in front of her dressing-table mirror staring grimly at her reflection.

She was such a fool. Brodie must know he had her in the palm of his hand. If she came back here, he would coolly take possession of her unless she could come up with some strategy for keeping him permanently at bay.

Brodie tapped on her door a short time later. 'Mrs Eyre would like to have dinner early tonight—she's visiting her sister, and wants to get away quickly.'

Donna went downstairs with him to eat the cold meal Mrs Eyre had put out—melon, followed by a salad with a platter of cold meat, and a gooseberry fool.

There were roses on the table from the garden—dark red ones with glowing hearts and petals like smooth skin.

'I gather your father will be coming home next week some time,' said Brodie. 'That's good news, isn't it? Mrs Eyre's already combing her recipe books for his favourite foods.'

Donna managed a faint smile, nodding. 'He looked so much better this afternoon—I hardly recognised him after the way he looked the first day.'

'If Gavin's going to be away, your father will be alone here,' Brodie said casually. 'Something will have to be done about that.'

She had hardly eaten a thing. She had no appetite. She felt like a mouse which had crept into an empty bottle left in a field—she was trapped and couldn't escape although she could see freedom all around her.

'You'll have to come home, Donna,' said Brodie in a soft voice, watching her intently, smiling.

She felt fever in her veins; a hectic iciness. He had her cornered and he knew it. She reached out a trembling hand and pulled a rose out of the vase and began methodically shredding it; crimson petal by crimson petal falling from her fingers in a passionate rain.

She couldn't answer, although she had already decided to do just that. Her eyes stared fixedly at the tumbling petals and Brodie watched her.

'Your father can't live alone, not in his state of health. It's either you or Gavin, Donna. I can't make you come home, but if you don't, Gavin won't get his chance to escape.'

Was that why he had gone to so much trouble to get Gavin an apprenticeship in the Midlands? Only then did it occur to her that Brodie might have done that deliberately, with the intention of forcing her back from France. He had a convoluted mind; it wasn't easy to follow the twists and turns of it even when you knew the motives propelling him.

It was at that instant that she decided to leave for Paris first thing in the morning without telling Brodie she was going. She had intended to tell him and Mrs Eyre this evening, but now she saw that if she was ever to establish her own right to make a decision, if she was ever to defy his attempt to manipulate and control her, she must start at once. Now, tonight, she must make a private declaration of independence.

She was going to Paris because she chose to—she was going on to Lyons with her friends because she chose to. If Brodie knew she meant to go, he would try to stop her. She knew that with utter certainty. He would threaten, cajole, persuade—somehow he would find a way of stopping her if he could.

So she wouldn't give him the chance to do any of that. She would take a leaf out of his book—if he could be cunning and deceitful, so could she! She would tell him she had a headache, in a minute, and go up to bed early. Of course, he wouldn't believe a word of it. He would smile sarcastically and think she was running away because she was so scared of being alone with him. But he wouldn't be able to stop her and because he was so confident of winning in the end he would probably let her go, and once she was safely in her room with the door locked she would quietly pack a few things.

Tomorrow when he had gone to the office she would get Mrs Eyre to drive her to the railway station and she would get the first possible plane to Paris.

CHAPTER NINE

MARIE-LOUISE didn't look radiant—she looked positively incandescent, thought Donna, as she watched her friend at the wedding reception, going from group to group in the hotel ballroom, kissing them in the French manner, once on each cheek for distant relatives, twice on each cheek for close friends and three times on each cheek when she hugged her grandmother, who had lent Marie-Louise the soft, goldy-white veil she wore. It was more than two hundred years old, that lace, and had been made by one of Marie-Louise's family here in Lyons. No doubt it had been pure white when it was first made, but time had conferred on it a gentle colour change—it was now a yellowing ivory. Among its folds gleamed pearls and tiny white roses, the coronet holding it in place.

The wedding had been very long and very beautiful; a sung mass with a choir hidden somewhere and a haunting echo of their voices coming back from the high roof of the mediaeval church. Looking upwards, Donna had seen angel faces among the dark wooden beams, carved gilded cherubs flying over their heads. The sun had shone through ancient stained glass, colouring the faces of the congregation. Marie-Louise's voice had sounded unfamiliar, husky, uncertain, but there was nothing unsure about her now—she blazed with happiness.

'You look wistful, *chérie*,' remarked Alain, leaning

over to smile at Donna.

'Sorry, do I?' She had been trying to smile for hours now. It wasn't easy because she envied Marie-Louise so much. It must be wonderful to be so secure in your love; to feel no doubts, no anxieties, no pangs of jealousy.

'Would you like to be getting married?'

'Is that a proposal?'

Alain laughed, putting up both hands in Gallic horror. 'Ah, no, *chérie*! I am not the marrying type. But you, I think, are.' His glinting eyes watched her thoughtfully. 'Yes, I think so.'

'Most people are, sooner or later,' shrugged Donna.

'This is true, but I am not most people,' Alain said with grateful fervour.

An hour later they danced together and almost bumped into Marie-Louise and her husband as Alain swirled Donna around, the full skirts of her strawberry-pink dress flying up in rustling layers.

'Having a good time?' Marie-Louise asked over her husband's shoulder, winking.

'Terrific!'

It was odd, but Donna already felt that Marie-Louise was different—from now on their lives would be totally separated, they might keep in touch, but it would never be the same again. Marie-Louise would have other preoccupations, other friends, other things on her mind. A wedding was the end as well as a beginning; one of the great divides of life.

They had a chance for a talk a little later when Marie-Louise and Jean-Paul stopped dancing and came to sit at the same table. Marie-Louise sent Alain off to dance with another girl in the party and chased her new husband away, smiling at him.

'Go and talk to your mother! She is all alone. I want to talk to Donna.'

Jean-Paul kissed her nose. 'Okay, *mignonne*! Don't forget, we leave in half an hour!'

'As if I would!'

'When women start talking they forget everything!' Jean-Paul grinned and went off, however, and Marie-Louise smoothed back her veil with a tender hand.

'Marriage is exhausting—it will take me a month to get over it. I don't know whether I'm on my head or my heels—I seem to have been rushing about for days now.'

'You look good on it,' Donna said affectionately, smiling back at her. 'It obviously suits you.'

Her friend laughed. 'Yes, I think so.' Her face became a little more serious. 'But tell me, *chérie*—what is this about your father being very ill? Alain told me a while ago. I'd no idea! Is it very serious?'

'He's recovering a little, but he has a weak heart,' Donna answered soberly, and told her about the events of the past week. 'I thought for a while that I wouldn't get to your wedding, in fact, but he was so much better that I thought I would risk it. I left the name and phone number of the hotel here with the hospital and my father's housekeeper so that if anything did happen they could reach me quickly, but in any case I've decided to fly back early tomorrow morning. I'm sorry to miss the fun Alain and the others are organising for tomorrow, but I think I ought to get back.'

Marie-Louise nodded. 'Of course. You must be very worried. It was good of you to come all this way when you had so much on your mind.' She leaned over and kissed Donna lightly on both cheeks. 'Thank you for the lovely silver fruit bowl. We will cherish it.'

'And you'll keep in touch?'

'Without fail.' Marie-Louise looked at her thoughtfully. 'And what will you do now? You won't stay in Paris, if your father is so ill?'

'No, I think I'll have to go home to live,' Donna agreed, sighing.

'It is a pity, I know how much you enjoyed Paris—but family is family.'

Donna smiled ruefully. 'How true!'

She didn't confide in Marie-Louise all the other problems on her mind. It wasn't something she wanted to talk about, and it wasn't the time or place for such confidences, anyway.

Marie-Louise eyes twinkled. 'Alain will be very disappointed. He's always fancied you and he probably thought he had a chance to get you alone for a while!'

Donna laughed. 'Too bad for Alain! He'll survive. There are plenty of other fish in the sea for Alain.'

The party continued for a long time after the bridal couple had left on their honeymoon. The band went on playing, the dancers went on dancing, people went on drinking and talking at the tables for some hours until gradually they drifted away in groups of two or three or more, saying goodbye to Marie-Louise's parents before they slipped away.

'I think we ought to go,' Donna murmured to Alain, glancing at her watch and seeing that it was gone ten o'clock. 'If I'm to fly back to London tomorrow, I ought to get to bed quite early.'

He made a wry face. 'The night's still young! I thought we'd go on to dance somewhere after we left here.'

The others in the group nodded cheerfully. 'Good idea! Let's do that!'

'I can't,' said Donna.

They tried to persuade her for a few more minutes. 'We may not see you for a long time! One last evening—come on, Donna!'

'Weddings depress me,' Alain said mournfully, looking quite lugubrious, his eyes dark circles in his ugly-attractive face. 'I need cheering up!'

Donna laughed at him. 'I'm sure someone will do that! One of your little flies!'

Their friends rocked with laughter. 'Mr Frog and his little flies,' they chorused. 'Yes, one will come buzzing around you, Alain!'

He gazed coaxingly at Donna. 'But I want you to come—just tonight, one evening together, just us, Donna.'

'I'd have loved to, but I can't, Alain, not tonight. Some other time we'll have dinner together and talk or whatever.' His friends hooted softly, but she ignored them, concentrating on Alain's reproachful expression. 'It's been such a scramble to get here for the wedding and I'm dead on my feet. I must get some sleep tonight.'

He shrugged resignation. 'Okay—but I'll see you back to the hotel.' He looked at the others, grinning at their amused expressions. 'You can go on to the disco club. I'll find you there later.'

'Much later?' they enquired wickedly.

Donna gave them a dry, irritated look. She knew what they were thinking—that Alain would stay with her for a few hours. If that was what Alain had in mind he could think again!

On the way back to the hotel, though, she realised

Alain had no motive in taking her back there except to make sure she arrived carefully. As soon as they were alone his manner lapsed into ordinary friendliness. His persistence with her had been purely for the benefit of his friends—and his own reputation.

It must be a bore having to live up to that, she thought. Poor Alain; did he feel tired every time he saw a woman?

With her, at least, he could talk of other things—books, plays, films. The subject of sex didn't enter into their murmured conversation.

When they got to the hotel, Alain came with her in the lift up to the floor on which they both had rooms. Outside her room he watched her unlock the door and switch on the light, then kissed her on both cheeks, holding her shoulders, as if she were a soldier getting a medal for bravery and he were a general.

'Don't forget us, *chérie*. I'm going to miss you—you'll keep in touch? You'll write now and then?'

She nodded, smiling up at him. 'Of course, if you'll write back.'

'I don't have your home address,' he said. 'Will you give it to me tonight—if you don't remember to write to me I can remind you!'

She laughed and opened her bag to find a pencil and paper. Alain came into the room and closed the door with his foot; the latch didn't click and she had no worries that he might be planning to stay. He stood politely watching her begin to scribble down her home address.

His friends would never believe that their relationship was platonic! She might well have smiled cynically at the notion if she had been told that Alain's friendship with any other woman was purely asexual. The trouble with men was that their ego formed their idea of themselves and everyone else accepted that self-image. Alain wanted to have a reputation as a great lover—or had done when he was younger. Now he was bored with it but couldn't shake it off. It had once been a halo round his head—now it was a millstone round his neck. Poor Alain!

She handed him the piece of paper and he glanced at the address before folding it and sliding it into his wallet.

'Have a safe trip back to England tomorrow,' he said, turning to the door. '*Au revoir, petite.* I hope your father is much better when you get home.'

The hotel was half empty, as they had noticed when they arrived, and now it was very still and silent, presumably all the other guests were either out enjoying themselves or fast asleep, so they kept their voices down discreetly, murmuring to each other in soft French.

'Goodnight, Alain.' said Donna, kissing his cheek. 'Have a good time tonight.'

He grimaced. 'I don't know why I do it.' The door stood partially open now. He turned to go saying, 'But I suppose I must join the others or they'll think the worst.' His eyes held a faint amusement. He took hold of the door. 'Now you can get to bed,' he said teasingly, and at that second someone pushed against the door violently and Alain tumbled backwards, taking Donna with him. Instinct made her grab at him to save herself falling. Alain collided with the wall of her room, a stunned expression on his sallow face. He threw his arms round her, grunting as if winded.

'Are you okay, *chérie?*'

'What . . .' she began, looking round at the door.

'Some drunk, I suppose,' Alain said in French, his tone disgusted.

Donna was staring at the man framed in the doorway; her face first white, then scalding red.

'I'll deal with him,' Alain assured her, gently shifting her to one side so that he could square up to Brodie Fox. He had seen him before, but he didn't appear to have recognised him this time.

Donna couldn't move or speak; she was too horrified. What was Brodie doing here?

'*M'sieur,* please leave before I call the hotel security,' said Alain in clipped French.

'I want to talk to you,' Brodie told Donna in English that had icicles on it.

Alain's head swung back to her, brows rising. '*Chérie*. You know him?'

Flushed, she began to say, 'Yes, he . . .'

'Get your boy-friend out of here before I spoil his face!' Brodie cut across her stammered explanation.

Alain's eyes narrowed on his face. 'I've seen him before, I think? Yes? In Paris at the Ritz, that was the man you were dining with?'

Half angry, half upset, Donna said, 'I'm sorry, Alain—you'd better go, I'll have to talk to him.'

He gave one of his wry little shrugs. 'Are you sure you want to, *chérie*?'

'Whether she wants to or not, she's going to,' Brodie said in Alain's own tongue, investing the French with considerable bite.

Alain considered him without seeming very impressed. 'He looks rather bad-tempered,' he said to

Donna as if Brodie couldn't understand him, in spite of the fact that he must now realise that Brodie did.

'You had better believe it,' grated Brodie through his teeth, Then he turned on Donna with a violence that made her jump. 'Get him out of here before *I* do!'

'*M'sieur* your manners leave much to be desired,' Alain said with enormous dignity, drawing himself up to his full height but completely failing to look any more impressive beside Brodie's six feet of muscled power.

'I'm not wasting any more time on him,' Brodie said, lip curling, taking a long stride towards him.

Donna leapt between them as Alain immediately tensed to meet whatever Brodie meant to do.

'That's enough! How dare you come bursting in here, throwing your weight around?'

'I am not scared of him, *chérie*,' Alain told her, dancing on his toes with his fists up. 'Let him try to hit me! I learnt to box at school.'

'No, I don't want any fighting in here—Alain, you'd better go now. Don't worry about me, I can handle him.' She hoped her voice sounded a little more confident than she felt. She suspected it didn't, from the searching look she got from Alain.

'You think so? It doesn't look like it to me! But if that's what you want, I'll be in my own room across the corridor—if you need me, you only have to call.'

Brodie was listening, his brows black and drawn above his glittering eyes. Donna ignored him and smiled waveringly at Alain.

'Thank you. I'll remember.'

Alain nodded and gave Brodie a long stare. '*M'sieur,* upset Donna and you'll have me to deal with.'

Brodie didn't bother to answer him; he merely

snarled wordlessly, holding the door open in a very pointed fashion. Alain went out, bristling, and Brodie slammed the door after him.

'How dare you behave like this to a friend of mine?' Donna burst out, trembling with anger.

'Friend?' Brodie laughed shortly.

'What are you doing in Lyons, anyway? You must have followed me here.' She was only just beginning to think clearly and a pang of alarm flashed across her face. 'My father . . .?'

'He's still holding his own—not that that bothers you much, or you wouldn't have come over here to meet your boy-friend!'

'Don't shout at me!' said Donna coldly, eyeing him with resentment. It was a relief to know that her father wasn't any worse, but once she had taken that in she found her mind filling with other, just as violent, feelings. Who did Brodie think he was? What made him believe he had the right to put her actions under some sort of moral microscope? She remembered Christabel Clair with mounting fury and bitter distate—Brodie was a hypocrite. If he thought he could walk in here and sit in judgement on her he was quite wrong.

'How could you do it?' Brodie demanded, looking at her as though he couldn't believe his eyes. 'You came here with him for the weekend—is he your lover?'

'Mind your own business!'

'It is my business,' Brodie ground out almost without unclenching his teeth.

'Oh, no, it isn't!'

'Damn you, I tell you it is!' shouted Brodie, making her uneasily conscious of the stillness of the hotel around them. Alain would have heard that from his room. She didn't want him coming back. Brodie was in the sort of mood where he might do anything, and Donna didn't want to find herself being turned out of the hotel in the middle of the night, or being taken off to the Lyons police station in a pair of handcuffs.

'Be quiet!' she hissed. 'How dare you come into my room kicking up a scene like this! I didn't ask you in here and I don't want you anywhere near me, so get out!'

He took a step closer and bent, his face a threat even though he didn't actually touch her.

Have you slept with that Frenchman?'

Scarlet, Donna slapped his face.

Brodie's head went back with the impact, a hot brand appearing on his cheek where she had made contact. For a second Donna thought he was going to hit her back, then he took hold of her shoulders and shook her violently.

'That's no answer! Tell me the truth!'

'It's all the answer you're going to get! What right do you think you have to question me about my private life? You haven't told me anything about yours, have you? And mine is a damn sight less eventful that yours!'

He didn't let go of her, ignoring her furious struggle to get free.

'I'm trying not to lose my temper!' he said, and she laughed in angry disbelief at this fantastic statement. 'What?'

'But I want the truth,' Brodie went on, ignoring that too. He appeared to be breathing as if he had just done an hour's jogging. 'Answer me!'

'Why should I?' Donna threw back, and that seemed

to be a strategic mistake, like pouring petrol on a fire, because Brodie broke out even more angrily.

'How could you let him come anywhere near you?' His voice thickened with rage; he shook her with such force that her hair flew all over the place; covering her eyes. 'I'd like to kill you!'

Donna peered at him throuh the strands of hair, her stomach clenching at the way he said that. If she hadn't known what a plausible liar and hypocrite he was, she might almost have believed he meant that.

'Donna,' he said huskily, the faintest softening in his voice. 'You're torturing me—tell me the truth. Why did you come here to meet that fellow? You aren't in love with him, you can't be.'

'Why can't I?' she asked rhetorically. 'Alain's a nice man.'

Brodie made a grating, grinding noise with his teeth.

'A lot of women are in love with Alain,' said Donna defiantly.

'You must be joking! That ugly little creep?'

'He has to fend them off with judo,' Donna said with an angry triumph.

Brodie's expression was incredulous. 'I don't believe it—but even if it's true, I can't believe that *you* fancy him.'

'Why shouldn't I?'

'Because . . .' Brodie's voice broke off, deepening. 'You know very well why, Donna. You belong to me.'

She went white, shaking. 'Oh, no, I don't. I hate the very sight of you.'

'No,' he said fiercely. His hands flew up to frame her face. He bent and kissed her mouth with a passion that made her head spin, his lips hot and insistent, refusing to let her pull away until her body weakened and her own emotions undermined her resistance. Her eyes closed and her fingers gripped his shoulders, her head sinking back under the force of his kiss.

When Brodie lifted his head again she was dizzy and sick with self-contempt. She had been so determined not to let him get to her this time. She knew only too well what lay behind his pursuit of her to France, why he was so angry at the very idea that she should find another man attractive. Brodie didn't care whether she slept with Alain or not—all that worried him was his own future with her father's firm if he couldn't persuade her to marry him. He wanted her half of the family shares, her voting power in the company. He didn't want her personally at all. He never had—it had always been Christabel he really loved, if he could love anyone.

He looked down at her, a smile curving his mouth—a smile of complacency, triumph, self-congratulation, she thought, hating him. His eyes had a drowsy excitement, his face was darkly flushed—if she hadn't known better she might have believed that Brodie was in the grip of emotions as strong as her own.

But the truth was that Brodie had forced her to betray herself, and he was cock-a-hoop about it.

'We'll get married right away, before your father comes out of hospital. He couldn't stand the excitement of wedding arrangements, it would be much wiser to make his mistake the real thing without bothering to tell him.'

Donna went ice-cold, swallowing on a hard lump in her throat. 'No!' she whispered. He thought he had won, didn't he? But he was going to find how wrong he was! For once in his all-conquering career, Brodie Fox was going to suffer a defeat—and at her hands!

He looked at her mockingly. 'Yes, Donna,' he said softly, eyes gleaming with total assurance. 'Don't waste any more of our time with arguing.'

'You really must think I'm stupid!' she broke out. 'Do you think I've forgotten Christabel Clair? I haven't. I'm not sharing you with her, any more than she wants to share you with me. You'd better get it into your head, Brodie! You're never going to marry me!'

CHAPTER TEN

BRODIE stared at her attentively. 'Christabel?' he echoed.

Don't pretend you don't know what I mean! You are still having an affair with her—you admitted it the other day. She rang you and you went out to meet her and didn't come back all night, and when I told you I knew you didn't even deny it!'

'I told you I was out most of the night, I didn't say I'd been with Christabel.'

'It was Christabel who rang you. I talked to her myself—I know it was her.'

He walked over to a chair and sat down, stretching his long legs with an impatient sigh. 'Sit down, Donna.'

'I'm not . . .'

'Sit down!' His voice cracked like a whip and she stiffened in shock and affront. But perhaps it might be wiser to humour him this once because he was frowning in a way which alarmed her, and anyway, she wanted to hear his explanation. She had no intention of believing a word of it. She knew what a liar and a cheat he was. But she might as well listen. Calmly, with dignity, she walked to the bed and sat down on the furthest end of it, far enough away from him to be able to move fast if he took a step in her direction. A bed wasn't the safest place to be when you were alone with Brodie Fox.

He watched her, frowning. 'When I told you why I broke off my engagement to Christabel in the first place, there was one important piece I left out of my story.'

She threw a barbed look at him. 'I noticed.'

'Don't interrupt!' he snapped. 'You want to hear the whole story—I'm going to tell you the whole story, but I don't want you interrupting every two seconds.' He ran a hand over his dark hair. 'Where was I? Oh, yes, I didn't tell you the name of the man Christabel had an affair with—you know him and . . .'

'I know him?' Her voice died away as Brodie fixed a menacing glitter on her.

'What did I just tell you? You've thrown me off my track again. You can say whatever you like when I've finished telling you, but until then for heaven's sake, shut up!'

'No need to shout!' she muttered. 'Well, go on!'

'Thank you,' he said through his teeth. 'I didn't want the story getting around for his wife's sake—and he has a couple of kids! I'd promised him I wouldn't tell a living soul. Give me your word you won't tell anyone, Donna.'

'I promise I won't,' she said frowning.

He watched her uncertainly, then said, 'It was Tom Reed.'

Her jaw dropped. *'Tom?'* She couldn't believe it. Tom's wife, Jinny, was so pretty, a charming girl with kind, direct eyes and a lovely smile. They had two children and had always seemed so happy. Donna had always preferred Jinny to Tom who was slightly boring; a rather pompous man with an inflated idea of his own importance, interested in nothing but his own success and his own view of the world, it had seemd to her. Donna found it difficult to believe that Tom Reed would have an affair with anyone, let alone Christabel. He simply wasn't the type. He didn't seem to Donna to have the imagination to be unfaithful.

'I told you I broke his nose—didn't you notice Tom's nose is out of true? It never set properly.'

She suddenly realised that she *had* noticed Tom's nose, although she had never connected Tom with the man Brodie had had a fight with over Christabel. At that party, in Tom's house, she had several times caught sight of his nose and had wondered if he had broken it playing rugger the way a friend of Gavin's had. It had looked like that—a bump on the end of it and a distinct twist to the right.

'I did wonder how he'd broken his nose,' she said slowly. 'I decided it was probably rugger.'

'No, it was me,' said Brodie with a sort of grim satisfaction.

'That doesn't prove anything,' Donna threw at him. 'You can tell me any story you like—how do I know it's the truth? For all I know Tom Reed did break his nose playing rugger and barely knows Christabel.' She fixed Brodie with a cynical smile. 'If he was the man, why did you see so much of him once you knew? I didn't pick up any hint that you had anything against him. At the time, I thought he was your best friend.'

'He had been,' Brodie told her curtly. 'I stood godfather to his little boy. I'm fond of Jinny, she's a very nice girl. After I found out about Tom and Christabel, I had an almightly row with him, as I told you. I didn't see him for weeks, but we do business together, we belong to the same clubs—if I played golf, I'd see Tom. If I went for a drink, I'd see him at the bar. I couldn't just cut him off without a lot of gossip and without hurting Jinny's feelings. Gradually it dawned on me that it was Christabel who was to blame, not Tom. He isn't the type to wreck his marriage over another woman, he loves his kids. We met and had a few drinks and he swore he'd never see Christabel again, it was over, so . . .' He shrugged at her.

Donna stared. 'But she was at Tom's and Jinny's party!'

Brodie fixed hard eyes on her. 'And that's where you met her, isn't it?'

She nodded.

'Tom told me that the other night.' His smile was grim. 'The night Christabel rang urgently needing to talk to me—she needed my help. Tom had been at her place that evening and had collapsed. He was rambling, delirious, she couldn't get any sense out of him and he obviously couldn't drive himself home. Christabel thought he might be dying—she didn't know what to do. I went there and found Tom with a raging temperature, so I put him in my car, wrapped in a blanket. He was stark naked—Christabel hadn't been able to get his clothes back on him. So I took Tom to a hospital, told them he'd collapsed in the bath at the club after playing squash. I think they believed it—but it was Jinny I wanted to convince, of course. I had to make the story convincing. I stayed long enough at the hospital to find out that Tom had pneumonia, a viral kind, they said. Comes on suddenly with a gallop, he'd probably caught it from someone. They said he was very ill indeed and might have pleurisy. They were scathing about people playing sports when they are obviously ill. Once I knew Tom wasn't in immediate danger, I drove to his house to see Jinny. I thought I ought to be there when she heard the news. She was quite calm, actually, but she wanted to go to Tom, she insisted on staying at the hospital all night. Her mother had to drive over from the other side of London, so I said I'd stay in the house until the mother arrived so that Jinny could go at once. The mother didn't get there until gone midnight, and by the time I got back to your house it was nearly three.'

Donna believed the story. It was too circumstantial to be invented—it was easy anough to check, after all. There were too many other people involved for it to be a lie—he couldn't get the hospital to back him up in a lie, or Jinny's mother.

'So Tom hadn't stopped seeing Christabel,' she said slowly.

Brodie's face was angry. 'He'd lied to me. He didn't know what he was saying the night he collapsed, he kept on talking in this funny rambling way, and I found out a lot of things—for instance, how you came to meet Christabel. She engineered that, twisted Tom's arm to get him to invite her. It was the last thing he wanted to do—he was terrified of Jinny finding out what was going on. But Christabel blackmailed him into letting her come to his party—she suggested that Tom told Jinny she was one of his firm's clients. Jinny was rather amused to hear that a top model was investing with Tom's help. It didn't dawn on her that there was any more to it, of course. As far as Jinny knew, she had the perfect marriage.'

Donna winced at the bite of his voice. 'Poor Jinny!'

'Yes.' Brodie got up from the chair and came over towards her. Donna was suddenly nervous of him again. She didn't like the look in his eyes.

'That night was the first time I'd seen Christabel in two years,' Brodie told her in a crisp, insistent tone, sitting down next to her on the bed.

Donna shrank back against the pillows. 'And all that time Tom must have been going on with the affair. How could he do that to Jinny?' Although she was nervous about having Brodie so close to her, she was angry, too. If Jinny found out how would she feel?

'How could he do that?' she said again.

'God knows,' Brodie said tersely. 'I was so angry I almost felt like telling Jinny, smashing the whole thing wide open. She doesn't deserve a guy like Tom. I felt pretty furious with him about the way he'd lied to me, but I knew Jinny would be totally shattered. I couldn't tell her. Maybe I should have done, I don't know—all I do know is, I couldn't.'

'Oh, no, you couldn't!' Donna agreed. 'But it doesn't seem fair that he should get away with it. Years of lying and cheating! And he knew Christabel had deliberately gone out of her way to break up our . . .' She stopped, eyes meeting Brodie's.

'Yes,' he said softly, dangerously. 'I finally found out from Tom that I had him and Christabel to thank for that. It seemed to be on his conscience, he kept talking about it while he was delirious. To do him justice, I think Tom's so obsessed with Christabel that she can make him jump through hoops. He's such a very ordinary fellow; not too bright in some ways, a careful plodder more than a genius. He's always done the right things all his life. Worked hard, been a good husband and father, a pillar of the community—in the beginning I think he had a little fling with Christabel out of sheer boredom. Just for once he wanted to live dangerously. And then he got hooked. He couldn't give her up. I don't know if I'd call it love; it's too feverish for that. Tom's addicted, that's all.'

He looked at her, and Donna felt suddenly very uneasy. There was a warning glitter in his eyes.

She looked away, swallowing, 'You'd better go—it's very late and I have to get up in the morning to fly back to London.'

'I've told you the truth. I could use a little truth from you in return,' said Brodie, ignoring that. 'What's going on between you and that Frenchman?'

She kept her eyes down. 'We're friends, that's all.'

'Just good friends?' he sounded sarcastic; he obviously didn't believe her.

She looked up defiantly. 'That's all! We aren't here alone—we came in a party of eight. A friend of ours got married here today, we've been at the reception. The others went out dancing afterwards and Alain wanted me to go, but I said I had to get an early night so he saw me back to the hotel. He was going to join the others later.'

'And he doesn't fancy you?' drawled Brodie disbelievingly.

'Alain has a different woman every day of the week. He has incredible sex appeal, but he's rather tired of it, poor Alain. I'm a friend, there's never been anything else between us.'

'He has sex appeal?' Brodie's brows rose in dark arches. 'You're kidding!'

'You aren't a woman!' Donna said drily.

'That's true,' he murmured, smiling. 'Want me to prove it?'

She shifted further away. 'I wish you'd get off my bed! And leave!'

'We still have a few things to discuss,' he said coolly without budging.

'We don't have anything to discuss!'

'Why didn't you tell me that you were coming to Lyons to a friend's wedding? Why did you just leave?'

'I told my father and Mrs Eyre—and left my address here in case of emergency!'

'You didn't tell me,' he underlined with a flick of those cool eyes. 'Why, Donna?'

'Why should I? I don't have to tell you anything! I'm a free agent. I can come and go as I choose!' He might have convinced her that he wasn't having an affair with Christabel, but she still didn't believe he wanted to marry her because he loved her. He wanted her father's firm and she was the quickest way to get it.

'You wanted to make me jealous!' he accused.

Her face was hot. 'I didn't! I didn't tell you where I was going because I thought you might try to stop me.'

'You knew I wouldn't like the idea of you joining that Frenchman at Lyons for a weekend, you mean!'

'I mean that I didn't want all the hassle I knew I'd get if I told you I was coming back to France.'

'It comes to the same thing. You knew I wouldn't be too happy at the idea of you spending time with another man!'

'I've been doing that for the past two years and you haven't known anything about it!'

His face stiffened. 'Has there been anyone else, Donna?'

She couldn't quite meet the probe of his eyes. She didn't want to admit that there hadn't; that would give him too much to crow about.

He suddenly caught her chin in one hand and tipped her head back to make her look at him.

'I love you, Donna,' he said huskily.

She felt a deep, fierce pain inside her chest. 'Don't lie to me! You want my father's firm, not me!'

'I've *got* your father's firm,' he said harshly.

Donna's body jerked in shock. She stared at him, unable to ask what he meant. His face was grim and taut; all angles, his jaw clenched, his mouth hard, his eyes fixed on her.

'I've had it for nearly three years,' he said shortly. 'I bought a number of shares before I joined the firm. I've been adding to them since and when I realised I wanted to marry you I suggested that your father sell me enough shares to give me control. There was never any question of Gavin being able to run the company. Not merely because his heart isn't in it, but because he simply hasn't got the right sort of mind. Gavin's no business-man—your father knew that. When I told him I was going to marry you, he agreed to sell the block of shares you were going to inherit anyway. He didn't see why I was doing it until I pointed out that I didn't want anyone to think I was marrying you to get those shares.'

She bit her lower lip, very shaky. 'Why didn't you tell me?'

'I would have done—those shares were going to be my wedding present,' he said shortly.

Donna closed her eyes. 'Oh, Brodie, you fool!'

'Yes, I must have been a fool to think you'd trust me,' he said with a dry anger. 'I believed you loved me enough to marry me without knowing for certain that I didn't want the firm. You never seemed to doubt it until you met Christabel. Everything was fine until then, but out of that clear blue sky you hit me like a hurricane and before I knew what was happening you'd gone.'

'But you didn't come after me, explain.'

'Explain what? I didn't know you'd found out about Christabel. You didn't tell me why you suddenly turned against me, remember. You just told me you hated the sight of me and left, and after the things you said about me I was in such a state of shock that it was weeks before I started thinking clearly.'

'But you must have wondered.'

'Of course I damned well wondered! I went crazy trying to work out what had gone wrong between us. Your father and I talked it over and he said he thought you were probably just too young to think of marriage yet. He said I should leave you alone for a year or so, give you time to have some fun, experiment a little.' He paused, looking at her fixedly. 'Did you?'

'In some ways,' she said, looking down.

'What ways?' His voice thickened and she glanced through her lashes at him.

'I learnt a lot of French, discovered how to cook, got to know Paris very well,' she shrugged casually, knowing she was annoying him.

'Stop playing games! You know what I meant!' he erupted, moving closer and watching her like a cat at a mousehole. 'Has there been anyone else?'

'No,' she said, half smiling.

'It isn't funny,' Brodie gritted fiercely, gripping her shoulders. 'Don't laugh at me, damn you!'

'Two years is a long time to wait,' she said, feeling the tension of his fingers with a certain satisfaction. 'Why didn't you come to Paris to find me?'

'Frankly, because there hadn't been a sign from you,' he told her in brusque impatience. 'I have my pride. I wasn't chasing you if you really couldn't care less. I thought if you cared, you'd come home sooner or later and then I'd be able to tell.'

'Tell what?'

He shook her briefly. 'Tell whether I'd be wasting my time to try again,' he said curtly. 'When your father started having these heart attacks I wanted to get in touch, but he didn't want you brought back for that, and none of them was grave enough to warrant ignoring what he said. If they had become really serious, I would have felt I had to disobey him. It wasn't until Gavin bolted and I guessed he'd gone to you that I followed him, and had a good excuse for seeing you.'

Donna looked teasingly through her lashes. 'Excuse? You felt you needed one?'

'Of course I did! I didn't want you thinking I was

following you to Paris because I couldn't live without you.'

'You're an idiot,' she said, slipping her arms round his neck.

He looked down into her half-closed, smiling eyes. 'I am?'

'How was I ever to know you really did love me if you stayed away from me?'

'There is that,' he accepted drily, his arms round her waist, pulling her closer. 'But it works both ways. How was I to know how you felt when you lived it up in Paris and seemed to have forgotten I existed?'

'I hadn't,' she said softly, staring at the passionate curve of his mouth.

'No?' His mouth came closer.

'I tried, but I couldn't,' she whispered as it touched her.

'Darling,' muttered Brodie, kissing her with a hunger that shook her to the depths. He pulled her down on the bed, holding her so tightly it wasn't easy to breathe. 'I love you so much,' he said, kissing her neck. 'I can't begin to tell you! I wondered if I'd still feel the same when I saw you again—two years is a long time, as you said, and although I hadn't forgotten you I wondered if I loved what I remembered rather than the real girl. Then I saw you in the doorway of that apartment and I knew it was all as real as the floor under my feet.'

She laughed, touching his cheek tenderly with one hand. 'Brodie, I don't believe it—you're a romantic under all the steel and flint. And I thought you were just a businessman!'

'Business is romantic,' he said, grinning. 'Gavin's too young and crazy to realise how romantic it is to make windows for people's houses, but you're no fool, Donna. You must understand! Every time I drive past a new housing estate I look at all those gleaming new windows and think . . . we made some of that!'

She kissed him. 'No wonder my father thinks the sun shines out of you! You think just like him!'

He stroked her hair, his face sober. 'Will you marry me, Donna?'

'Yes, please,' she said, throwing pretence to the winds.

He kissed her again, slowly, deeply. 'I'll make you happy.'

'We'll make each other happy,' she corrected, and Brodie laughed.

'Yes, that's what I meant. One thing, though, if Gavin does take this job in the Midlands your father will be alone in that damn great house.'

'I'd forgotten Gavin's interview—how did it go?' she asked.

'They seemed to like him, and he certainly flipped over the work they're doing. They offered him the apprenticeship and he has to let them know Monday. The one problem bothering him was your father.' Brodie looked uncertainly at her. 'How do you feel about living with him after we're married?'

'As long as you're there I don't mind where we live,' she said. 'And I couldn't leave my father alone—you're right. I'd already realised I was going to have to come back home if Gavin left. I'd booked on tomorrow's plane and I was going to wind up my affairs in Paris in due course.'

'You mean I wasted my energy rushing after you like this? You were coming home anyway tomorrow?'

Donna made a face at him, knowing he was teasing, seeing the happiness in his eyes, the lines of content in his face.

'At least you made yourself clear, at last,' she said.

'There are no more secrets, are there, Brodie?'

'One or two,' he said silkily, pulling her down on the bed again. 'But they aren't going to be secrets for much longer, darling. From now on we're not going to hide anything from each other.'

A thought flashed through her mind as she curved against him. 'But where did you get the money to buy the block of family shares?' she asked, and Brodie groaned.

'Didn't I tell you? I inherited my uncle's money automatically when he died. He didn't make a will, he wouldn't have wanted me to have it, but as I was his only living relative I got it all the same, so although he didn't intend it, he's responsible for bringing us together.' He laughed drily. 'He'd be furious if he knew!'

'Maybe he'd be pleased,' she protested. 'Give him the benefit of the doubt.'

Brodie eyed her through his lashes. 'If *you'd* given me that, we wouldn't have wasted two years.'

'I'm sorry, darling, I'm sorry,' she whispered, contrite, kissing his ear and moving on to his neck, her teeth softly grazing his skin.

Brodie's hands explored and she shivered with pleasure, her eyes closing. Very soon there would be no hiding-place, no pretences—only the intimacy and honesty of love.

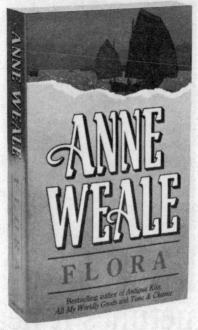

Next Month's Romances

Each month you can choose from a wide variety of romance with Mills & Boon. Below are the new titles to look out for next month, why not ask either Mills & Boon Reader Service or your Newsagent to reserve you a copy of the titles you want to buy – just tick the titles you would like and either post to Reader Service or take it to any Newsagent and ask them to order your books.

Please save me the following titles:	Please tick	√
BREAKING POINT	Emma Darcy	
SUCH DARK MAGIC	Robyn Donald	
AFTER THE BALL	Catherine George	
TWO-TIMING MAN	Roberta Leigh	
HOST OF RICHES	Elizabeth Power	
MASK OF DECEPTION	Sara Wood	
A SOLITARY HEART	Amanda Carpenter	
AFTER THE FIRE	Kay Gregory	
BITTERSWEET YESTERDAYS	Kate Proctor	
YESTERDAY'S PASSION	Catherine O'Connor	
NIGHT OF THE SCORPION	Rosemary Carter	
NO ESCAPING LOVE	Sharon Kendrick	
OUTBACK LEGACY	Elizabeth Duke	
RANSACKED HEART	Jayne Bauling	
STORMY REUNION	Sandra K. Rhoades	
A POINT OF PRIDE	Liz Fielding	

If you would like to order these books in addition to your regular subscription from Mills & Boon Reader Service please send £1.70 per title to: Mills & Boon Reader Service, P.O. Box 236, Croydon, Surrey, CR9 3RU, quote your Subscriber No:..................................... (If applicable) and complete the name and address details below. Alternatively, these books are available from many local Newsagents including W.H.Smith, J.Menzies, Martins and other paperback stockists from 12th March 1993.

Name:..

Address:...

....Post Code:........................

To Retailer: If you would like to stock M&B books please contact your regular book/magazine wholesaler for details.

You may be mailed with offers from other reputable companies as a result of this application. If you would rather not take advantage of these opportunities please tick box ☐

Forthcoming Titles

DUET
Available in February

The Emma Goldrick Duet	KING OF THE HILL IF LOVE BE BLIND
The Charlotte Lamb Duet	HEAT OF THE NIGHT HIDE AND SEEK

BEST SELLER ROMANCE
Available in March

ECHO OF PASSION Charlotte Lamb
THERE IS NO TOMORROW Yvonne Whittal

MEDICAL ROMANCE
Available in March

THE DOCTOR'S VISITOR Alice Grey
MAJOR INCIDENT Grace Read
ROGUE VET Carol Wood
MORE THAN MEMORIES Judith Worthy

Available from Boots, Martins, John Menzies, W.H. Smith, most supermarkets and other paperback stockists.

Also available from Mills & Boon Reader Service, P.O. Box 236, Thornton Road, Croydon, Surrey CR9 3RU.

Readers in South Africa - write to:
Book Services International Ltd, P.O. Box 41654, Craighall, Transvaal 2024.